See R 182.
P. 290
907. 0000

Bishop Beaver presented throughout this book. A good background in diocesan history.

# CAN SPRING
## BE
## FAR BEHIND

# CAN SPRING
# BE
# FAR BEHIND

JOHN ASHLEY

**VANTAGE PRESS**

New York        Washington        Hollywood

**FIRST EDITION**

Published by Vantage Press, Inc.
516 West 34th Street, New York, New York 10001

Manufactured in the United States of America

Standard Book No. 533-00968-5

# CAN SPRING
## BE
# FAR BEHIND

# PROLOGUE

On July the nineteenth 1850 Kate Horan was born in a tiny house set in a plot of cow-pasture land, in the singularly unattractive town of Belleville, Ontario. She was one of the six children of immigrant Irish: James Horan who came here at thirteen in the wake of the little famine of 1831 and his wife, who had been born Mary Ann Duggan. In later years, despite Kate's totally Irish background, most people thought she was French.

Her formal schooling was to stop at fourteen; for fifteen years she was to be principal of St. Jerome's School, as well as a teacher and was to be a pioneer in the field of higher education for the sisters of a large community. She never in her life had any formal courses in nursing; but she was to head a whole chain of medical institutions and to become the first president, if not the organizer, of the New England Conference of Catholic Hospitals.

As a girl she knew no boys except her brothers; through nearly seventy years of active life she influenced and was intimate with Bishops and grubby little urchins, with millionaire executives and untouchable staff doctors, with workmen and tradesmen and above all her pets, drummers, and house-to-house canvassers.

When she was a child, her family had at times almost not a penny to rub against another; however, for years and years she was to buy and to build and to run million dollar enterprises begun without funds, supported by begging trips and bazaars, despaired of by every prudent person, and left ultimately flourishing and solvent.

She had probably never seen a professional play, certainly had never danced or engaged in unladylike and tomboy sports, had little ear for music and no very great taste in art; she admittedly was unacquainted with the masterpieces of literature and had no time for trivial fiction. In architecture and the construction of buildings she had no practical experience whatsoever, and yet she directed and even

7

engaged in all these activities herself, with a pen and a ruler, drawing the plans for the first buildings—which oddly enough stood up—reportedly climbing scaffolds and clambering over beams, directing shows and dances and musicals, coaching in readings, in decorating. There is testimony to her skill in many of these areas, and it is remarkable that in the legacy of construction and adornment that she supervised, though much of it now is dated, she left behind almost no real atrocities. Fortunately one architectural horror for which she was responsible has been torn down.

Her personal life too is replete with improbabilities. Since she was singularly warmhearted and affectionate, she allowed herself no intimates until she was seventy-five. She gave total devotion to her superiors but was rejected by each one of them. With a strong sense of family, she was estranged from her relatives for years, and even to the end, there is no sign of reconciliation with the older sister whom, with girlish hero-worship, she had followed into the convent.

Her obedience frequently went beyond the bounds of reason, yet when faced with a great decision she was defiant. As a superior she was full of little tendernesses and of measures harsh beyond modern belief. In her poverty and in her legislations concerning it, she was in many respects rigid; yet there are constant accounts of her hidden little gifts to subjects and lay-folk, where her natural generosity overcame her almost penurious spiritual convictions.

She was broad and forward looking; yet her structuring of her religious group to conventual legalism and cloisterization has been blown away by the breeze through the windows of Vatican II. Her cult of professionalism led, where she did not wish it, to the administrator nun and the momentary demise of the bedside nursing sister—a situation which tomorrow will remedy. In her lifetime her educational dreams were shattered and renewed. Now, after her death, her inevitable triumphs of the massive expansion she had envisioned and brought to reality, seem, in the new accent of smaller numbers, more personal commitments, retrenchment after spreading too thin, concentration of ministries, all to have been counter-indicated. But the "why-did-theys" of our moment reveal no more than a lack of historical sense. And

8

those who say it have no comprehension of the *Zeitgeist* of the times of Kate Horan or the pressures from personal convictions and from all contemporary external compulsions. The questions that we ask: How did the nuns ever get that way? and What is happening to them now? do no more than reveal a polarity of attitude. Were they serious questions their answer might be meaningful. As it is, they are no more than examples of deplorable rhetoric. For it must be remembered that, though she was far from average, she was a typical great nun of her moment, and the pattern of her greatness can be multiplied over and over again, in every outstanding superior, every nineteenth-century foundress, even to attitudes and principles, to regulations and achievements, to identical anecdotes and constantly repeated generalizations. The reactions to these magnificent women were also remarkably similar. There were some of her subjects in the old days who said that she would most certainly be damned; there are some of the survivors, who pray to her now.

So it was that Kate Horan, who had had almost no formal novitiate training and precious little personal direction of religious structuring, started that significant and sometimes formidable congregation of women religious, the Sisters of Providence of Holyoke, was given their very name, lived among them for most of her ninety-three years and has been proclaimed as their acknowledged foundress.

This was Mother Mary of Providence.

JOHN ASHLEY

# CHAPTER 1

While she was still a young child the family moved from their distant cottage to a larger brick house near the center of Belleville. It was far from a large house, but it had seven windows, rather a good door and a small stoop at the front. It was nearer James Horan's work and the school for his children. And besides, the famine Irish were arriving, building their shacks near where the Horan's had once lived, and perhaps it was dangerous for young girls to be out after dark. It was certainly bruising for young boys if they ran into mobs from another county.

James Horan felt that he had done well now and the future looked even brighter. It was a far cry from the day when he had come in terror, with his little brother by the hand, out of the hunger that was Ireland, and the stinking black of the hold of the pestilence ship that had vomited them out at Nova Scotia.

There were many aboard who would stay awhile in the maritime provinces, earning enough to get them passage to America. Forever after, they would be known in New England as two-boaters. Others would settle down for the fishing and the wild winters, and Boston would call them herring-chokers and off the ice. But the Horan brothers, at thirteen and nine, pressed on to the West, following the river, until at last they came to Belleville and went no further.

Perhaps it was because James knew something about smelting, from his father's forge, that they settled in this town. At thirteen, he would have been three years beyond the working age for lads in Cork, and Martin had only a year to go, until he was ten, to be a man. But having passed through the proud city of Kingston, with its thousand islands, and the pretty town of Deseronto with its river and its falls, the two boys stopped at Belleville.

Even its proudest inhabitants do not claim any great beauty for Belleville. It is crowded, as if there were no more land beyond, as close as it can get to the tip end of Bay

11

Quinte, and the spire of its church surmounts the smoke-stacks of its mills only by dint of perching itself on a cragged little hill. The stream that cuts the town is intent and curious, as if it were bent only on business and to get away as soon as possible.

Yet it was here that the Horan brothers had remained for many years, though they themselves and their future families fled from the town when they had the opportunity.

But James did not settle for the slavery life of the furnaces, nor did he condemn his little brother to the grim desperation of the new mills. In Canada, he discovered the working age and the custom for children was not to leave school at ten, but an amazing fourteen, and he himself could have been still at school had he been born there. But James was a strong lad, and he could easily pass for fourteen, which of course he did. Besides, where was the money to come from to support young Martin if not from him? He had been a man long now. 'Twas not for him to go back to the scholar's bench. Besides that, it was not eternity as the years went, before he had got himself a little forge and set up a shop, where at least a man could step outside of his own door, and breathe in the air, such as it was; and Marty, he discovered, was the bright one. He was a scholar in the schools, and before he had come here at all, he had got up to the Bull in "Reading-Made-Easy," and in Mathematics, what with that he had learned from Father Ghoeghan—he was the one they made Bishop later—wasn't he way ahead of the native British and Canucks, and them with only millhands for teachers?

So before he was twenty he had sent Martin all through the free academy and was putting him through the College of Regiopolis in Kingston. And for himself he was doing well, with a smeltery now, and hired greenhorns to help him.

When she was very old, Mother Mary of Providence was to write in her brief autobiography that her father was in the foundry business, possessing two plants, one of which was in Belleville, one in Syracuse and it may have been true or it may have been the romanticizing of the old.

In any case, James had done well, now with a real brick house in town, with a fine family of four boys and two girls.

12

If the boys, though not wild at all, had a tendency to stray, if they looked with great gray eyes at the distant places, if the West were in their hearts and in their feet—had he not himself sailed the Western seas when he was thirteen years old?

As for the girls, the older one, Elizabeth, had the brains of a man and she took after her uncle Martin as a bookworm— but after her mother as a thinker. Yet she was like the boys too, like himself perhaps in her dreams of adventure, and also, he admitted, in the extremity of her sensitiveness. For like him she was thin-skinned.

Katie, the little one, was a different kettle of fish. You couldn't say she wasn't bright. She was devoted enough at school, but she was no Martin and no Elizabeth. And she wasn't shy at all. But she just never went out. Romps with the boys meant nothing to her, though when she did play with them, to please them, she was as strong as a little bull-calf, which was unexpected and odd for a wiry little thing no bigger than a wren. To hold one's own in the rough-and-tumble with four brothers and a big-boned sister demands stamina, and she had that all right, the quiet one.

Once, when she thought she was alone, he caught her dancing in the meadow. How she had learned he would never know. But it was beautiful, like coming on one of the little folk.

He accepted the fact that he himself would never grow close to her or she to him. He was a shy and silent man. Sixty years later when she was to write about her family, she does not mention his early death, and has nothing to say at all about him except the bare facts of his beginnings. Yet now it pleased him that though she modeled all her actions on her more brilliant sister, she worshipped her mother. And that was right. He could understand this. Though, as the children did, he went in fear of his wife most of the time, it was a fear that was worship, not terror. She was so far above him, it was a wonder and all.

He never could understand how he had got her.

There are some women who are aristocrats by blood, and some who are aristocrats by nature. Ann Duggan Horan was born to be a benign despot.

She had had certain advantages that James had lacked. She

had come here from Ireland as a little child and had picked up the speech, not of her parents, but of her companions, in that area north of Lake Ontario where English, as spoken by the middle classes, is the best in the world. She spoke with a precision not quite as clipped as Dublin, not as lockjawed as New England, not as slurred as Oxford, but her vowels were differentiated and her consonants were clear. Having learned English from her mother was to be a great advantage to her daughter in the years to come.

Ann's education, though limited, was that of a young lady of her time, as trained by the nuns, and though her voice was very light, she had a good ear, and her taste in music if sentimental was no more so than others of her period and was anything but cheap. She had excelled in needlework in the convent school, and her proficiency was to stand her in good stead in the years to come. She always deplored the fact that she knew no French, but the racial identifications that were to lead to the rebellions of the eighteen-forties, separated the two Canadian cultures even in her schooldays. It would not have mattered very much anyway, as she would never have been exposed to French literature, reading nothing all her life that was neither instructive nor improving.

No matter how much she insisted that she had never really been a nun, and in a way it was true, since she had never taken vows, having been turned down at the end of her postulancy, she had never been anything else until she married James Horan, and even then, though she bore him six children, she managed—as is the way with many an Irish girl—to maintain her spiritual virginity.

She became a mother. If her domicile was a matriarchy, as indeed it was, there was never a word of complaint from James and her children. They all put her on a pedestal, from which she never fell, and perhaps, in reality, that was her proper position. Nor was she ever a *mom*. When their time came, each of her children grew into a personal life, each went on alone without her—in itself a tribute to her dedication and her selflessness.

There is a myth about the Irish mother and the vocations of her young— that old ma had the vocation and the children entered religion and a lifetime of agony—that it always turns

14

out this way in the myth until at last they collapsed or withered.

Since Ann Duggan's life had been strictly conventual, it is not strange that she brought the same pattern into the home she built. There was a time for everything; duty came first, and it was sacred; pleasure, if there were anything left over for it, was not a bad thing—but it did not have the sacredness of pain, and you couldn't offer it up in union with Our Lady of Seven Dolours the way you could your troubles; and one thing you never did, or never even thought of, was to offer up your joys. Troubles and religion were related, as the Church kept reminding you in all the devotions. You began every morning by announcing to the Holy Queen, Mother of Mercy, that you were poor banished children of Eve, and to her you sent up your sighs, mourning and weeping in this valley of tears. Centuries of slavery, oppression and social hopelessness had gone into those prayers. And though the liturgy of her church had its Gloria and its Te Deum, and though Easter was its greatest feast and Sunday was a day of rest, yet all joys were overshadowed by Good Friday, the Fast and the fish, the Way of the Cross and the black requiems, and the Duty of Mass on Sunday which was above all things.

Now it must not be thought that Ann Duggan's catholicism was a religion of gloom as were some of the more severe sects around her. On the contrary, it was a faith of consolation, which, though it took for granted its need, made suffering meaningful and gave to the agony and the endurance always a kind of shining grandeur.

With sense of duty, Ann's religion had behind it a long history of legalization and had come a far cry from the easing of the yoke that its founder had promised.

History from the beginning had plagued the Catholic Church. The lifting of many of the older Hebraic tribal laws had felt like a liberation, but its primitive founders were of an unshakeable rabbinical tradition. The Church grew and identified itself with Imperial Rome, whose claim to glory, outside of its militarism, was its advances in Law. It flowered in the Middle Ages, which was the true Age of Reason, when even the mystery of God was explained and explicated, and when the highest claim to learning, and therefore the greatest intellectual influence, was to be Doctor Utriusque Legis—a teacher of both laws—Ecclesiastical and Civil. And now, in the nineteenth century it had entered the age of codification and was to produce its Code of Canon Law, the Index of Forbidden Books, the lists of the exact shades of difference between an imperfection and a Venial Sin, between a Venial Sin and a Mortal. In such a moment did Ann Duggan live, and toward such a structuring was Katie Horan destined to play a part. If Ann Duggan never questioned its value, no catholic woman of her time ever would because the Council of Baltimore had made such advances and was to have such tremendous influence over all North American Catholicism.

How often Ann Duggan Horan said to her boys of a Sunday—the girls never needed it—"If you don't get up out of that bed and go to Mass, you'll all go to hell," and she had thought, "And if I don't get you up I'll be as guilty as you are." Though this was not very good theology, and though the Church itself and even the rigid moralists of the Council of Baltimore said something far more subtle, it was certainly an accepted attitude of the faithful, and indeed it was taught both in the schools and from the pulpit. If you did x or y you would go to hell; it was not so clear that if you did z you would go to heaven. But at least negatively there was a neat clarity about this religion, which the Protestants, God help them, did not have.

Yet it must not be thought that Ann Duggan or her contemporaries or her brood, lived in a perpetual kind of hell-fear or did everything because of a dread of excommunication. Hell was as real as it was to the Presbyterians, and the hell-sermons of the Jesuits (the mild ones) at the conclusion of the Mission were almost as good as the more Dantesque fires of the Redemptorists (the strict ones). Both of them brought many a man to the pledge. As for excommunication, neither Ann nor James nor most of the neighbors knew anyone except those who had got mixed up with marriages and couldn't Receive. Even her daughter was to be acquainted with only two excommunicants, both priests, one of whom defied the bishop and the other who started a heresy.

16

No. The attitude was quite different. The laws were there. Ann knew of them and the thought might even be of need in some bad and improbable moment of life. But to Ann, hell and excommunication had no more practicality than capital punishment does to the law-abiding. Little fines you might expect your husband to get and good fat penances from some priest with ulcers was not unknown to the best of them. But anything beyond that was as removed from their lives as was hanging. You only read about such things.

Her own father's answer to a young priest was significant. She thought about it often and told it to her children. Her father was eighty then, if he was a day, yet rain or storm he climbed his way to the church on the hill, always on Sundays and holy days of Obligation and not infrequently on weekdays when he could. He said he was doing it as a penance for his sins. Yet once when he was laid up with rheumatism, the new curate said to him, "You know, Mr. Duggan, you don't have to climb up that hill any more. If ever you want me to, I'll bring you Communion." The old man had smiled at him and thanked him. When he was gone her father had said, "Now there's a real fine priest for you. But the poor boy! He thinks I go because I have to." And then, more to himself than to anyone else, he muttered, "Can you just see our holy Lord coming to the likes of me when I can crawl up to Him? And God knows, when I'm on my deathbed, I'll be glad enough to have Him come. He can come down then if He will. But for the Easter, I can get up the aisle." Then aloud: "How far is it now till Easter?"

It was at Easter they went to Communion, and the forty days before were too short a time to get ready and try to be worthy of it. Ann knew as well as the next one that you never could really be worthy. It was all right for the nuns to go more often. Had not she herself gone, with a holy fear in her, on the great feast days? And for the priest, didn't he have a duty to say Mass every day? It showed what a holy life you had to lead, to be a priest of God.

The Easter Duty. These were words to her. Duty? Like her father, as she prayed would be the way of her children after her, how could you think of a duty when God allowed you to have Himself for a moment once a year? Or the Obligation

17

of Sunday Mass, when once a week at least you could follow the words and the movements that were rich and familiar and mysterious, when God, from the Elevation to the Priests' Communion, would be upon your altar, then to be locked away in the Tabernacle where you could visit Him sometimes, in the stolen and slipped—in moments of an afternoon?

The fish on Friday was, of course, different; but it was a great symbol to her race, as strong almost as the Mass on Sunday. It was the sign of the Catholic, and it meant more to the Irish than to other Europeans. The French were pretty good about it, but she had heard that the Italians were lax, in the Pope's own country, and though she scarcely believed it, she had heard that the Spanish didn't have it at all. How could they call themselves Catholics?

In her own land and down to her own time, fish on Friday had been the strongest sign. Though she had not herself experienced it, having come here too early, she knew that what her husband had told her was true, and that in the Little Famine, when only one potato crop had failed, the Gentry, the Gauls that was, had tempted the starving. They would feed you if you ate their meat-broth on a Friday. If her people had buried the skeletons even of children, it was better than to defy the laws of God's Church. For that is what it would mean. It would be giving up the Faith. Oh no. It wasn't the eating of a little meat that was a mortal sin but the rejection that the gesture meant. And that surely would send you to Hell. It was as clear to her as it was to those who hated the Pope. The Protestants did that sort of thing to try you, and if you yielded, they despised you and laughed. She even heard that they were doing things like it to the south of them, in the States, luring Irish into their churches. But it would be a snuther and a scamp, in her father's words, who would be caught dead worshiping with them, even if you lost your job for refusal, which, they said, many a poor man did.

In this, and in many things, these were the enemy: the Protestants.

The best thing you could do was to avoid them. Let the men tip their forelocks in a gesture of respect, let them say funny things so that the native sons would laugh and dine out on a new tale of Irish wit. Let the women who worked for the yanks mother their children and wash their clothes and lay on a bit of the blarney, which did no harm. But don't let the young colleens butter up to them, for who hasn't heard of a girl who . . . but the less said the better.

They didn't want you marrying into them, so take them at their word and marry your own. They resented your young being in school with them, so send your children to the nuns.

She believed this firmly and was bolstered in her views by the example of the Canadian French around her, though they seemed to her to lack ambition for their children. But like the Irish, they didn't want to mingle. They had their own language, and that helped the barrier. Though three years before Kate's birth the French had lost their rebellion and were now really under the Queen; their spirit of separatism, she thought, would never die. Though they shared the faith of the Irish, they did not care to share churches, and already the small towns were having their French Church and their Irish Church. Monsieur Le Cure would put up all kinds of obstacles to a mixed marriage—an Irish lad and a French girl. If you lost the language (French), you would lose the faith (Catholic). What would happen to the children of such unnatural alliances? So the Irish schools grew; so the religious communities of priests and nuns split into French and Irish.

Now Ann Horan saw that there was a new split. It was within the Irish themselves. She had been only vaguely aware of the pattern of social consciousness, when her friends had thought she had thrown herself away on James—and James himself had never lost the idea that she had married below her station. She had come close to being Canadian born. He had come here fifteen years later. Her parents had come freely and by choice; he had been driven to the western lands by hunger. The few years made a difference.

But she was quite aware now of how vast that difference was. The hordes of famine Irish that swarmed upon them, the way they lived, the terrible conditions of their shantytowns, the inability they found in adapting to any kind of a decent life outside their own ghettos, their drunkenness, their brawlings, their diseases—though it made your heart bleed for them, it also made your stomach turn over. James could talk

19

to them, she could not. She met them at Church. The same faith—the same race—the same history was never enough for Ann Horan. If her younger daughter was a reclusive child, there were not many neighbor children of whom her mother could approve. And neither the natives nor the French would have her. And to do her credit Ann Horan made for her little ones a happy home where they had everything. What more was there beyond?

In the meantime the native sons smiled at their native wives. If to them now there was less and less social distinction between church and chapel or church and kirk, or between church-and-kirk and the other sects, there still was some advantage in being Episcopalian or Presbyterian; but they prided themselves on their liberality in this New World. You could have a Methodist as a friend, and a few scattered Baptists were acceptable. But the Canucks and the Paddies were Catholic. Quite a few French were gentlemen, but they must have been Huguenots and the Irish of the fox-hunting breed, whether from Kerry or Cork, must originally have been Orangemen. The earlier settlers were Scotch-Irish, whatever breed that might be.

The native sons were really amused now that the famine Irish had arrived. They said with some surprise, "Why, you know, they even have a caste system among themselves!"

"Do they really?" their wives asked, who had never noticed. "What does it depend on?"

"The thickness of their brogues, I suppose."

Sometimes they said with approval, "You know the older ones here look down on the new ones just as much as we do. They resent the way they live. They call them 'Shanty Irish.'" "Oh? And do they have a name for—for the better ones?"

"'Lace curtain,' they call them. Isn't that good? Lace Curtain."

And the lady smiled and said, "Isn't it wonderful how witty the Irish are?"

The Irish had some virtues. Many were really quite lovely, and there was no question about it, the colleens were beautiful. Of course they got fat and coarse as they grew older. No wonder, with all those children. But the insupportable fact was that you really couldn't do anything with them. They were Papists. All you had to do was to look around and see the ignorance and dirt and poverty of the lower classes in Catholic countries. With great cathedrals, too, and rich, fat priests, like the French Canadians. Every impoverished village was centered around a vast basilica. They were building more, in very bad taste, all the time.

These people! What could you do with them? Though they were all right if they kept their place.

It was into such a world that Ann Duggan bore her younger daughter, Kate.

# CHAPTER 2

Katie Horan did not get her social sense from her mother, but from her older sister Elizabeth, whom she secretly emulated and remembered as being constantly censorious. As a child, Kate tried very hard to please Elizabeth. It was not easy. She knew, deep within her, that her quiet father loved her. Her mother did not fondle children, but the little pat and the bright, quick smile were readily there. Though Elizabeth scorned and loved the boys, there was nothing that Kate could do that would win approval.

One day, when she was very young, she cut her hair in bangs, the way Elizabeth wore it. It came out craggily and uneven, and she kept cutting it until she was suddenly afraid that there would be nothing left in front to cut. But when she looked in the mirror she was sure that Elizabeth would know what she had done it for and she knew too, that this way she looked a little more like Elizabeth. She fully expected approval.

When Elizabeth saw it, she let a cry out of her, "That Girl!" and ran at once to tell her mother. It was not that her mother would not have eventually seen the monstrosity, but it hurt that Elizabeth had not let nature take its course.

Her mother said, "Katherine," she never called her Katherine unless she disapproved, "why did you cut your hair?"

Couldn't she see? Katie looked across at her sister, at her straight bangs, at her tawny hair fluffed up high on her head, caught at the base of the neck by a tortoise brooch surmounted by a hair-ribbon and hanging in neat curves halfway to her waist. Maybe it was because she had forgotten the hair-ribbon, Katie thought. Maybe because she had forgotten to see how her hair looked from the back. Or just because her hair was darker than Elizabeth's and would never catch the sunlight in it, filling it with glints of gold.

Her mother said: "Katherine. Speak up, now. Why did you cut your hair?"

Elizabeth was shrill. "Why can't that girl talk like everybody else? All she ever does is mope."

Then Katie told her lie. The lie was to be a symbol to her, like the pears of St. Augustine. Later she would do a great penance for it.

"I didn't," she said.

"What do you mean, you didn't?" Elizabeth cried. "It's cut, isn't it? If you didn't cut it, who did?"

It would have been bad enough if she had lied to Elizabeth, but it was her mother who had asked the direct question again.

"If you didn't cut it, who did?"

Katie said: "The groundhog cut it."

That evening when the boys came home they roared and shrieked when they saw her, and when Elizabeth said, "Look at what the groundhog cut!" they kept gasping and shrieking, "Groundhog," until at long last their mother said, "That will be enough, now," but she added not very audibly, but clearly enough, and not as if she thought it was that funny, "Groundhog."

Though this was almost insupportable, it was nothing to what had happened before.

When Katie had lied, her mother had looked at her for a long time waiting for her to retract. But the nature of silence was already in her, and there were no words. Then her mother sent Elizabeth from the room, who assumed a rather petulant frown at her banishment, just as if she would have enjoyed seeing Katie's disgrace and punishment.

When they were alone her mother said with a terrible disappointment in her voice: "Up to now I have always been able to trust my children. They have told me the truth. But now one of my own children," and looked straight at Katie, "I never can believe again." She said no more.

All the rest of that morning and through the dragging afternoon, infinities stretched out before Kate Horan. Year after year she would tell her mother things, terrible and true things about herself. Her mother would never believe her again. Only for moments life would brighten, and Katie could foresee, years ahead, when after a thousand and a thousand times of telling the truth, her Mother would finally say, just before she died, "Now I can believe at last that all my children tell the truth. At last I believe you, Katie."

But the vision would fade. Never again could anyone, anyone in the world believe her. Yet as the afternoon wore on another funny thing happened. A groundhog came with shears and cut her hair. The groundhog became very real. She even prayed to St. Jude, whom she had just discovered from the Sisters of Loreto in Infant School, "Make the groundhog real! Make it have happened the way I said."

No groundhog came to testify.

She tried her best that day to make it up. A tiny little girl, she picked up all the boys' scattered things and put them in the wrong places. In despair, she got into the cupboard and found the ammonia, practically crawling into the cold oven with it, to clean out the grease. Her tears that had silently run down her cheeks, for she had not bawled nor cried aloud, and that had dried and stained at last, were renewed by the fumes; and when, of course, Elizabeth had pulled her out of the oven and had said in her best diction, as if speaking a piece, "Oh, you are a sorry spectacle. Go clean yourself," she had run out of the house for the first time all day, down to the pump at the well, sinking her swollen face into the cold water, wetting and gnarling what remained of her hair.

When she could see, she noticed a tiny emerald grass snake that had been disturbed from its sun by the spill. It wriggled off, into the woods clean and bright, visible for quite a distance.

She had never liked snakes. Alone of all woodland things they had frightened her. but now she followed the snake with her eyes, and she said, "I wish I was you."

Every incident of that day became etched upon her memory. Except for one thing. She forgot that.

Her father had not scorned her, not laughed at her. Impersonally he had looked at her and at her hair. He had said: "It will grow again."

She remembered even the next morning when Elizabeth, as usual, had accompanied her to school. Her sister had taken her by the hand, as she always had, and that was comforting because Katie had been afraid that today she would reject her, particularly when she had been dressed and her mother had done the best she could with a plain ribbon, tightly pulling her bangs into a forehead-torturing upsweep, and Elizabeth had said, "I'll be ashamed to be seen with you," at which, her mother, for the first time, defended her.

"That will do, young lady. You'll never be ashamed of your own sister."

With that they had gone on hand in hand. They parted wordlessly, each for her own class in the two-roomed schoolhouse, Katie for the infant-classes, Elizabeth for the scholars, large children between eight and twelve years old; though there was one massive girl named Arvella Titus who was fourteen, and a French boy, whom they suspected of being part Indian, whom the youngsters exaggerated into eighteen but who was actually thirteen by the parish register. In due time, Arvella was to prefer her Gaston to the mills and they were to be married. It was their grandson who became the illustrious Titus Lindsay, who won his elections, not only because of his real ability but also because of his unbeatable mixture of bloods.

So Katie went to her slate and wrote and Elizabeth to her books and dramatic recitations, and each into her own world.

On Elizabeth's side of the wall, Sister Benigna reigned. She was the kind of woman who felt that her students' dislike of her was a tribute to her fairness, her excellent discipline, to her worth as a teacher. In later years, she thought they would be grateful to her. Their callous and contrary opinions now were without any value. She trained them well. They did their sums, and they could spell. Their handwriting was legible. And they knew right from wrong.

She often said that there was no youngster in the world who could fool her. Her principles were more punitive than corrective, and she believed thoroughly in catching a culprit, not in preventing crime. As witness, the time when she had detected that the boys whom she had sent to the woodshed to stack wood against the winter, had built themselves a retreat beyond the outer stack, where they could loiter. They would never forget the day she had caught them. One of them later became a Monsignor.

Then there was the day that they had put a live skunk in her desk drawer. When she had come in, the smell had been

25

woodsy but not unusual. It was only when she opened the drawer and touched something furry that the skunk became frightened. She simply closed the drawer calmly and ordered Gaston to shut the windows. If she could stand it the children could. And though through that day there was a good deal of coughing and that night a good deal of scrubbing out clothes with lye soap, an incident like that never happened again.

Sister Benigna was much admired by the parents.

And with the boys, among them the Horan brothers, the apocryphal tales grew of how they had outwitted her. That they really never had turned over the girls' outhouse, with Arvella in it, or never had plugged up the chimney on the first day of the new fires so that there was no school for a week, was irrelevant over their late beers in the Western taverns. Her punishments, too, assumed heroic proportions. She had, in the story, lifted John Horan right off the ground by his ears when he was quite a large boy. That is why, he told them around the bivouac, his ears flapped so now. Though Sister Benigna's prophecy that they would love her in the years to come was not fulfilled, it would have pleased the old lady to know that her scholars indeed remembered her and that she had grown into a legend.

On Katie's side of the wall, Sister Thecla had been chosen for quite different attitudes. She exuded peace. She ran her bilingual and tri-level classes with unperturbable calm, and if as she grew older, her good humour increased her girth, that only made her more maternal. It was quite clear to Katie that Sister Thecla believed everyone, and, as in the story about the monk, which she had heard, if someone told her there was an elephant outside the window, she would have gone over and looked out.

Sister Thecla was what Katie needed that morning, and as usual, she was a completely substantial relief.

The infants loved Sister Thecla, and some of the little girls wept when they left her, but they all wanted to cross over to the other side, not only through the ambition of being older, but from being allured by the challenge of Sister Benigna and the young wonder of whether they could meet it. For no one could tell tales about Sister Thecla around campfires in the

26

wilderness, and when they grew up, most of them could not quite remember her name.

How much of Sister Thecla's maternity brushed off on Kate Horan, we can never know; but certainly some of Sister Benigna's disciplinary methods were absorbed. Certainly, if there is any educational value in emulation, both nuns had an effect upon her, as well they might. For they were the only teachers she remembered from the eight brief years of her schooling.

Katie's desire to advance into the intriguing world of the Upper School was intensified by her adulation of Elizabeth. Her sister was the best scholar, and there was not a boy among the students who could touch her in declamation — though there were some, fresh from the schools of Ireland, who were faster at sums — none was more accurate. Her brother John was her equal in geography until, toward the end, he fell by the wayside because he discovered that it was possible during the study times, when his grade was not reciting to prop up his huge atlas before him and Delia O'Connor — who had lately developed a rose-bud mouth from furious efforts to hide her almost buck teeth. Between him and Delia there was what Sister Benigna called "Room for the Holy Ghost," but the Holy Ghost is, after all, a Spirit.

The time for Katie to pass into the advanced grades happened to coincide with Elizabeth's graduation, which of course, far overshadowed it. But another thing happened, too. There was no set time then, as there would have been in a more structured and less casual system, for all the children to advance together to another grade. When you had finished your lessons and could recite them all by heart, you went on to something else. And so it was quite three weeks later that Sister Thecla noticed that there seemed to be an echo in Kate's replies, and that indeed, she was repeating over and over again, what she had already mastered. Sister Thecla gave Kate a little rundown test, and laughingly passed her on to Sister Benigna.

Katie had not mentioned the oversight. Among several sacred rules that her mother had instilled into her, there was one that said: "Bear with patience and resignation the Crosses which the Lord sends to you." To the naturally reticent child who, only in her dream world could even confide in her Mother, this rule of patience under God's Will was inextricably bound with another dictum: "Never tell anyone outside the family what goes on under this roof," which though not as holy, was as binding for, "What will the neighbors think?" kept the Horan clan as tight-lipped and as aware of outside social acceptance as any Chinese.

Grimly, Kate Horan kept to herself the fact that she had been passed over. She waited out the three weeks, sharing nothing of Elizabeth's triumph, and finally simply announcing at home that she was now among the scholars of the upper classes. Her brothers had forgotten to mention it.

It was taken for granted in the family that Elizabeth would go on. The brothers could scarcely wait for their emancipation at fourteen; Kate was too young yet to know whether she was smart. The older sister had all the talent in the family. And at Elizabeth's last day in class, when the parents all came and squeezed themselves into the larger back seats, there was no doubt at all that she must go on.

Elizabeth's declamation was the finest thing Belleville had heard. In choosing it, Sister Benigna had been torn between the works of a poetess named Adelaide Proctor, whom she heard was a Catholic and a nice woman, and a favorite selection of her own from the works of Cornelia Hunt, the Sweet Singer of Ontario. Native talent must be recognized. Cornelia won. Elizabeth's rendition was unforgettable. Her gestures on "Follow the Stars", which was the main moral of the poem, and since repetition is the mother of learning, it came in again and again, making you think it was night — the graceful way her hand went up. When she came to the end, which informed you that even if you failed it was good that, though sinking in death to the sod, your tears on the breast of God, if you looked and followed the stars, you would reach to heaven's bars.

Of the younger children, perhaps because she alone followed it, only Kate Horan was confused by the anatomical difficulty. She never was to care much for poetry. But for the adults who were present, there was scarcely a dry eye in the audience.

When Uncle Martin came up from his foundry business in Syracuse, which he managed for his brother James because it was hard in those days for a young Irishman, no matter how good his education, to break into more learned fields — and had not his renaissance Jesuit teachers told him that education was for life, not for jobs — the matter of Elizabeth's further training was settled. The high hopes that had built his brick house in Belleville in '53, and the satisfaction that James Horan had felt rising up in worldly ways from the position from which he felt he had pulled his wife down — had been dashed by the panic of '57. It had been no easy thing, when the mills were closed, to keep up a house and a family of six young children. Ann had stretched things and made do. The starch would never come out of her, he knew, but he could see the flame of resentment, immediately subdued, when after Mass their mill hand neighbors, yesterday from the shanties, had with their mouths full of saliva and their black hearts filled with the victory of their envy, said when they saw the patch in young Edward's breeches, "Tis a neat sewer you are, Mrs. Horan," or when they had heard Patrick Henry's dry agonizing cough, disturbing his Reverence during the two sermons, one in English and the other in a strange Canadian French with an Irish overlay, they would say with malicious sweetness, "Oh, that poor boy of yours. If it were mine now I'd be that worried I couldn't sleep. And talking of sleep, though it's none of my business at all, is it true you have the windows open on you all, to the night air?"

Those who went by in the night to see if their windows were open had little to do, Ann Horan thought, and it was a wonder they could see at all, the condition some of them were in. What she said was: "Fresh air never hurt anybody."

She said it in her perfect English, and her head went up while the little jaunty feather on her hat seemed to straighten itself and stand erect. As they stalked briskly down the hill, Elizabeth in wonderful facsimile, there was a loyal pride and a fear of comeuppance in the breast of James Horan. He would walk down more slowly, he and his little one, and he never could tell on which side Katie was, for she never talked at all.

Ann Horan never talked either, at least not to complain. Her own silent phrase — which she seldom used because her daughters would not understand till they were mothers, and

29

the boys, never — was: "She kept all these things in her heart." It cleansed her of bitterness. It united her to the Woman of the Seven Swords.

To James Horan, she did not need to speak. Yet his wife's defiance had a reverse effect upon him. The work that he had once loved now was dull and flat, and secretly he welcomed the days when the forges would be cold and to have no smelting jobs came in at all. Very secretly, he was glad that John was ready for the mills. Perhaps if there wasn't any money to send her on with, Elizabeth, like a dutiful daughter, could work at the spindles.

For three months that is what Elizabeth did. She would rise up early before it was half light, so as to take the long way in the dark. She dallied or ran, to avoid the other mill hands, when the whistle blew for dismissal. On Sundays she took to going to High Mass at eleven, at which only the pew-holders were ever to be found — the rich people with their names surrounded by mother-of-pearl on the sides of the pews, and looked down upon by their names in the stained-glass windows as if they were saints. None of the mill girls or the living-out girls would be there.

When she was at home, Elizabeth never answered the door. This was much to the delight of Kate. Kate knew that — when company was with them a child's place was to be seen and not heard and never to let out a peep; — she had almost from infancy formed a violent attachment for casual callers. She was the delight of tramps. Tradesmen who came by with carts to sell produce from door to door, wonderful wagoneers with gleaming pots and pans and spices and teas from the Orient, found in her their best ally. But she was ravished by drummers — traveling salesmen, they called them later — and no matter what tawdry calico, disintegrating household utensils, impossible medicines that cured all, if whatever they produced from the depths of their battered bags were not purchased, Kate would be devastated. The bag that closed without a sale tore at her heart. The sight of their discouraged shoulders, as she followed them with her eyes down the long street, set her quite aback.

Now at least since Elizabeth shunned strangers, Kate could rush to greet them, entertain them whereas Elizabeth

30

cowered away. If she could not buy anything, at least she could bring them a cup of tea. They were romance — exotic. They came from far places and would return into them, and not one of them but was nice to little girls.

That was Kate's only consolation during those three months, when everybody, even her Mother, was worried about Elizabeth, afraid, as they said, that she was going into a decline.

For herself, Elizabeth almost prayed that she would. She envied Patrick Henry because, of all the children, he was not strong. If her own physical health, with all its youth held up, she contracted in those few weeks an incurable disease of the spirit. It was odd too, she knew. She had not been forced into this disgrace. She had chosen her work bravely and with her eyes wide open; but her work, she knew, had broken her mother's heart. Never again could they walk down the street together, mother and daughter, with their heads so high.

She was a mill hand.

She had felt a fierce joy the day that she had announced her decision. Now what was the matter with her? Not that she wouldn't go on with it — she would. She would till she dropped. But she wouldn't have to be one of those girls.

She could smell the one next to her. It was worse, because day after day, no matter how often she rebuffed her, the girl beside her remained unfailingly kind. Worst of all, what the girl called her! Liz. Even her father only slipped into Lizzie and pulled himself out of it after one look from her mother. Liz. Liz the mill hand.

The name and the fact never left her. No one ever called her that to her face — never. But she could hear it, and it was true.

In her thoughts she made the rebuttal to her family. "Yes. And I did it for you. I did it when nobody else would. And a lot of thanks I got for it." It was worse because she never could say it. How could you answer a look that said, "mill hand?"

After about nine weeks a thought came into Elizabeth's mind — an answer to prayer. It came to her in church on the last day of a "nine-day Novena" that the Passionists gave.

She would become a nun.

If you were a nun you would dress in a habit, you would change your name, you might be sent to the missions.

To the amazement of the family, after supper that night, Elizabeth dressed herself in her Sundays. When they asked her where she was going, she said, "out."

In the bright evening, with her head high, she stalked up to the convent. The lay-sister, whom she had seldom seen except at Mass, let her in, and she had time enough to panic in the long wait before Sister Benigna, for whom of course she had asked, appeared. Perhaps they would only take her as a lay-sister, now she was a mill hand.

She plunged in boldly. "Sister, I've decided to be a Sister. A Sister of Loreto."

Sister Benigna smiled tightly.

"Nonsense," she said, dismissing the whole idea.

Elizabeth was nonplussed for only a moment. "Why?" Was it because she was a —

"Because your mother is half a nun and your sister has a vocation if ever I saw one, and because that Father Florian gave a sermon I could have killed him for."

"It was a beautiful sermon."

"Pooh! Putting ideas in your head."

"It did not! I mean, Sister —"

"How long have you thought about it?"

"Lots of times."

"Now, really. Every little girl thinks about it sometimes. It keeps popping up at Benediction. Some nuns I know trade on it. 'Did you ever think about being a Sister, dear? Yes? Well you know what it means to resist a vocation? Just supposing that Our Lady had said no to the Incarnation.' Oh, I can hear them, just."

Elizabeth tried hard to think of the consequences of such a negation, but her theology failed her. Nor was this the way she was supposed to be thinking, if she were really following Sister Benigna.

"How old are you Elizabeth?"

"Fifteen — almost."

"Mm hmm. And I can't remember you mentioning it to me once. And of course you haven't talked it over with the pastor or your parents or anybody at all, have you? You just

32

heard a voice out of the Tabernacle or something equally silly. So go home like a good girl and grow up. Meet a nice boy or something where you work." So she knew didn't she? "and marry him someday when you're old enough."

"Oh, Sister, I never cared for boys."

"That's only part of your trouble. Now Elizabeth, I'm going to tell you something for your own good." That was Sister Benigna for you. She was always telling people something for their own good. "You're a bright girl — for Belleville. And that doesn't say much. You're not bad looking, but you'd never launch a thousand ships. And you're as proud as the rest of the Horans and that's saying a good deal."

"You mean you won't take me?"

"Nobody in their right mind would take you now. Or maybe some would. But not in their right mind. Some of them take anything nowadays."

Elizabeth clutched the last straw. "You mean, maybe some day? When I get older?"

"The wonders of God never cease. And that's all you'll get out of me. Now go along with you."

On the way home, through side streets, Elizabeth thought and thought. Her own mother had rejected a vocation. The words of Father Florian returned to her. It was a terrible thing to reject a vocation, and how could God bless the children of a girl who had refused to be Christ's spouse? She could see clearly now how God was visiting the sins of her mother on her and how He had rejected her, her mother's child. There was no blessing on her.

But what could the nun have meant about Kate? Why, she scarcely even knew her. A little girl like her. She could just picture Katie as a nun. She never even dressed up like one.

At home she laid away her finery and said nothing to anyone. She was too ashamed. Her shame lasted until Uncle Martin came and everything changed.

Everyone listened to Martin Horan, even then because of his success in Syracuse. The American value system sanctioned him. More, his education set him apart, putting him in the society, small but exclusive, of doctors and lawyers and teachers and made him a man to be reckoned with, even by the clergy.

At this moment he was not at the peak of his career and was still technically in his brother's employ, though the day was not far off that, with the decrease in James' ambition, and his loosening grasp upon business, Martin was all but forced to take command. Though the panic had hurt him, it had had one effect contrary to that which it had had on James.

Perhaps it was his identification with the States that had served to spur him on. He was a naturalized citizen now, and his Canadian years were becoming as remote a background to him as his origins in Ireland. He was a number one American.

In the States, though, as he told his Canadian relatives, these were perilous times. With business just now coming out of the doldrums, there were ugly rumors. In the North, there was a new book sweeping the country and stirring up the hotheads. He didn't like the book much, even if it was mostly on the right side, because he found in it a subtle attack against Catholics. Not everyone could see it, Martin said, and his brother nodded, knowing that it was Martin's better education that made him read between the lines — but if you followed it carefully you would find that the Protestant slave owners like St. Claire, his name was, were fine to their darkies; but as you got down to New Orleans — the Catholic part — they treated their niggers worse than dogs. Legree. He was the villain. Do you follow? Legree — a bad spelling for Le Gris. New Orleans French. Catholic. Martin wouldn't let a child of his read the book. And you know who wrote it, don't you? Harriet Stowe. And who was she? Why, Beecher's sister. You know. Beecher the Preacher, from Litchfield. There were stories about him, too. They say he is almost a Unitarian — you know, those people who do not believe that Jesus Christ is God.

You have to be careful nowadays. There were those fellows around Waldon Pond with all their highfaluting pagan pantheism. Know what Emerson said? "I thank God every day I live in Concord, where the steeple of no Catholic Church is visible."

Oh. You had to be careful about what you read nowadays. He hoped his brother's children were allowed to read only good books.

34

Ann nodded her approval. Only one of the books Elizabeth had picked up didn't seem quite right. It was about Pilgrim's Progress, and it was full of slurs. Ann had burned it, and Elizabeth had cried. She said it was a classic.

Then, Martin went on, there was a new dark horse they were building up for President. He was a rail-splitter lawyer without any education. James nodded his approval of the insinuation. Anyhow, Honest Abe was dead against the South, or maybe he was just for New England cotton. Some of his views against the right to own slaves went against St. Paul. No. He himself would not be a slave owner. But logically he couldn't deny his brother a right that God had given him, now could he? Abraham Lincoln did just that. But you could understand why. Abe was a God-fearing man, they say, but he didn't believe in any one religion — didn't join up with any church. Can you fancy that, now? And what with that and the fact of his lack of any training in logic, you couldn't really blame the man. But you could blame educated people who were taken in by fallacious argument, couldn't you?

Anyhow, there wasn't any real worry. Douglas would get in, and maybe he could save the Union.

Would there be a war in the States? Ann Horan worried. The rebellions of '37, that strange three-way encounter, with Mackenzie for the English speaking and Papineau for the French, against each other and the Majesty of Queen Victoria, had never really stopped, perhaps never would. Only the year before Kate was born, while Ann was heavy with her, Lord Elgin had been stoned in the streets of Montreal. In the last years another group, Fenians, they called them, were rekindling the fires of secession with that smoldering, and sometimes flaming intensity, of which the Irish were peculiarly endowed.

Ann was glad that her boys were too young, and that her severance from the new hordes, who, with adequate reason considered the Queen who had starved them as the most cruel tyrant since Cromwell, had protected them from the Fenians and the raids in the night. Though she looked at John and thanked God that he was only sixteen.

James Horan looked at John too but with more doubt

than his mother had. He had seen the eyes of the boy as they filled with that growing hero worship that is so beautiful and so troubling to behold. He had seen him hanging on every word of his fascinating uncle from the States, and never, if he could help it, letting his uncle out of his sight. What they talked about on their walks together during Martin's visit, James thought he knew. But he had always known the wandering that had been in his sons, the wandering that he had had once and was losing by now.

It was no surprise to James Horan when, in the dusk of the evening in the moth-time, with the men smoking their pipes, and Ann's strong tea getting weaker and milkier as it descended to the youngest—that though the main debate centered around Elizabeth, the ultimate decision determined the future of John.

Martin Horan was, under his new American breeziness, a sensitive and perceptive man. Though his eye was on John, his heart was with Elizabeth. He himself had been spared from the mills and by this stalwart and defeated brother who sat across from him. In one stroke he could repay the debt that he owed. And if, by chance, his shrewd foresight envisioned the possibility of an ultimate advantage to himself, that night he put it down like a bad thought. True, James' business had flourished because of the rebellion; and in case of a war between the States, who knows what needs there might be for smelteries and what a boom might be just around the corner? It was an ill wind that blew nobody good. But war was a terrible thing. He meant it when he said it. War was a terrible thing.

"Now what will you do with Elizabeth here?" he asked, broaching the subject that had been in the girl's prayers since his arrival.

"What can we do?" Ann asked, by way of answer. "She's a brave girl—and there isn't much money for us now, save what she brings in."

"It's a hard thing for her," Martin said. Elizabeth felt as if she were poised upon a peak until at last her uncle added: "Is it needful?"

"If it weren't, do you think I would let a daughter of mine go to the mills?" For the first time Elizabeth knew the shame that her mother shared with her. It made a difference.

"Suppose now" Martin took the pipe from his lips and tampered with the bowl—"Suppose I were to help out a bit. Just by way of compensation. To pay up an old debt I owe."

James spoke feelingly and for the first time. "There was no talk of debt between us, Mart."

"I know, I know. It isn't that, that I mean. Let me put it this way. Suppose now that young Johnny-my-lad comes back to the States with me. I could give him a bit of salary and I could learn him the business."

"Teach," Kate's mind corrected. "Teach him the business."

Ann Horan stirred her tea, carefully shook the last drop from the spoon back into the cup and laid the spoon down clean on the dry saucer. "It is a thought that has passed my mind," she said, to her husband's amazement. "It does not come as a new thing to me. If we had a little money from John," she said, "we could send Elizabeth to the nuns in Kingston. They're the cheapest nearby, but Elizabeth could learn from them." She looked carefully at John and avoided even a suggestion of criticism of her husband. "It would be a good thing if we had another man in the family, to be a smithy, the way things are now." Then she turned directly to her husband. "What is your word on it, James Horan?"

Kate knew. She always knew. The woman made the decisions, but it was the man who stated them. It was the right way.

"For Johnny I think it's a grand thing, and for Lizzie it'll be the salvation of her, I'm thinking." Then he shocked them indeed. "But for all that, I say no!"

"No is it?" Martin asked, incredulous and lapsing a little into the soft lilt.

"And why, James Horan?" Ann stirred her tea again, letting the man object, as he must and confident of her ultimate victory.

"It's only another way of charity, it is. Why what could the small chap be earning? Ask yourself that now. And it will be a black day when the family starts supporting my children. I say no to it all."

It was a tribute to their faith in her, that neither John nor

Elizabeth wavered or doubted for a moment that their mother would win. But it was John whose adulation of his uncle increased, if it could.

"Well, now, well now," Martin was saying. "I'd anticipated that one So I've got, as they say, an alternative suggestion. It's just this, James." He stroked his handsome and silky mustache the way John had always fancied captains of industry would stroke them. Seeing him do it seemed to make the fuzz on his own upper lip feel an inch longer. "It's this way. As it stands now, it's you who owns the smithy."

"It is."

"Then suppose, if it's welcome to you, I buy you out. Bit by bit, as I couldn't all at once. There'd be no charity in that, and I want to say now whatever happens, the future's with the States not north of the border. And I'd fix it up so that you'd always hold onto a large slice of the business, even if you wanted to take it easier later. Even if, God forbid, something happened to you, you'd leave Ann and the children provided for."

Deep within him, James gave a sigh of relief. It was what he really wanted, wasn't it? The ambition that had driven him in his youth had evaporated, and he was tired.

His answer though, felt like his death.

"I can't say no to that. I have a duty. And I'm not getting any younger—he was forty that year—"and I guess it's for the best."

"It's God's will," said Ann, shaking her head, for it clearly was.

And neither of the brothers was guilty of the slightest intention of irony when Martin concluded, "You can't say there's any charity in this deal, James," or in his brother's reply, "No. There's no charity there."

So it was settled. Not for a moment did it cross the minds of John or Elizabeth that it should be settled in this way. Certainly it never entered the heads of their parents to ask them what they wanted nor to consult them in a decision that was to frame and change and groove all their futures. How would the young know what was good for them? And the fact that the young were in this case delighted—that the gleam returned into the eyes of Elizabeth—and that John wanted to say in his best Americanism: "That would sure pleasure me," was only an added bonus and, in its way, irrelevant. The decision was made.

After one week John left for the States. At the end of the summer, with her head high again, for after all, she had only worked during vacation, Elizabeth set off for Kingston in new furbelows.

Ann did not weep as she saw her children departing, though she kissed them in public before they jumped into the stage, as no Canadian Frenchwoman would dream of doing, right there in the open. She kept her tears for that night, in her flannel nightgown, she knelt by her bed, her great sobs shaking her.

Kate saw her, having heard and crept to the door. As swiftly as she had come she crept away, not to be witness to her mother's disgrace. Alone in her own room she heard her father come up the creaky stairs and close the door behind him, uniting her parents. Beyond the partition her three brothers lay snugly together.

Kate Horan was alone.

# CHAPTER 3

As to her contemporaries in Belleville, Kate's reactions to the mill workers and the shanty dwellers separated themselves completely from the more class-conscious attitudes of her mother and from her sister's shame of association.

Kate's identification with the out-society was not learned by contacts with her schoolmates. Her mother saw to that, and her own inclinations made her aloofness an easy obedience. As she advanced in the upper grades, she became more and more reclusive.

She had only one close friend, Emma, of whom her mother approved and from whom she found sympathy. She walked to and from school with her every day. She confided in her. During the play periods the two girls were inseparable and exclusive.

There can be no doubt that Kate's self-claustration tendency affected Emma. But there was something in herself as a child that produced her withdrawal. For society and contact, her mother and Emma sufficed. Even her association with her brothers became meaningless. The romps with them practically ceased, or were at best endured.

But for whatever cause, in these years of growing, her attitudes toward the less fortunate did not include rejection. For the girls whom Elizabeth had repelled, the girls caught in the mills, Kate had not pity but a strange childish respect; and for the shanty children whose parents sent them to school, despite all hardship and need, she conceived the beginning of what could only be called admiration. For those whom she saw emerging into a better world, and there were many, she had a strange, shy and silent affection. For the rowdies and the slothful and those who had learned early to blame others for their lack of progress, she developed a strong anger. These people were her own. And they were defeating the cause.

Though there were mainly religious motives proposed by her mother, and these she valued, there was one bit of worldly advice that never left her. She would always remember the words and tone of voice, in which they were given.

Her mother said: "There are other things more important, Kate, but there are only three things the world will judge you by. How do you dress? How do you speak? How are your table manners?" She pushed a rebellious and still ebony hair back under her sidecomb and she added: "Be a lady first, and whatever else you're going to be, second."

Kate maintained her diction, so that its precision was without consciousness: the perfection of her table manners flowed over into a rare discrimination in good food; her mother's skill with the needle never became hers, but she was imbued with a sense of fine materials and elegance of cut. She found at home and at school that what she saw others do, she could usually do a little better. This discovery had a double and sometimes contradictory effect upon her. Where her observation led to an easy accomplishment and improvement, she became bored, knowing that she could always do it and could call upon it when it was needed. If the skill were difficult, mastery was a compulsion.

In school this ability at learning by observation could not alone bring her to the head of her classes. She was not remiss in the rote of memorization, or repetition or accuracy. Indeed, in verbal skills she became devoted to the exact words of the endless and daily memory gems, which were all so very improving. But she had no flair for imaginative expression; her declamatory style was too repressed for her moment; and though she could do it if necessary, she found it as against the grain to stick in similes and metaphors and figures of speech to "enliven her writing" as to make the studied gestures to be more graceful when she spoke her pieces. In other words, she was no Elizabeth.

In the one area of assimilation by observation, she was a genius. But that alone, does not make one a teacher's pride. Even Sister Benigna, for all her shrewdness and experience, did not observe that little Kate learned things differently; but when she learned them, she knew them better than the other scholars.

And so Kate Horan never really liked school.

What she fell in love with, at this time, was Kingston.

41

She and her mother went several times to see Elizabeth. From the very first, Kate knew that it was her city.

There are some proud towns that wear an air of distinction that they never shed. Some of them are not more beautiful, some do not have any more rich historical legacy than their more humble sisters, but everyone brags of having come from them. They are widely and strangely scattered, sometimes in most unlikely places. There is Litchfield, Connecticut, quite different from Terryville; there is Appleton, Wisconsin, not much more charming than Oshkosh; there is Lafayette, Indiana, which thinks itself New Orleans; and there is Victoria, so distinct from Vancouver.

Now Kingston has reason for its pride. Kate smelled it at once. Though its streets descend to the Cataraqui River, they do not clutter and crowd the river bank or huddle as they do in her birthplace. There is room for graciousness. And the Cataraqui spills in a wide stream into the magnificent breadth of the St. Lawrence, which had just flowered the roots of a thousand magical islands. The Cataraqui, too, bears with it romance, flowing down from the site of the Comte de Frontenac's Fort, which he built as a defense against the Indians.

Across on a hill stands another more recent fort, where Kate never tired of going, to hear the half mythical, often droll accounts of its building, how it was made to defend Canada in 1812, when there was fear still, from the Ohio Rebellion, and how it faces the wrong way, for wasn't it built from the plans for Kingston, Jamaica, confused by the architect, who, thrown into chains, committed suicide while on his way back to Europe to be executed?

She knew of the very recent grimness, when in the Rebellion of '36 the fort had been a prison and a place of execution and dark suffering dwelt in its black holes.

It was all sunlight now, and she was allowed to see the brilliant uniforms of the imperial troops, the pageant of the changing of the guards and one bright sunset when a Scots regiment was in residence to hear the skirling. The pipes raised forgotten Gaelic echoes in her blood.

Near the center of the city was another barracks, divided in two sectors by a narrow street, down which she often

42

went. But these barracks chilled her with their gray bleakness, particularly the one to the north, since it was almost abandoned now. And another place did not suit her fancy, since it, too, made of the same gray stone, looked to her eyes almost like the barracks. It was Regiopolis College, which she came upon after a leisurely half-hour stroll. It, too, was a forbidding structure. She did not know then that both the barracks were to be her homes, or least of all, that one of the seminary students whom she saw distantly, playing ball in their soutanes, was to change and influence the whole course of her later life.

(Mr. Harkins was blurred in the indistinction of a crowd.)

In the main, however, there were enchanting things about Kingston. It had quite recently and for four years, been the Capitol, a distinction which, like Philadelphia and Richmond, it could never forget. Furthermore, its great, gangling, loose-limbed hero, a rich-man's Abraham Lincoln, whom the town would always claim, though historians might deny, as the true founding father of the Dominion, was very much in evidence. Sir John MacDonald's ambling gait and assumed backcountry drawl did its best to offset the almost feudal splendor of his family's estate, Heathfield, toward the west boundaries of his city, and to which when his political career was over, like Washington to Mt. Vernon, he was to retire. In the years to come, both the barracks and Sir John's palace were to belong to the congregation that her sister helped to found, and, for a time, to which she would bind herself.

Symbolically too, Kingston meant a change for the better in Elizabeth or in her attitude toward Kate. After the first news of their initial visit, Elizabeth seemed more happy to see them, to introduce them to her new friends. Why should she not? Mother and daughter were smartly, and Kate even jauntily, dressed. The little girl had impeccable manners and impeccable speech. And Kate was so eager for Elizabeth's love that she did not wish to accept what she soon suspected—that Elizabeth was showing them off, and through them, proving the superiority of her own background. Her new appearance of warmth was not totally altruistic. This became unmistakable on her rare visits home at Belleville. During them, she could and did revert into her constant disapproval of her younger sister.

Kate had always thought that Elizabeth was beautiful. She had taken for granted that she herself was the ugly duckling, hopeless now of ever being statuesque, which was the praise-word of the moment. She knew she was a scrawny little thing, all edges of elbows and knees, and was delighted when the styles and her age allowed her dresses to conceal her knees and frilly pantaloons to cover ankles; furthermore, it was a relief to her that female knees and legs would never be mentioned in her presence, as a lady again. Even ankles would become insteps.

The new view of her sister came accidentally at the convent school. Kate's withdrawal tended to give her the quality of invisibility. As she sat motionless and tiny behind some asphodel, two of the *jeunes filles* passed through the great hall, neither seeing her nor lowering their voices—and she knew they were talking about herself and her family.

"I don't care what you say," Maud said to Bridie, "I just think it must be hard for them."

"Why? What's so hard about it?"

"Well, how would you like it if you were so plain and you had such a beautiful mother? And how do you suppose their mother feels—trying to dress them up to look like something, as if clothes could make them into anything you'd like to look at twice?"

"Heavens! I never thought of that," Bridie agreed and, as she had been taught in the convent, added something charitable. "But at least Katie has beautiful hair."

Then they were gone. Only the sudden mirror remained.

Kate looked at her sister. It was true. Elizabeth was plain. Her clothes distracted you, but they were the product of her mother's good taste. As for her personal endowments, it was her posture, her poise, her perfect grooming and above all, that ineffable self-assurance that beautiful women wear and not her features, not even her hair—for the ringlets, as Kate saw them now, were stringy—that deluded you on first glance.

Her mother? Odd, she had never considered her mother's beauty. It had always been there, was taken for granted, like the lily-loveliness of the Virgin Mary. Kate studied her mother intently now.

Her hair had suddenly gone pure white, over black brows,

making her look like the last queens of France. Though Kate had never seen her when the perfect rose of Erin was on her cheeks, the texture of her skin, the whiteness of it was so flawless and still so unlined, that the resemblance to the *Grande Dames* of the *Ancient Regime* was startling, for you would swear that only a delicate powder could have produced this perfection—uncharitable to a lady who would have considered powder and rouge a mortal sin.

Yes. Her mother was beautiful.

When she returned to Belleville she looked at herself in the mirror, and committed vanity, which she duly confessed next Saturday. No. Her sister was better looking, there was no doubt about that, but she herself, she knew had better hair. She had never really noticed it before, but it was soft and full and glossy, waving in the natural curls that Elizabeth had to induce by artifice. Besides, she thought, examining her face with some care, she was pert. Her mother was beautiful; Elizabeth carried herself well; but she was pert. She would rather be pert.

She went about being pert for considerable time after that, and it may have been her pertness that attracted the *boy*. She was to remember it years later, how he looked that day: how his hair curled over his ears, how he had not yet grown up to his nose, and the eager fox-terrier look about him. It was to be to her always her one and only symbol of romance. Because the boy deliberately waited to walk home with her and Emma! He did not quite get up the courage to ask if he might carry her school bag, but he did manage to walk on her side, pushing Emma almost onto the lawns.

Kate liked it. Yes she did. Though when she realized that she liked it and recognized it as a temptation, she managed somehow to get Emma between them, and they walked the rest of the way home that way, while Kate felt, for the first time, lonely and strange, as if she would have liked to walk next to the boy, and get the aroma of him, as she had before, that smelled like bread and butter.

Never again though was she to allow this to happen and was to limit her male acquaintances to her father and her brothers. She squelched the boy. The day she found an apple in her desk, she took it gingerly and put it where it belonged—on top of his desk, where it gleamed red and accusing, a symbol of rejection. He never tried any stunts like that again.

She did not feel particularly self-righteous about her act, but she knew that she must discourage him. It was perhaps the first inkling of her vocation, which was to follow with great surety almost at once.

When she became a nun, Mother Mary of Providence never denied that Elizabeth's entering the convent influenced her deeply, or much less that it was her sister's choice of congregations that determined her life's dedication to the Sisters of Charity of Providence: though the year before 1861 and all its tragic events served as a preparation for both the Horan girls. In the very first days of the Civil War, their newly americanized brother John enlisted in the armies of the North, and remained with them for four bitter and dangerous years.

It was not Martin Horan's fault. Indeed, as his own business increased with the war needs, it was opposed to his own best interests that his nephew and apprentice ran off to the wars. Yet, though the family of James Horan must have or should have sensed this, they felt that since Martin was *in loco parentis*, he should have seen to it that no such dangerous folly be tolerated. It made the Canadian Horans more careful guardians of their three younger boys, lest they get any foolish notions in their heads, and it sent a chill through their mother's heart whenever her boys told brave tales of the Negroes whom they helped to their final experience of freedom. Somehow the dangers of the boys became more and more associated with blameworthiness on the part of Martin Horan and the coldness that developed between the American and the Canadian brother, together with the United States distrust of British feeling during the War between the States, this did not help James in his now inferior position in the blacksmith's shop. As Martin's fortunes rose, James' business dwindled and trickled almost to nothing. To Martin, it meant operating at a loss in Belleville; to James, an almost welcome cessation of concern. His family felt no real want—only a little pinch at times—and also a disturbing awareness that they were really living on

46

Martin's generosity.

Above all, however, John's physical dangers—accounts of which he delightedly sent home to his family as all soldiers do—the worry about the romanticism of the other boys, plus the increasing financial problems, drove the Horans even more to their knees. The novenas now were perpetual, the rosaries incessant.

No doubt but the family's increased worry and devotion made it easier for Elizabeth to enter the convent. Not that they would have any objection to having a daughter a nun, which was a mark of God's favor, but perhaps her choice of congregation might have been an obstacle, had they not seen in it a certain sign that if they made the sacrifice, gave Elizabeth fully, like Isaac, that God would fulfill His part of the unspoken bargain, keep John from danger, and assure the stability of the younger boys.

For Elizabeth had chosen not the well-established and completely respected Sisters of Loreto. Of all things, she entered a new, struggling group of nuns, not fully accepted in Kingston, who behaved in ways that shocked the pious, such as begging from door to door. Granted they were hungry, it was still a funny way for nuns to act.

But Elizabeth, remember, had felt rejected by the Sisters of Loreto. She would not try them again. And once she knew that the Call was real, since it would not go away, the only other nuns around were the new splinter group from Montreal, who had just arrived in Kingston and had taken over the barracks that Kate had found so formidable. In fact, Elizabeth was only the third postulant to enter the new convent. She was fifteen then. Desperately, the nuns over-worked, understaffed—welcomed the little girl. "She is mature for her years," they said. Perhaps she was. She had worked in the mills.

# CHAPTER 4

In 1842 a group of laywomen who had labored together under the leadership of Marie Emmelie Tavernier Gamelin for almost fifteen years—first in the caring of the old and abandoned and later, expanding their services to the cholera plague, the starving Irish of the Famine, all the waifs and strays of the rapidly overflowing city of Montreal and by 1843, under Bishop Bourget—were granted the Rule of St. Vincent de Paul, received the holy habit and began the structuring that would form them as Daughters of Charity. In this they were repeating a pattern, from day-dedication to cloisterized monasticism. Each step in formalization was received with rejoicing until precious few remnants of their original dedication remained.

Less than twenty years later and ten years after the death of Mother Gamelin, a new vitalization occurred along with the establishment of the community at Kingston. The very stiffness of the chronical account of this foundation is in itself indicative:

"On the twentieth day of January, 1861, his Lordship, Right Reverend Edward John Horan [no relation] Bishop of Kingston, Ontario, visited the Community of the Sisters of Charity of Providence, in the Motherhouse known a *Asile de la Providence* and presented his petition that three or four sisters be given him to commence a foundation in his Episcopal City of Kingston. Reverend Mother Philomena, who was Superior of the Institute at first refused alleging for reasons that no Members of her Community could consent to separate themselves from their Mother House; also that the Missions of Oregon and Chile were calling loudly for an increase of Sisters and that under the circumstances, she could not spare Sisters for Kingston. Not to be dissuaded, the Bishop renewed his petition, in which he was supported by the Bishop of Montreal, Right Reverend Monsignor Bourget, and on the twenty-eighth day of August, 1861, the new foundation was accepted by General Council of the Community.

Among other things, it is noticeable that the objection of the General Superior was overcome in eight days, along with the reluctance of her community to leave the Mother House and the needs of Oregon and Chile. Equally noticeable is that the capitulation was due to the combined force of two who were non-members of the Congregation, but they were Bishops.

Even the chronicler notes that such precipitance was not usual; that generally such matters were decided only after mature deliberation supported by fervent prayer. But she goes on to observe with detached objectivity and without any provable tongue-in-cheek that on the twenty-eighth day of August the council met with the Bishop presiding. The Mission was duly established.

Be that as it may, on December 13, 1861, four Sisters arrived at the British center of Kingston and of these foundresses only Sister Mary Anselm McAuley could speak a word of English.

Then to the regret of all there was a repetition of the relatively unstructured life of Emmelie Gamelin's first days. Four women could scarcely adapt themselves into a fully integrated or regulated community or least of all constitute themselves a novitiate when applicants joined them with a real mistress of novices or a real noviceship regime.

To such a group Elizabeth entered, and after a semi-cloistered postulancy, received her white veil from Bishop Horan and was plunged immediately, ready or not, into the work.

Sister Mary of the Seven Dolours was the name they chose for her. She was not allowed to visit her home, but now at last her family could drop in at the convent almost as often as they wished. Later visits were reduced to once a month, then to three times a year and once a year during the novitiate.

The period 1862 to 1866, which included the usual time for Sister Dolours' postulancy and novitiate, became in the annals of the Sisters of Providence of Kingston, the heroic age, the age of the giants. Later they were to romanticize the poverty, the dedication, the cold of these pioneer women in their Canadian winters; but it was to be years before they reached the point of emulation.

Like many a nun in these and the times to follow, Sister Dolour's training was by doing. During this long period there was precious little theoretic instruction in the spiritual or conventual life or precious little patterned and formal education. When at home in Kingston, the tiny Community tried to live a cloistered life, but with the practical burdens of their existence upon them, it was more of a token than a reality. And it was this lack of legalistic regularity that made the laity reject them, since to their picture of what nuns should be like, these ladies did not or could not conform. Only one nun complied with their picture. Sister Edward rarely went foraging but stayed in the convent like a regular sister.

It was somewhat different among the people of the outlands to whom they went abegging. The response of the peasants was warm and generous; the clergy sometimes reacted somewhat adversely, but after all the nuns were siphoning off from the parishes the pittances that would have come in the collections to build and maintain the sometimes huge and cathedral-like churches that were rising in the hamlets of the wilderness.

The winter of '63 was bitter cold with a swirl of blasts that swept from the Arctic to Andersonville. The girl, now Sister Mary Dolours and the ascetically fragile lady, Sister Mary John, who was scarcely older, but professed, bundling themselves up as best they could, froze on their open sleigh from Epiphany to Ash Wednesday. They returned to Kingston only four or five times to deposit their collections; and in the hope of finding a warmth that was seldom possible in the frigid cells of their barracks where the sisters huddled as much as possible in the one small heated room, in which the cook-stove served many purposes, and dreaded the damp chapel, to which only Sister Edward went with any regularity, her fingers blue on her rosary. But it was worse to have to retire to their rooms, and it was with reluctance that most of them removed the holy habit, in reverence, before they tried vainly to make a sleeping bag out of the frigid sheets and the ancient blankets that had been thinned to unprotectiveness by many an over-washing.

The money that the Sisters brought back with them went

50

at once into the general till, and its usage was known only to the Superior, Mother Mary of the Blessed Sacrament and her bursar and assistant, Sister Mary Andrew. Only once when she was a very young religious did Sister Dolours mention this lack of communication to Sister Mary John.

"I wish," she had dared to say as they drove along in one noontide slackening of the cold, "I wish they'd tell us sometimes where our money goes to. After all, we make it for them."

Sister Mary John, a gentle girl, took a moment or two to answer. In that moment she remembered that Sister Dolours was not yet fully formed, and that God did not promise to send them Religious, but women of the world, who must learn, not know by intuition, what it was to be a nun.

She said: "Little Sister, soon you will be taking your vow of Poverty. Then God will give you the grace to know that any money we collect is not ours, nor any disposing of it. And in the Community there are no *they* and *we*. All of us are instruments whom God has chosen, *superiors* and *subjects*. And it is better for subjects not to question superiors, because subjects have not the grace to make decisions. But you will know all this when you take your Vows." Sister Mary John believed implicitly in the mystical gift that they called "The Grace of State." This meant that when one was given an office, an ordination, even motherhood for the married, Almighty God sent the wisdom necessary to the duty. It was a charismatic theory held by the best minds of the Middle Ages and the Renaissance, extending upward to the coronation of Kings and Popes. For if God gave the duty of rule, He must, reasonably give the virtues necessary to good rule. It was a theory held more tenaciously by superiors than by subjects who occasionally saw contradictory evidence.

Though Sister Dolours felt vaguely uneasy about the answer, she did her best then and later not to voice her objections, putting them down into the back pockets of her mind, regretting them when they burst out remotely catalogued as "bad thoughts," though that shibboleth meant something quite different and utterly unmentionable, except in Confession. The Grace of State was almost as fundamental as the Natural Law.

51

Yet had the subject sisters known what was done with the money they earned or collected, they would not only have been satisfied, but amazed; for it seems incredible to an outsider how generations of nuns managed to exist on the pittances they received. Yet Superiors had a mystique of their own, also sanctioned by the best minds of the past. It was a theory of Divine Providence, based upon the care of sparrows, which held that if God wanted a work done, he would send the means. Their conventual mythology supplied example after example of unforeseen material deliverance at the imminent moment—but not before—of absolute catastrophe, which implies a rather sadistic sense of humour in the Deity. Yet this mystique, all apocryphal stories aside, seemed to work, and is a matter of fact, to which this document gives contributory if merely suasive evidence.

There were, however, two other areas related to this pious theory. One was good. The unquestioning subordinate could relegate all financial worries to two people—the Superior and the Bursar, accepting what they received as from the hands of God. Filled with this spirit, they could live, as many of them did, like rather restricted lilies of the field. The other fringe result was not good. Living as most of them did and do, on scrimping but Providence-trusting penury, they saw no reason why others could not do the same. This led to the appalling underpayment of their help. Under the guise of assisting the needy, they employed semi-cripples, debilitated aged, moronic incompetents or in the higher echelons even of teaching, professionally unequipped and unaccredited lay people, who because of various lacks were unemployable elsewhere and out of desperate need would accept a pittance—of which the payment was not infrequently unconscionably delayed. Yet to do them credit the Religious never once thought of this as gross social injustice—taking advantage of the needs of the poor to defraud them of a living wage. For did not the religious live this way themselves? And were they not and are they not abetted by their desperate retainers, who edified by the example of their employers, drudge in the Service of God and are troubled in conscience if they press for adequate or timely compensation? But these

52

more massive considerations never troubled Sister Dolours. She just wondered what happened to the money. For she was to become adept at begging, and in later years and from farther abroad, she was to return home with very adequate sums indeed!

Yet it would have done no harm for her Superiors to share their accounting with their subjects. At this time the Sisters of Providence of Kingston were sheltering as many orphans as they could accommodate. Following Mother Gamelin, their foundress' example, they housed and fed and washed numberless indigent, frequently querulous old women. These young and old were permanent. But in addition, the doors of the portery were never closed, and there came to them off the streets, without questioning, the girls big with child, the women of the road, the runaways. The clothing that the nuns begged and even the food did not go for themselves but for the migratory and the indigent.

During these four years also, the Sisters had, out of their pitiably small numbers, dedicated their services to the local women's prison, a distance of some miles, which they walked to when they could, or when, with reluctance, they must ride, paid for their own transportation. While they were there they prepared the Chapel for Sunday Mass and trudged home with a basket of altar linen that they mended and cleaned and starched with scrupulous devotion, for might not a crumb of the Body of Christ fall upon it?

It is significant of their financial condition, that there was great rejoicing when, after four years of gratuitous service, the news leaked out to the subjects that they received a check for one hundred and fifty dollars, or about thirty-eight dollars a year from the Inspector of Prisons for their sacristy labors and were promised an annual allowance of twenty-three dollars, a little less than fifty cents a Sunday. Of course the instructions and counseling of the female prisoners, the taking of them in after their release, was never compensated for. This was a work of zeal. It would be almost sacrilegious to be paid for this.

Their needs were supplied by Divine Providence, abetted by Sister Dolours begging from the English-speaking, and Sister Mary John from the French Canadians.

53

The two mendicants had hoped that the winter of '63 would modify by February of '64, but though there had been a thaw and the temperature was statistically higher, a dampness settled in by Ash Wednesday and the white, dry blizzards of the winter turned to a biting and clinging sleet while the dampness crept through their shawls and garnitures into their marrow. The sleet froze on the horse's whiskers and made strange icicle patterns from his nostrils.

They knew before three o'clock that they could not make it to the nearest rectory nor were they sure from their last experience, that they would receive more than a grudging welcome. As it was the beginning of Lent, they had begun their fast and the cup of coffee and single slice of unbuttered bread that was all that they had allowed themselves, manufactured no heat from within. If they were caught here on what looked like a tundra, when nightfall came, it would be hard if not dangerous going.

It seemed to them, after their decision to seek shelter, to be an eternal distance with no perceptible human habitation. The scattered farmers here were still cutting their way out of the wilderness, still in the defiant process of turning the forests into pastoral and arable land.

Sister Dolours fought down the panic in her breast; Sister Mary John's lips were moving in prayer. "Send us a house, Lord!" which was rather an odd prayer when you think of it from Olympian security.

At last God sent them a house. It was a hovel, really, camouflaged by the drifts that had conquered the zigzag wooden snow-breaks. The sisters momentarily tethered the horse, who resented it, to the visible top of the gatepost, and then slithered and skated down the remains of a path to the only door. They knocked in ladylike fashion at first while Sister Dolours feared, since they saw no smoke from the chimney, that the shack had been deserted, and Sister Mary John's confidence in God's providing was tested but not found wanting. Then they beat upon the door with a curious sense that some living thing was within—though they heard no sound, felt no stir. In desperation they pushed open the unlocked door.

There were five children within, kneeling in terrified

prayer around a table. Though the oldest child should have been able to replenish the fire, it had gone out. Her eyes were not quite bright. From the grate there came now much smoke little heat. But the enclosure was out of the extreme cold.

When the children saw the nuns, all but the littlest one who cried in fear, they ran and buried their faces with love in the sodden and cold skirts of the sisters. Sister Mary John beamed upon them, but Sister Dolours stirred up and replenished the fire. Sister Mary John tried her French patois on them, but they gaped back at her till Sister Dolours tried them in English, which they answered with rich and unconverted brogues, which elicited that Da had gone to Church, that Da should be home.

As the nuns busied themselves caring for them—the baby in particular, who was in an outraged mess—Sister Mary John could not resist giving her novice companion a little homily. "Do you see, Sister, what is the meaning of the Holy Habit? It is not we as women whom these children love. It is our garb—it is all the nuns in the world! How fortunate we are to be clothed in Christ!" And the young sister experienced a massive tender feeling of identification with the thousands of Brides of Christ clothed everywhere in the uniforms of love, and with joy, she shed her individuality.

But at that moment there were loud cries from the children and a more personalized love—action of thumping and banging and little side-warfares for position, as they greeted their Da after he had burst through the door.

"Na, Na," he said. "Didn't I tell you to be kneeling at the table when I came in?" And seeing the nuns he added, "and leave way for the good sisters who have blessed the house by their coming," and as the nuns also knelt, not knowing why, he added, "I glimpsed the buggy at the post, excusing the language, and I'll get your horse in the shelter after the doing."

With that he took a collection envelope from his pocket, and beginning with the nuns and including the infant in arms, he smeared the foreheads of each with the black and holy ash of Lent, saying as he did so, like a priest, "Remember man that thou art dust, and unto dust thou shalt return," pledging even the infant to forty days of Lenten fast for sins.

When the ceremony was finished, the father who suddenly seemed exhausted sat down heavily. "I'll tend to your beast in a tick."

Sister Mary John was all tact. There was no possible room for them here. "Oh it won't be necessary, sir," she said. "We only paused for a moment to warm ourselves. We'll be going on in a jiffy." Sister Dolours looked alarmed.

"And where will ye go?" he asked.

"To the nearest rectory—the convent," Sister Mary John replied.

"Ye'll not make it," he replied. "Tis the back of beyond. Tis twenty miles if a foot, and it's four now by the clock. I'll tether the horse." He rose wearily.

"Where were you yourself?" Sister Dolours asked.

"At the Church, of course. Where else would I be this holy day of obligation?"

It was irrelevant to tell him that Ash Wednesday, though a holy day, was not of obligation. "How did you get there? And back?"

"On Shank's mare." He pointed to his legs. "What did God give me these for?"

"Glory be to God," Sister Dolours lapsed into the Irish, and then practically, "When did you eat last? Was there nothing along the road?"

"There was not. And 'twas last night since I had the morsel."

Sister Mary John, comprehending, took up the thread. "Oh, you poor man!" she cried. "So you fasted for Holy Communion."

The father enlightened her, poor innocent soul. "Tis not for the likes of me, sinner that I am, to approach the holy table till Easter time. 'Tis grand for you, holy souls that you be. But not for a poor layman like me."

"But you didn't need to fast just to go to Mass," Sister Dolours burst out and was silenced by a glance from Sister Mary John.

"So I was taught in Mayo," he said, "and excusing your better knowledge, I'll teach my children the same." Now he presented a stubborn wall to them, a man talking to mere women. "Now I'll go shelter your beast," he said, "and ye'll stay for the night."

With the slamming of the door, the sisters scurried to the larder and the stove. They found some potatoes, some coarse bread, some herb tea, and when the father returned, laden down with such blankets as were not needed for the horse, the potato water was beginning to boil, sending up a warm and soothing steam.

The man dumped the blankets, all save one, in the corner near a second bunk. "The boys can sleep on these," he said, pointing to the heap, "and you can rest in the big bed, if you don't mind the two of you." Carefully he was adjusting the reserved blanket for a screen across the corner where the nuns would repose in all modesty.

"Where will you sleep?" Sister Mary John asked.

"On the outside of the boys—between you and them. They're scamps," he grinned, "and they might be tempted to peak in at you. They're scallywags," he said. The little boys, too, grinned with delight, like imps.

While the children dropped off to sleep one by one—two girls and the infant in the bunk, two boys in the blankets on the floor—the father and the nuns talked until very late about the state of the world and of the church. It was almost nine when after the politest of yawns all around, that they went to their respective resting places.

The morning, thank God, was bright and brittle. After their breakfast of bread dipped in the tea, the nuns prepared to go, the father bundling up their blankets, hitching up their horse. But while he was busy outside, Sister Dolours had proposed that they give him some of the orphans clothes that they had collected, but Sister Mary John had only shaken her head. "I wouldn't do that," and though Sister Dolours did not understand at the moment, she did later. For just as they were about to depart, the father scowled in mock severity at his young.

"Is there nothing you have to give to the good sisters for their orphans?" he demanded. The children, except for the baby, looked sheepish. The baby only looked old and disapproving.

"Oh no!" Sister Dolours cried! "We did not come to

beg—and was just caught by Sister Mary John's cough from adding—"From poor people like you."

"Arr, I know that," he said. "Sure if you came to beg, I'm such as might give you nothing, I'm that mean."

Somewhere he found a sack of flour. He said to his oldest, not quite bright one, "Measure out a quarter of it for the orphans." She understood, and did so with some undue generosity, then her father answered the unspoken objections. "My nippers aren't orphans while they got me. And herself is alive and God will send her back to me. She has the weakness," he said.

The weakness. Consumption, tuberculosis. Call it what you will. Hacking out her life in bloody coughs while she carried her last child. Living somehow through the wild winter to the spring and the agonizing childbirth.

What the father told no one, nor ever would, for it was such a thing that no decent man would speak of, was his intimate relations with his wife. Like poverty of the spirit to the rich was the purity of his wife to him. His Mary had been obedient to him, but through their marriage she had maintained her mystical virginity.

Many's the night, he remembered, he had prayed to Our Lady for strength, but as the children were proof, there had been times—

After the babe came, he would see the strain in his Mary's eyes until she had been churched and could go to the sacraments again. Then he would pray the harder, try harder to respect her. As penance she offered the birth-pangs, God's punishment on Eve, and now her illness, which came into the world with the fall of mankind. But what could he do, who had brought this on the pure woman he loved?

How did a sinner like him dare to go to Holy Communion even once a year?

His mind came back to his guests. "She's with the good sisters in Kingston," he told them. Then it came out that she was spending the long winter in their own community and the bond between them all strengthened, until the nuns barely escaped without the rest of the bag of flour.

During the twenty miles of jewelled morning, on their way to a gruff and reluctant permission to stay at the rectory,

Sister Dolours asked: "What was his name?" and Sister Mary John puckered her forehead and replied: "I don't know. I don't think he told us."

"But then"—Sister Dolours laughed dryly—"We didn't tell him ours."

Sister Mary John smiled into herself. "We have no names, Sister. We have given up our names with our families and with our worldly garments." And then she added with some rueful humour, "What externs ever remember our names?"

It was to such tales as these that Kate Horan listened during the next three years; and though she sat quietly, there was wonder in her. And in the daydreams of her rather solitary life, the same kind of vision that had inspired her father and uncle came to her—the same kind of hunger and driving force that was to put the compulsive fever of far places in the blood of her brothers.

Then a second thing happened. In the summer of 1865 the Sisters of Providence came to Belleville, so that she could see and touch them. Her first schoolgirl crush centered upon the extremely young and extremely nunnish superior, Sister Mary Edward, who appealed to her for all the reasons that she could not find in the sister of her blood. Sister Mary Edward, though indeed so young that she could not be appointed by the Bishop of Kingston as a true superior, but must be termed "Sister Servant," had nonetheless acquired all the conventions of the authentically conventualized sister. She knelt endlessly rigid in chapel; she answered on the first call of the bell, leaving even her duties unfinished; she never once broke silence, raised her voice or her eyes, or skipped her prayers either of obligation or of devotion; she never sacrificed her Rule to coddle others, deviations which too often were motivated by the desire to gain esteem among men.

To Kate's almost inborn value of self-discipline, encouraged by her mother, came Sister Mary Edward as the ideal and model. Sister Dolours was too unmortified to satisfy her completely. And the fact that Sister Mary Edward treated her with distant reserve, exactly as she treated everyone else, made her occasional notice, the more devastatingly desirable.

As to the others of the new community, there were only two, if you didn't count the laywoman who taught music—Miss Meagher from the town. These two also were attractive and both young and demure, as befits the novices that they still were. For what Kate could scarcely realize was that Bishop Horan had chosen, and the Kingston Community had accepted under episcopal obedience, that the Belleville community be founded by three untrained novices, to pass on and to create that peculiar charism that they called "The Spirit of the Congregation." For Sister Mary Edward was herself a novice.

Nor did Kate have the slightest idea of the upset that had happened in Kingston when the Bishop pounced down on them with the decree that the already burdened and cutoff community there, should send three of its sparse numbers to establish a new mission. The very thought was appalling, and who could blame the sisters if they sent three of the more expendable—three novices instead of three professed—and as the Chronicle of Kingston says, with delicious understatement, the three Foundresses "Set out with no other guide than the mandate of obedience."

That the two other novices under their Sister Servant did not experience the full joys of Christian living, is not in itself surprising, that they persevered in their vocation and established a meaningful community, is miraculous. It was also this simply perceived dedication that influenced Kate Horan.

But the loss of personnel was nothing when compared with the greatest blow that was to befall the Kingston community in that year of 1866.

There were among them only two remaining foundresses, one of them, their Mother Superior. She had already made her duty-visit to the Montreal Motherhouse and had assured her sisters that her travels for the year were over. They were disturbed therefore when they saw that she and her assistant, the two mature women, the two heads of the house, were preparing for a further trip. Nor did they say a word, since they had been commanded under Holy Obedience to hold their peace. Once only the nuns found the assistant, Sister Mary Andrew, in tears, and even the control of their superior could not keep the strain from her eyes.

One Tuesday—without a word of farewell, without a good-bye—their two leaders departed forever from them. But when they had gone, the Bishop came himself, and in one flat sentence informed the community that he had personally dismissed their superiors, sent them back to Montreal—since he didn't want any foreign influence in his diocese. And then he whipped out of his black bag two little dolls dressed as nuns—but as such nuns as the Sisters of Providence had never seen.

"My nuns," said his Lordship, "will change their habits. They will copy this dress that I have got for them from Ireland. And my sisters will remember every time they put it on that they are not French, but English-speaking Canadians of the Regiopolis Diocese."

It is no doubt sentimental, that the abandoned children wept almost as much for their change of clothing from the uniform and garb they had kissed each morning as for the loss of their leaders. They also resented the time-consuming preparation of the fluted linen dimity that the Bishop had chosen for their headdress and very really suffered from the burdensome expense of the Irish linen aprons they were forced to wear upon their daily rounds.

There was then a complete severance of the Montreal and the Kingston community in personnel, in uniform and the Bishop hoped, in spirit. There was resentment in Montreal, and that hurt worse because the sisters in Kingston longed to be reunited to the congregation they had chosen, joined and loved. But they could not tell the beloved in Montreal. For they were commanded to silence.

They obeyed.

Thus there came the great separation and the lasting rift.

# CHAPTER 5

It is not unexpected that Kate Horan at fifteen determined to be a nun and that she actually applied for admission to her sister's precarious congregation. She was not exactly turned down, for the need of novices was great, but her entrance was delayed for four years as it turned out. The reasons given for the delay illuminate the opinion that her contemporaries had of her glamorous sister Elizabeth. The congregation had accepted Sister Mary Dolours when she was too young, and though, by the Bishop's appointment and contrary to their desires, she was now the treasurer of the Kingston Community; they would not take a chance on the baby sister until she had attained more maturity! That they told this in complete frankness to Kate is in itself amazing to anyone who knows the tight-lipped secrecy of nuns about their internal affairs.

Kate's own secrecy was inherent. Though she had formally applied for admission to the religious life, she had not consulted her mother and did not report to her the decision of the religious. For four years she did not speak and of four years she speaks too little.

She had been inspired to declare her vocation by the experience of an Ignatian retreat called The *Exercises.* The facets of insight, which were then called Lights, that were to abide with her to a long, vivid memory was her Election, the center of the Exercises where the exercitant chooses a way of life. To her, it came forever, after the Meditation on the Call of Christ to the Apostles. She could recall exactly the words of the Jesuit Retreat Master:

"What was the difference between the Rich Young Man, and the twelve apostles? The Rich Young Man was satisfied with life in the world, and apparently lost his soul, since Jesus wept; though the Apostles had many faults, they answered the call of Christ fully and became his closest friends.

"They responded generously, leaving all. They responded

62

constantly, remaining faithful to Christ through three years, and after that, even to martyrdom. They followed constantly, for though they may have sinned like Peter or doubted like Thomas, they were given the grace of perseverance. They accepted their vocation; they kept the faith to the end.

"Only one of them was a traitor. Judas betrayed Christ, and as we know, 'Better that that man, the son of perdition, had never been born.' On the revelation of Christ we know that the man who lost his vocation, after vowing himself to Christ, is certainly in Hell.

"So you, my dear young ladies, can see what it means to reject the Call of Christ. The Rich Young Man did not follow Christ because it is harder for the rich to get into the kingdom of heaven than for a camel to get through the eye of a needle; Judas, who was already a religious, left Christ for thirty pieces of silver, and he hanged himself when he realized what he had done.

"Are you sure you have never heard the Holy Ghost whispering to you 'Come, follow me?' Corresponding with God's grace will you determine now to stay with Him until death, and not to be one of those few, but unhappy souls, why try vainly to live in the World after they have joined the happy household of the Lord, and become Brides of Christ?"

Kate was filled with a wonderful new feeling that was certainly the Call of Christ and the voice of the Holy Ghost. It was half exultation, realizing that God Himself had picked her out from millions to follow Him and to be His bride; and half with acute dread, that if she did not accept this great grace, she would lose her soul or worse, be damned forever with Judas, if having accepted it, she should ever leave the convent.

Hence, she applied for admission. When the nuns asked her if she felt she had the grace of perseverance, she answered with an outburst of emotional affirmation rare to her. Even so, they did not accept her.

Though this moment was the deepest experience she had yet had, her silence about it may be understandable; but her inexpicable reticences about the next four years of waiting, produce a disturbing mystery. Her journal is relatively detailed, but the most important facts of her life are embarrassingly missing.

In 1869, when finally she was accepted and entered the Sisters of Charity of Providence of Kingston, she finds herself living with her mother, in Watertown, New York. There is no further mention of her brothers or of her previously prosperous uncle in nearby Syracuse, no reason assigned for the leaving of Canada. We know only that she and her mother had lost or left a larger house in Watertown for a small cottage. There is no mention any more of the foundries of the past; and the burial records of her Uncle Martin show his occupation as laborer not owner or manager. But no matter what comedown he had had in the world, Martin left to his children and their descendants a legacy of education that enabled them to claim dignity in living and a breakthrough into the professional and business world.

But of her father we know nothing. She is utterly silent about him, with not a single mention of his death; and the city records of the places in which he might have been buried are silent too. Whether James Horan died during this period or went with his boys he simply disappears, seemingly even from the memory of his daughter. He was a quiet man.

In her autobiography Mother Mary of Providence speaks of her mother as a milliner, but perhaps we can see her better as a widowed or deserted woman eking out a precarious existence by her needle, as do the standard and cliche heroines of bad Victorian fiction. It may even be that Kate's education ceased at fourteen, not only because as she asserts, there were no available nuns' schools in Watertown, and she did not wish to expose herself to the Protestant environment of the Public School, but equally because she was needed to do full womanly duty in keeping up the house while her mother supported them.

Although her formal education stopped now, she began the self-training that she was to employ all her life. They had moved into the small cottage from the larger house where they had lived, and their former dwelling was now inhabited by an expatriate Canadian family, like themselves, but differing only in that the new family was French. With that exquisite ear for verbal sound that was her natural gift, Kate detected, though she knew precious little French, that the French this family spoke was different, somehow better, from the millhand patois she had heard around her as a girl. As a matter of fact, Eloise, the daughter, had gone to the better boarding schools as a child and spoke true French as beautifully as she spoke English badly.

The two girls entered into a pact. They would teach each other to speak their languages without an accent. Though Eloise doubtless profited, Kate emerged with flawless French; so that in later years, released from patronymics and therefore nationality, as nuns are, she was often mistaken for a Frenchwoman, and with some naughtiness went to no pains to deny it. But then, it was the time of the French nun, and she was not alone in her lack of candor.

Also, she read. Not novels — God forbid. The Scotch-Presbyterian woman next door called them Fables; the Swedish-Lutheran boy, Harken, crept into the barn to read the new installments of Dickens, and hid the sheafs under the hay when the Deacon, his father, came near; and the Catholic Mrs. Horan shared her neighbors' disapproval of what could be dangerous to a young girl's mind, and was a waste of precious time to anybody.

Kate read improving books; and why she hid them from her mother is as mysterious as why she did not confide in her that she had applied to the convent. But one day she was not quick enough in hiding her book and her mother bore down on her and snatched the volume.

It was Reeve's Bible history.

"Hmmph," Mrs. Horan snorted. "There's nothing the matter with that. Why did you hide it?"

In agony Kate answered, "I don't know," which was doubtless the truth.

"I don't understand you. I never stopped Elizabeth from reading. She always had a book in her hand. I only scolded her when she neglected her work. I don't mind good books — just not trash."

"Yes, mamma."

"But in the future, young lady, I want you to be more open. I don't like this furtive business. You're too sly."

Kate knew it was true. But what could she do about it?

There was a self hidden within her; and if she were to reveal it she would lose it.

And now — from her increasingly pious reading, from her secret and treasured waiting for a reply from Kingston, saying they would accept her — the usual self-imposed austerities of the person aware of a religious vocation began.

She went out less and less, making an eremite of herself. And then, perhaps from too great exposure to the fur-belowed women who came to her mother for dresses and hats, huge hats and prinked bonnets, she took a strong stand against vanity, punishing herself for having so often, when her mother was out fitting a customer, dressed up in the fine clothing that was almost finished, looking at herself in the mirror, and almost, but not quite ever, swaying her hips. And she loved the feel of clothes, heavy velvets, smooth satiny goods and silk.

Her greatest sin had been the day when she had asked her mother for a great orange plume for her hair.

"I think it's silly," her mother had said, "but nobody wants that thing," but gave it to her.

In her remorse, Kate in turn gave it away to Eloise, who, as a matter of fact, was never seen wearing it.

So then when her mother was making the necessary yearly trip to New York, to see and copy in her mind the latest fashions, she looked her daughter up and down and said, "I've got to get you some new clothes. You look a sight," and Kate had dictated very firmly what they were to be.

"I would like a brown and white checked dress," and then she added, without a sob, "and a sailor hat — with a blue band and streamers."

"I thought you wanted a willow plume," Mrs. Horan said in surprise.

"That was silly, wasn't it?"

"I suppose it was. What color straw?"

"Black."

"With a blue band and streamers? Well. I never."

But she returned from New York with the brown and the white and the black and blue, and Kate wore it. Bravely.

Weeks later she had only one qualm about it. Much to her surprise, one day in early August her mother had said, "I must go to Philadelphia for The Exposition, and I'd like you should come with me."

Had she been a demonstrative child, she would have flung her arms around her mother, but she only said, "Yes, mamma," and Mrs. Horan looked at her, bewildered. "At your age, I'd be dancing in the streets. You're a caution. Don't you want to go?"

"Oh, yes. Very much, mamma."

"Then you might show it. And by the way, I'd better make you a new outfit."

The visions of Philadelphia in gorgeous array could be controlled only during the daytime. In the half-sleep of night, they beset her with vanity.

That it was all an illusion of the Tempter became clear enough, when the letter from Kingston arrived, accepting her for the fifteenth of August.

Now she must tell her mother. There was even some letdown in the fact that Mrs. Horan did not seem to be in the least surprised.

"I have a duty, too," her mother said, "in seeing my children settled in life. If you feel that God calls you, go. And do not think of me."

Kate thought of her very much, all her life, even when the image and memory of her father had completely faded.

On the fifteenth of August, 1868, the Sisters of Providence of Kingston, Ontario had expected to be spiritually overjoyed. Two or three years ago they had been allowed the privilege of nocturnal adoration of the Blessed Sacrament, like real nuns. In the beginning they had allowed externs to join them, relieving some of the night watches, but since the Separation they had done all the vigils unaided. If it meant an extra sleepless hour for their aching limbs, who would object to that in the presence of the Lord. Many of them offered the physical discomfort for the sins that were being committed in the world, at those hours of the night.

Now, refreshed from their Ignation Retreat with Father Nash, who had even ended with the Contemplation To Attain Divine Love, instead of shingling it in with the Resurrection, as so many Jesuits did, the Bishop had allowed them to conclude with the Forty Hours Devotion, and there, before the exposed Blessed Sacrament in the gold monstrance — the white Deity with the rays coming from it — the tiny peripheral at which they gazed, centered without distraction — flickering of the candles, the scent of incense and flowers — the dimness, the occasional mystical monotony of the chant, the constant repetitive litany or rosary — there had been induced in them that exultation and disembodiment, which the religion of the West had inherited from its Oriental origins. From this they had emerged to the first real election of a superior that their new congregation had had.

The Bishop who was present in purple had lead the invocation, "Come, Holy Ghost, enlighten the minds of Thy faithful" — and they felt indeed, that they were in the Upper Room, as Father Nash had described it, when jets of fire had stood over every head and the sound of a great wind had been about the Apostles.

The lots fell upon Sister Mary Edward. From now on her commands would be, to them, the Will of God.

Then His Lordship broke the spell of their spiritual self-hypnosis. "Very well, Sisters," he said. "I approve your superior. But we don't need to go on with this." He fumbled in his cassock, below his pectoral cross, and came out with a scrap of paper. "I might as well appoint the others. It will save time. There aren't that many of you anyhow. Yes. Here they are: Assistant, Sister Mary of the Cross; Treasurer, Sister Mary of Seven Dolours; Mistress of Novices, Sister Mary John; Councillors, Sister Mary Jane de Chantal and Sister Mary Sacred Heart. There they are."

In her new position, Mother Mary Edward attempted to speak for them, voicing their mutual alarm. "But your Lordship", she began.

"Yes, Sister," his words hissed.

"It is not according to our Holy Rule. We must elect these officers — she was not even being coherent. The Bishop did not help her. "The Rule says —"

His Lordship waited through a stunning silence. He looked at them all, white, shaken but not daring to speak. "I am the Rule," he said clearly. "Let's be quite clear from the beginning. You are now a Diocesan Congregation, and you

68

are in my Diocese." And then he glared at the new mother general, "It's a fine thing to begin your career by defying your Bishop."

"I didn't mean to do that, your Lordship."

"Then don't. That's all there is to it." Almost perfunctorily he gave them the triple blessing, as they fell to their knees. Mother Mary Edward tried to leap up and bob down again to kiss the episcopal ring, but Bishop Horan stopped her. "That won't be necessary. All I expect from all of you is obedience."

He was gone. Mother Mary Edward glanced around at her new staff. If her glance lingered for a fraction of a disapproving moment on Sister Dolours, who though a good beggar, was a very bad bookkeeper, or if there was the slightest hint of despair as she looked at her two new Councillors, who had caused her such disapproval in Belleville, it was scarcely noticeable except to the elect. Then she too, disappeared, and the nuns went their silent and separate ways.

At the door a little postulant stopped Sister Dolours. "Your mother and your sister are waiting in the guests' parlor — quite a long time."

"I know," Sister Dolours said. Long enough for the Bishop to show the rest of them what he, at least, thought of her. The look that she had got from the new Mother General — I mean, Sister Servant — she had not missed.

So it is no wonder that her family found Sister Dolours, who was dying to talk, and could not, a little strange, and Kate Horan never really recovered from the chilliness of her reception.

She had been in a strange state of terror, living in a world of unreality, since they had arrived at Kingston. Though she was familiar with the convent, she saw it now, really saw it now.

It was still a barracks, with forbidding high stone walls, a formidable iron gateway, a heavy iron knocker on the impregnable door. The single cross surmounting the turret could not make it any less an army quarters than the similar graystone fortress, still occupied by soldiers, on the opposite side of St. Lawrence Street. Even the parlor in which they met Sister Dolours was more military than monastic, with its rush chairs in straight lines, a dull rag carpet and black and white religious prints — some stained as if coffee had been spilled on them—on the battleship gray walls. Katherine Horan smelled mildew and loneliness.

When she had said an all too abrupt farewell to her mother, Sister Dolours led her into the nun's garden, an enclosure in the center of gray walls, where the direct rays of the sun could only reach at noonday, looking she thought, for all the world like a prison courtyard.

There were fourteen nuns there, sitting in their stiff new habits, on stiff wooden chairs, erect; for a nun did not lean back for comfort.

She knew, too, and wondered, that as if at a signal, the group that had been grim before her coming galvanized into sudden chatter and laughter, edifying the new postulant with what the Rule called for: "All shall exhibit happiness, rather than any less moderate or contrary emotion."

And then an extraordinary thing happened. As her sister introduced her to the nuns, each one knelt down before her. Sister Dolours whispered, "Kneel down, kneel down." She did so, popping up after the first one but remaining fixed for the rest. Then each nun knelt and embraced her chastely and kissed her with dry lips on each cheek, saying in formula: "God grant you the grace of perseverance."

She was going to need it, she thought, even after she was allowed to rise and sit among them, and their laughter, not hers, rose.

So it began. The grace of perseverance was granted to her for seventy-four years.

## CHAPTER 6

In the bitter January of 1866 the young priest, Patrick Harkins, came to Holyoke. He was thirty-two years old and had been ordained at the Seminary of Laval University only two years before, during which time he had held only one curacy at St. Rose's Church, Chelsea, Massachusetts; and from the civilized environs of Boston to the Holyoke he found, this was a far cry indeed.

"Well," he said to himself that night, as he tried to get the cold out of his bones, exchanging it only for the damp of the cottage that served as rectory, which had been closed up for days and left fireless and of which he found himself the solitary inhabitant, "there's no place to go but up."

He had trudged the streets of his parish. Great ugly rows of mill houses were rising, becoming shambles within a year of their completion. In this city of 5,000 people the tenements of Canal Street, built for workers on the dams and in the mills, seemed to him to house the majority of the million and a half Irish immigrants who, during the decade before, crowded into America and who worked for five dollars a week.

Yes these reeking shambles — without sanitation when, in building the dam and the canals, the river was stagnant as it frequently was, and frozen scrofulously now — were para-disiac, compared with the terrifying shacks that still re-mained from the pioneer days of fifteen years ago when the Irish first came.

They had built their own huts in a day by sinking four uprights in the river-bank mud; over these they hoisted a roof of overlapping boards, and on the sides they left a door and cut little holes for windows; then they banked turf up to the eaves. In the vee of the roof there was a loft, and there they and their spawning progeny slept.

Though many of them had moved *en masse* from these reeking huts to their new jerry-built quarters, they had tried to retain their tribal identities, and there were areas that he

71

must learn — for they had staked out years ago, the domain of The Kerrys under John Delaney, and the warring Connaughts under their own autochthonous Daniel O'Connell. And they warned him even that day to be careful at night, for though no one would willingly harm the holy priest, bringing perhaps the Blessed Sacrament to the dying, the gangs might mistake him as he crossed from one territory to another.

In Irish parish, or less respectfully, the Patch, the Kerrys and the Connaughts united for only two things — the Sunday Mass and against the forays from Baptist village, with whom they maintained a constant and often bloody feud. The Baptist villagers, in turn, lived in a state of somewhat more civilized warfare, shown only by the more gentlemanly black eyes of their respective juvenile scions—with their betters, the congregationalists of both antipathetic members of the First and Second Church; but they owned the mills, contracted for the canals and ran the banks, and they never were to be seen in the Patch even by day but managed their tenants and their workers from an aloof and sanitary distance.

There was still a third group quite distinct but somewhat less involved. For cut off by language, they had formed a ghetto of their own and had as far as possible retained their French Canadian ethos and mores and could not even be said to join their Irish neighbors at Mass — for though they were physically present in St. Jerome's Church, they were as segregated and cut off, as if they had already had a church of their own. Because the Irish had begun to arrive in 1850 and the Canadians came down in 1852, the Irish considered themselves the older settlers, for could they not remember the coming of the Canucks; and the Canadians considered the Irish, in their hovels, since they had recently arrived on this continent, as barbaric Johnny-Come-Latelys, compared with their own seventeenth-century migration.

Now in 1864, as the nations and Father Harkins realized, all the enmities were bitterly increased, for what could you make of the young? The hordes of youth returning from the Civil War, where they had learned new and immoral ways, and the first generation now getting a whiff of the freedom in the air of America, were not like their parents, God knows.

72

to whom *their* parents had been second only to God, and to whom the word of the Priest had been God's law. It was so no longer.

What was happening to the young? 'Tis no wonder they shot Mr. Lincoln, though 'twas God's justice in a way, what with him going to a theatre on Good Friday, and though there were prayers for him, you wondered sometimes if they could work. And of course he was a Protestant, poor man.

The young priest, rubbing his feet in his cold house, and distracted by wondering if he could ever learn to darn his own socks, had not been theoretically unaware of these conditions. But they were his problems now. And he had had so short a time being a priest and protected a good deal by his old pastor at St. Rose's, who was none too eager to have the young curates mingle too much with the parishioners because he was of the mind that assistants went and came whereas pastors were the fathers of the flock. So the pastor did the baptizing and the marrying and the burying, and woe betide any strange priest from outside the parish who tried to horn in on these. The curates heard the confessions, took the sick-calls and counted the collections whereas the Order Priests came in only for the missions and were respected according to how little surviving contacts they kept with St. Rose's after they went back to their monasteries or from whatever kind of place they came.

Now Patrick Harkins knew, "I am the Pastor." The thought never crossed his mind to determine not to be like the priests whom he had known and honored, or least of all, to change the pattern, which as far as he could see, was in the established order of things, as certain as the rising and the setting of the sun. But he did determine to do several things. Tomorrow he would visit his Mission Parish across the river in Canal Village, at the Falls; he would write and ask his sister Grace to come at once; though Grace was a little fey, she could set his house in order at least until he had a woman of discreet years to watch over him. In two weeks he would sit down and write out everything that needed to be done.

Then he would do it.

The list that Father Harkins read was not in the order of importance, but his comments were informative, and he left for later annotations on sites for constructions, filled in dates of purchases and sometimes appended costs. Some things took years; some he did immediately; but all were accomplished and later implemented.

He was still alone as he read over the list, though Grace was to arrive within a week. At that moment he could only read the left hand column, it lenghtened to formidable proportions. His jaw set, his cragged handsome young face practiced the lines that were to be set with determination in the years to come. He ran his hands through the wire-curly hair, which went perfectly with the rest of his strength. He felt no motivation of ambition and was unaware of determination, not having room for anything save seething anger as he looked at the left hand of the incompleted list representing such injustices, enslavement, neglect — and yes sin.

What he said was perhaps less a prayer than it might ideally have been. He said, "My God!"

Before his reading of the list was far advanced, he knew what was to him the number one problem. It was the *drink*.

There were four saloons to each block of tenements; they called one street intersection, between the Connaughts and the Kerrys "Benzine Corner" and in back of it was where the rolled drunks lay and the men committed mayhem on each other, and the stinking shacks still survived called, "The Dog's Nest." Though the more respectable Yankees spoke only of the drunken Irish, and though it was against the tenets of the Baptists and Methodists, there were plenty of Swamp Yanks who didn't get their crops in when the cider was ripe; and there were plenty of proper old ladies who had headaches in the morning, were known to swoon when in company and had to lie down on the sofa. A fine example, too, that General Grant was to our boys drunk even in battle. Of course the elders always talked about the booze hitting the young, or the women about their men; but it was many a white poll that was bloodied, and in two years Father Harkins had got many a whiff in the confessional, during the Women's Mission, while they told him that they did nothing at all; God knows they were good women, they did nothing at all.

Above all, though, he thought, there were the owners of

the saloons, and they were Irish, too. Though everyone knew that there was a curse upon them, they grew richer and moved up the hill with the Protestants, and they sent their sons to Holy Cross in Worcester to become doctors and lawyers and some even Monsignors. That the Protestants had their own Temperance Societies, he knew, but you couldn't traffic with them, now could you? He never did.

If he found conditions a little better, even to the signs of drink, in Canal Village near Hadley's Falls, his heart went out to this cut-off flock, and he took his hat off to their devotion. There was no bridge over the river; and on Sundays they crossed by ferry or by rowboats above the dam. When because of floods or floating ice no boats could cross, they went by foot the long and dangerous way round: over the railroad trestle at Willimanset. As for the ferry and boat fares, he sighed, to think of the pennies that could have swelled his meagre collections.

As for his own personal finances, he was for his time a rich young man, and his small fortune must have come from his family. Certainly his money did not come from his own earnings — from over the brief period when he worked for Messenger Brothers in Boston, though his local biographers claim that his employers pleaded with him to remain in the field of commerce. But he left very shortly for his seminary training in Kingston, then later in Laval — therefore he could not have put aside the large sums we see him spending out of his own pocket: for properties in the next few years and then selling it to Bishop Williams for one dollar. These charitable expenditures amounted to at least eighteen thousand dollars, a sizeable sum at any time, and making doubly ironic the allegations made against him and his people, at the end of those two years.

Using his own funds, Father Harkins was expeditious about his purchases and building, but the Temperance Society retained precedence at least in his mind. He had his pulpit for thundering propaganda; and he had most of the women who suffered on pay nights on his side.

There were of course the usual number of morning-after-never-agains, and the repeated pledges for life; but within a few months there was a noticeable cut-back in liquor consumption in the Patch, enough to cause growls from the ginmill owners, but growls that never reached his ears — for it was not long before there was an awareness that this young bristly Irishman could growl back. Besides, the owners and tenders of the saloons had themselves, to fight with their uneasy consciences, and their superstitions that made them certain that every stroke of ill luck that came their way was the direct act of a punitive God. So it would not do to aggravate the crime by open resistance to the good pastor.

No. The opposition, when it did come strongly, arose from others who were fighting for the same cause — the Protestant Temperance League. To speak of a rift between this organization and what Father Harkins called the St. Jerome Temperance and Beneficial Society, is ridiculous because there had never been a moment of cooperation. If this seems odd, since both groups were working for the same good cause and since the only overtures came from the Protestant group that was summarily rejected by Father Harkins, it must be remembered that there were reasons on the side of the priest, valid enough to him, and to most of his Catholic contemporaries.

At that time, it was thought that one of the greatest sins that could be committed was what the theologians called *Participatio in Divinis*, which meant a Catholic joining with heretics in their divine worship. In the schools of the day it was the Catholics who opposed mutual prayer and scripture reading, and Catholic children would remain belligerently silent during the Greek doxology after the Lord's prayer, "For thine is the Kingdom and the Power and the Glory" and who, presumably, closed their ears to the sonorous phrases of the King James version of the Scriptures as read each morning by Miss Chips.

How much more heinous it was then to go to a Protestant Church for a service; and even if there were no formal worship, the minister would ring in a prayer. While his congregation bowed its communal head, you could spot the Catholics staring at the ceiling.

"Worship the same God?" the missionary priest intoned from the pulpit of St. Jeromes'. "Nonsense. Our God says he is truly present in the Blessed Sacrament, here on the altar;

76

their God says our Holy Communion is a piece of bread. Our God says that Our Blessed Mother was the Virgin of Virgins, and their God says she had a brood of children, other than our Lord, Jesus Christ. Their God says in some of their Churches, and this I know, that Christ Himself was not God, but only a man like the rest of us. How then can they call themselves Christians? They are well named Protestants — protesting against all that we hold most sacred. Isn't it silly then for them to expect us to join them in protesting against ourselves? But we are the Catholic Church; our doors are open to all men; we affirm the True Presence, the Virginity of Mary, the Divinity of Christ. Let the others come and worship with us. We cannot join in a worship of a false God who reveals nothing but lies. A lying God is no God."

Father Harkins copied this down for his notes and used it vigorously when he assailed united prayer, which was often.

Then there was the problem of proselytizing. There were rumors, and some of them well founded, that the separated sects lured Catholic children into their congregations, giving them outings and games and even food, making rice Christians of them. For the adult backslider, it was obvious how the few who went over, prospered in a worldly fashion and those who became Masons did very well indeed, moving up rapidly from the flats. And every Catholic knew what those Masons were.

On the other side, the Protestants perceived that while the Catholics had nothing to offer their children, the Church held the mighty club of love. Young people got carried away, and the Priest, Patrick Harkins, refused to witness a mixed marriage; therefore many a poor Yankee boy or girl, hopelessly in love with an Irish lass or lad, would have to convert to Catholicism before Harkins would see them married. The priests had so filled their subjects with the idea that if they were married in a Protestant Church, all their children would be bastards — though this teaching was against the law — that they would be living in sin and ultimately go to hell, that the Catholic party usually stood out, and the Protestant who would have become a Moslem for love had to be baptized again — contrary to the Creed — and have as many Catholic children as nature and fecundity could provide. So the Roman Church grew with the generations, and its list of converts seemed impressive to those who could not see through its wiles.

Father Harkins boasted that until Canon Law finally forced him, he never once witnessed a mixed marriage. All his spouses were good firm Catholics baptized conditionally, in case the first one did not take, having received their first Communion, and when possible, confirmed. That the instructions took hours upon hours, did not cause him a moment's regret. Truth was from God, and truth must always conquer. In his witness, it always had, and the results were the fine Catholic children, and his outstanding converts, who, since they had discovered and renounced the evil of their ways, were, as was often said, better Catholics than the born ones.

In some ways, but not all, Father Harkins admired the French, though perhaps they pushed their opposition to mixed marriages too far, always mating from within themselves, holding as they did that even the loss of language, let alone the mixing of blood, was the first step toward the loss of Faith. Then, too, they opposed the public schools, as he did also, though their language barrier made most of their children immune to propaganda whereas his young ones were gradually sopping up new and subtly heretical indoctrinization. The ideas some of the brats came home with! And the way they were being filled with the idea that they were smarter than their parents because they had a little book-learning! Something must be done.

For two years the tensions grew between the two temperance societies, and, from his pulpit, the priest made the cleavage complete.

Early in 1870, Mr. Skiddy Wood, the great temperance revivalist, fresh from triumphs in Boston, with pledges thick upon the city, came heralded to Holyoke.

Father Harkins received a courteous invitation to join in the first great rally in the Second Baptist Church. He saw through it at once. The Yanks knew very well that he, who had taken such a strong position against his congregation joining in any way with the Protestants, were putting him in a dilemma through the cause that was dearest to his heart. What would his people, and rightly, think about their pastor who went to a Baptist Church? But if he did not, how his enemies could twist it! He read it again. "Invited to join with all the Holyoke Protestant ministers and share a place in the pulpit of the Second Baptist Church." He could just see himself doing that.

Another thing he knew. The Protestant Temperance Society was just another means of proselytizing. All their bad cases were Catholic drunks; all their reformed were now respectable Protestants, revoking the evils of Rome with the evils of drink.

He sat down and wrote them a note saying that he had another engagement that evening. Had he left well enough alone; the editorial attacks in the newspapers might not have been so violent, but he preached a strong sermon to his flock, which produced the following retort:

"The Lecture — Father Harkins on the platform — He challenges Comment.

"The lecture of William Skiddy Wood on Monday evening, although devoted to a description of criminal proceedings at the Tombs, and the terrible debaucheries and crimes that doom so many to Blackwell's Island, death or the madhouse, was of considerable merit otherwise, while its moral tone was of the highest and best order. The lecturer having introduced his subject by alluding to the formation of bad habits as the first step down towards all shame and ruin, declared that the only remedy and safety from the impending doom was repentance; that every besetting sin must be avoided, as God saw and counted all. He spoke of the value of a good character, both to a man's happiness and his success in life and of the blessings that ever wait upon virtuous deeds, and the calamities that attend or follow the evil ones. He exhorted all to exercise Christian charity towards the poor sin-cursed wretches that ask alms or pity, for upon this charity may depend the issues of life or death. The habit of drunkenness is an abomination in the sight of Almighty God, and if men indulge in it they can look for no mercy. Our prisons, lunatic and other asylums were peopled by those who had lost health, character, or reason by this fatal indulgence, and for the salvation of those not yet confirmed in evil habits, and for the salvation of those on the brink of the abyss, societies must be formed and every influence of human sympathy or Christian love must go out toward, and constrain or allure them into the paths of virtue and happiness. The speaker then proceeded to describe that terrible crowd daily arraigned before the authorities at the Tombs, in New York, nearly all of whom are the victims of strong drink and are charged with drunkenness or some crime which is its legitimate fruit. Disgustingly ghastly was the picture of squalor, of rags, of blackened eyes and broken forms, of all ages and sexes, of men mangled in desperate fights, of women with their faces beaten to a blue jelly, giggling and winking in their grim glee — outcasts of society — demons in half human form. Twenty of these wretches per day are transported to Blackwell's Island, few to reform, many to delirium, almost all to return again to the haunts of vice and crime.

"We will follow the speaker no further into the horrors of New York but will commend to all whose blood and brain are not yet turned by alcohol, that [sic] repentance and speedy reform of life and character, which the speaker enjoined as their only remedy or safety. The lecture was a sermon of power, pathos, morality and Christianity, and its matter and manner filled with the highest thought and deepest feelings, produced an impression upon the audience who echoed its sentiments by frequent applause. And here we let the curtain fall, and pause, that those who do not wish to linger and listen to the final farce may seek the tranquility of their homes to ponder in peace upon the soulful sentiments of the sermon.

"It is not often that a sermon is supplemented by a farce; and when we look for a farce of this character we descend from the church, go below the theater, and find its fitting fribble in the tent of the circus. There a tawdry pretender sways his mock dignity, and claims for himself the rightful ownership of all the virtue, valor and animals in the caravan. But he is habited like a jester, professes to be a pretender and would not deceive the veriest fool; but where a man in the guise and occupying the position of a gentleman, goes upon the stage and swings his arms and acts the clown, claiming that he and his society contain all the virtue of a townful of

80

men, denying to all others the common concession of sincerity, without which society is chaos or a despotism, the ignorant will be deceived, for they will fail to discover that the first is a gentleman in the guise of a clown and the last [sic] is a clown in the guise of a gentleman. Father Harkins uttered language to the following effect concerning the clergymen, Rev. Dr. Peet, Rev. Mr. Trask, Rev. Mr. Adams, and Rev. Mr. Bigelow, who proposed and invited his [Harkins'] cooperation in the temperance meeting for Fast Day evening: They knew I had a meeting appointed for that evening, and they knew also that I would not attend a temperance meeting at the Baptist Church, and they are not sincere in the work of temperance. I tell you there is no sincerity in them, charging them, thus directly, with uttering a false statement in the expression of their wish to have him unite with them on that occasion. He said also in substance that there were few Catholics present who heard the lecturer's remarks who did not feel that the man had disgraced himself in making them. He thus casts himself beyond all social recognition, and openly proclaims himself the enemy of all social unity or peace, and his bishop must judge whether or not it is safe to commit the care of a large congregation in a rapidly growing community to one whose notorious lack of erudition is made painfully apparent by the sad lack of those nobler qualities of heart without which even learning is a curse and ignorance an abomination. It is painful to comment upon the unfortunate address of Father Harkins. Many of the members of his church are our good friends, and although differing upon points of theology, we have been glad to join hands with them in every reform that would tend to promote temperance, morality and peace, yet we must not hesitate while we hold as sincere the interests of the whole community, to denounce this shameful attack as a disgrace to his priestly office and an insult to a community that holds its clergymen in highest esteem. It should ever be remembered by public men that "Zeal without knowledge is fire without light" and that "Envy shooteth at others and woundeth herself."

"The following letter of Father Harkins, handed to us in the Baptist Church after the temperance meeting, contains no hint of any other feeling but one of generous sympathy, not only with the cause, but with the clergymen engaged in it; and we can only charge his subsequent declarations to some unworthy afterthought to which few men would have given public utterance:

Holyoke,
April 6, 1870

"Rev. Mr. Trask,

"Dear Sir:
As I have made arrangements to be engaged in our church on Thursday [Fast Day] it will be impossible for me to be present at your temperance meeting. I am with the cause.

I am, Rev. Sir,
Very Respectfully,
P. J. Harkins"

The unworthy afterthought had been a mounting sense of chagrin at the dilemma in which he had been put, and a choleric certitude that the plot had been deliberate. Nor was it the first attack which had been made upon him. A little over a year before the Baptist Church Letter had contained the following, thinly veiled vilification:

"March 1, 1869: Baptist Church Letter

"The duty of providing for State Paupers is no small trust and we cannot close our annual statement as Overseers of the Poor without calling attention to the increasing tide of pauperism that is steadily flowing in upon the community. There are scores of families in this town that are painfully destitute of the common necessities of life. There are sick persons and needy widows with little children who are incapable of supporting themselves and children; they are obliged to solicit aid from the town authorities or suffer from hunger and cold. More than two thousand dollars have been distributed to this class of persons during the past year and all or nearly all are "Members of the Roman Catholic Church in good and regular standing" and who have contributed liberally to the support of the religious organization to which they belong.

"Now the social and religious interests of the community demand that some more effective plan shall be devised and carried into execution for the relief and support of the worthy and suffering poor in our midst.

"We believe that the truest and best interest of a Church consists in making provision for its own poor and if the Roman Church . . . would give attention to this important element of living Christianity by following the Christian rule adopted by every other religious denomination in town providing for its own poor, it would not only relieve a vast amount of sorrow and suffering, cheer the sick and helpless, and in the hour of death save many a body from a pauper's grave, but it would also secure a more abiding and heartfelt respect for their religion."

"According to the Town Report, the total State Welfare expense for the year amounted to $1,568.32 including 29 burials that cost $242.60.

Patrick Harkins did not, perhaps, appreciate the worry that the Town Fathers, representing the citizenry, had about their budget. In the startling purchases of land and houses that the Catholic pastor had effected in four years, they saw valuable tax holdings now immune from civic revenue; he saw only the good that would be done on his properties. But the record of his purchase is alarming.

In 1866 he had bought the lot at the corner of Dwight and Elm Street, and the house that had been Father Sullivan's (his predecessor) rectory for $3,400, and then two other lots for $850 apiece, and a huge lot on Elm and Hampden Streets, for which the records vary from $3,060 to $5,695. In 1868 he had bought the land belonging to the tribal leader, John

Delaney, for $800, and the following year began, at last, to build himself a rectory. But he stopped that, and converted it at a cost of $18,000 into a convent for the Sisters of Notre Dame.

This last venture came about unexpectedly. The City Fathers comdemned the frame school on Elm Street and determined to build a large new and brick school directly opposite his Church. A public school, with all its proselytizing, was to lure off his innocent children. So he went without a proper rectory for a while longer, moved the frame school to his own land, and refitted it for $4,000; and since the Notre Dame nuns, by rule, could not teach boys, he started a boys' school of sorts with his sister Grace and a cousin and two or three other laywomen as teachers.

Nor had he been idle at what was now becoming known as Hadley Falls across the river. In 1867 in his own name, later sold to the Bishop for a dollar, he had bought land in South Hadley, turned William Cook's house on North Main Street into an orphanage for the children of Holyoke, and was in the process of building a church nearby, to be called St. Patricks, named, as one wry parishioner pointed out, for the Patron of Ireland and for himself.

Doing no good for his people? That was a bitter jest, surely. In his eyes, the tax-free land was contributory to the people of Holyoke. How much money did his parochial school children save the town? Did the orphans taken off the township mean nothing? Until his arrival, they had meant just that — nothing. Not a penny had been appropriated for them or for his further projects: a home for the aged, who suffered and died like flies in the tenements; or even for a decent hospital, which he vowed he would get. And as for a poorhouse, what interest did they have in his poor?

How many had he fed and clothed personally? How many were cared for by the laymen who were to become the St. Vincent de Paul Society? And a pity it was that the town buried those it had allowed to die, to the exorbitant sum of two hundred and forty-two dollars — and, God help us — sixty cents. And the implication that he had been bleeding his people — that stung — when he had depleted his own hoard, and had borrowed from his sister. Or what of the benevolent part of his Temperance Society? Benevolent they had been till it hurt.

No. The key was in the bitter sentence: "The increasing tide of pauperism that is steadily flowing in upon the community." Let the poor go elsewhere — not to sacred Holyoke. Cure the conditions by paying the laborer five dollars a week, and closing the better jobs to them unless they turned Protestant, though even then they were handicapped; for their Irishness was a blood in them, which they could not change, and the accents of their tongues betrayed and barricaded them.

So it was no imprudent afterthought that had made him open fire from his pulpit upon his enemies but the righteous anger of a man with a whip of cords. Moreover, it would be contrary to his temperament and of his race had he been silent under attack. Men like that, with the social passion in them, their enemies call fanatics; their friends call them zealots.

It was in his nature to lash out. He had done so in Hadley Falls, in an unforgettable sermon when Carew, his get-rich-quick neighbor, battening on war profits, arrogant now with the sign over his Glasgow Mills, "No Irish Need apply", and turning at last on the parish of St. Patricks' and the Church of God that was to be built there. And this from the man who had split his own Congregational Church down the middle and, after failing to subdue his own minister, had erected a rival Congregational Church to the tune of $25,000 with his own lackey-boy in the pulpit!

Oh, there were bitter words, Patrick Harkins said that day from before his altar, as he put the curse on Carew. No one forgot the prophecy: "Many of you listening to my voice will see it come to pass that the black crows from Mount Tom will roost on the eaves and the swallows will nest in chimneys of the empty Carew Mansion. In the name of the Father and of the Son, and of the Holy Ghost, Amen."

Those who heard, lived to see it happen. Less than a year later the twin sons were born dead; old lady Carew followed them within two years; young Francis Carew, the oldest boy, was killed by a runaway horse on High Street; in '78 Carew had to eat humble pie, and he rejoined the other congregationalists; in '81 the old man died, and his three surviving grandchildren chose to become expatriates, living in France; and two years later the black crows from Mt. Tom rested on the eaves, and swallows were nesting in the chimney.

You could see it yourself, couldn't you?

But usually his angers had more positive effects, and his wrath was turned more upon the causers of violence than the violent. He did not condone his own people for their gang-wars, but he deplored them more if they were between the Kerrys and the Connaughts, destroying each other, than when they joined to pit themselves against the common enemy. His penances were mild for that, though he suspected that such battles were seldom fully spelled out but cloaked under a formula like, "I lost my temper, but they started it," or "I had a fight in self-defense." He knew that you could keep an oppressed people down by grinding poverty and broken hopelessness; but he knew, too, that if once they had a breath of freedom or an upsurge of hope, destruction would blaze like a fire. It had done so during the Reign of Terror in France; it was doing so now among the emancipated blacks in the States.

So it was with mixed feelings that he read the account of a man whom he and all the world loved and admired, Bishop John Gibbons, later to be the great Cardinal of Baltimore. He was sorry for the Bishop and his fright — but he understood the Negroes because he understood his own people of the Patch. He read that day in 1868:

"The night I arrived in Wilmington there was a torch light procession of the emancipated slaves, many of them now holding office and domineering over their masters. If one can imagine an enormous crowd of Negroes, most of whom were intoxicated and all of whom were waving torches in the blackness of the night, one can very easily imagine the impressions of a new and very young bishop."

Oh well, It was a troubled world. And there was always the drink.

The priest though, reserved his greatest wrath for divisiveness among his own, and he would never forget how seething he had become by a letter from another priest, mind you, and countersigned by his Bishop, attacking the very nuns whom he had admired from a distance in Kingston. His own wrath was impotent, for the happening was in Syracuse, out of his domain. But he was mightily warmed by the answering letter from a Catholic gentleman who took up the defense of his sisters.

## A WARNING!

EDITOR OF THE STANDARD: — SIR:

We are so often imposed upon by parties pretending to collect for charitable purposes, that we deem it our duty to warn the people against imposition.

By a Decree of the Plenary Council of Baltimore, Female Religious are prohibited from going outside of their Convents and at a distance for the purpose of making collections. The Bishops are called upon by the Ecclesiastical Decree not to permit or tolerate Female Religious of their Diocese to violate this regulation. The people are therefore warned against encouraging parties, who pretend to collect for religious purposes, as such are either IMPOSTERS OR DISOBEDIENT AND UNWORTHY RELIGIOUS."

[Signed] Rev. Joseph Guerdet,
Pastor of St. John's,
Rev. James A. O'Hara, D.D.

Reply to the above.

EDITOR OF SYRACUSE STANDARD: —

I saw in your paper of Thursday, a communication purporting to have come from two Catholic Clergymen of this City, warning people against giving charity to Female Religious (not the Catholics alone, but the whole people) as they were *IMPOSTERS OR DISOBEDIENT AND UNWORTHY RELIGIOUS.*

What a strange warning, emanating from the followers of Christ! No charity to be given, unless it passes through the hands of those Reverend Clergy! Has the day arrived that if I meet a poor man or poor woman that is hungry, shall I let him or her die, unless I have the permission of clergymen to contribute to their wants? O Religion! What a mockery is thy name!

Again they charged that the Sisters referred to are Imposters, well knowing at the time of so charging that it was utterly false, as the writers of that article were well acquainted with the relatives of one of the Sisters, who reside in this City and are some of our most respected citizens; moreover, one of the Reverend Clergymen knew that this Sister was born here and baptized by our late beloved and holy Priest, Father Hayes, and he so certified, over his own signature, when the Sister was joining her Order. They also state that nuns are prohibited from going outside the gates of their Institution. Those Reverend Clergy would do well to read up and inform themselves, to learn the difference between Nuns and Sisters of Charity. If there is no difference, why did the Sisters of Charity go to the battlefields in the late American War?

They also charge that the Sisters are DISOBEDIENT AND UNWORTHY RELIGIOUS! Oh, thank Heaven that you, Reverend Clergymen, are not now, nor ever will be, their judges at the great Judgment Day! The simple story referred to is that they reside in Kingston, Canada, and are founding a house of Providence, as a Home for the Poor and Destitute of every creed. They are travelling by the authority of their Bishop, and by the authority of their Lord and Saviour, Jesus Christ, and not for self, but for the love of God and His Poor on earth.

Hoping God will assist them, as He knows no bounds to His Charity or to His blessings, is the wish and prayer of a Catholic.

From afar Father Harkins sprang to the defense of Sister Dolours and her three begging companions. He vowed that day that these would be the nuns for him, these women who, he knew, simply were not afraid.

## CHAPTER 7

For fifteen interminable months Kate Horan remained a postulant. A postulant is one who, though living the full life of the religious, is not yet received as a novice, who wears a bonnet instead of the white veil, and is not yet clothed in the holy habit. Whatever there was about Kate that held up the decision of her superior to accept her, certainly it was not her lack of patience or her silence under the obligation of drudgery.

She said nothing at all when she was assigned to the old men's ward, then in the old women's ward. Perhaps she had made a mistake when Mother Edward had asked her what her preferences were.

"Oh, if I could only work with the small boys!" She betrayed her eagerness, and never did so again. She learned to mortify her desires, never to express a preference. She became aware that those more crafty than herself sometimes suggested a distaste for what they most desired.

So she was put to work in the kitchen. She rather enjoyed the change; and though preparing something edible out of the meagre material and thinning out the supplies to feed the old women, the old men, the orphans and the nuns was more of a challenge than there had been in helping her mother with the always adequate provisions of the Horan family, she enjoyed the work well enough. It was the sister in charge whom she did not like, a massive and florid woman from County Mayo whose black hair, constantly greasy, grew out of her cheekbones, and who spoke in the sweet lisp affected by little and pious nuns, as she gave her constant exhortations to a better life.

"If Our Lady dropped a spoon on the floor, she'd wash it real careful, now wouldn't she?"

"What would St. Joseph say if he came into a kitchen like this?"

"Now we must be learning about holy poverty. Did you ever see the likes of the amount of potato you scraped away with the skins? Enough to feed a village in the famine." In the future Kate parboiled the potatoes before she skinned them.

The incessant refrain coming in the child-voice from the massive woman almost drove Kate crazy. "Child dear, will you ever realize this is God's House?" Kate thought that she realized it adequately.

After the usual month of this *kitchen trial*, as they called it, the Reverend Mother, with thin lips compressed, said to her, "Sister Horan, it has been brought to my attention that you do not like the work in the kitchen."

Kate liked it well enough. It was only the sister she did not like. But to say this would be against charity, so she replied: "Is that so, Mother?"

Mother Edward, who in all things, followed the pattern, went on. "Hence, I am returning you to the kitchen for further training. You must learn that God does not view the nature of the work and sets no store on likes and dislikes."

Sister Horan, who as yet had no name in religion, tried to be humble, but this backfired. Thinking of the kitchen sister's constant reproofs, she said, "I fancy I'm not much good at cooking."

Mother Edward's blondness assumed frigidity. "Those are scarcely the principles of a religious. God does not look at the success of the work, only at the intention."

There was a paradox here, the girl knew. The House of God demanded that every detail be perfect; but God didn't care about that, only about the motive. It was odd.

The superior concluded: "So, until you learn what it is to be a good religious, you will return to the kitchen."

The learning process lasted for an entire year. Monotony dulled time and meaning. Pious exhortations melted into each other. The months became an endless succession of pouring grease drippings on stale bread. The poor and the sisters were fed.

She rebelled only once, emerging from her daze to realize how much time had gone by and wondering if she had been completely forgotten. She approached the very door of the superior, through which no one ever went voluntarily.

"Sister Horan!" said Mother Edward, who was almost, but not quite, caught exhibiting the emotion of surprise. "What brings you here?"

Kate was daring. "Reverend Mother, when are you going to give me the habit?"

To that question Mother Edward did not reply, but instead picked up something quite different. "The habit?" she asked. "Is that what I heard you say?"

"Yes, Mother."

"The what?"

"The habit, Mother."

With perfect articulation the Reverend Mother said, "The *holy* habit." She left an icy pause. "Holy," she added.

"The Holy Habit," Sister Horan repeated, again as if by rote.

"Because of your lack of reverence, which may partially explain my hesitation in receiving you, you will announce your fault in the refectory at the evening meal, and for your penance, say the *Miserere* once. That is all. You may go."

That evening Sister Horan knelt on the rough floor of the barracks messhall and while the other religious, after a first glance, hid their embarrassment by looking away, Sister Horan confessed her fault and parroted the Latin of the *Miserere*. She had picked up the Latin from the chapel chant, and she did not know it in English.

They accepted her at last; and when the day and the hour came she went into chapel with the other sisters. Time passed. After an hour or so Kate found that she was alone, the others having crept out softly one by one when they realized, first, that the Bishop was late and finally came to the conclusion that he was not coming at all.

An hour and a half after schedule, Bishop Horan came into the chapel and the sisters rustled back softly. The ceremony began, the beautiful ritual for the clothing of nuns, but Sister Horan found no joy in it. The one thing that stood out above her fatigue was the moment when she saw her shorn hair at her feet. In her despoilation a qualm of conscience shook her — her past vanity in her beautiful hair. Now, though she had no mirror, she could see how hideous she must look, a little sparrow of a thing, a bird draggled in the rain.

91

With her new white veil bound about her shorn head she came out from the sacristy and as her sister, Mary of the Seven Dolours knelt and gave her the ritual kiss of acceptance, the novice thought: "You are more beautiful now. I only had hair."

The Bishop gave her the triple blessing and retired. He had not apologized for his lateness nor did he now. All the sisters knew how busy a Bishop was. But he did smile just a little at his namesake, and as a result of the morning he would not forget her, as he did most nuns.

She had completely slipped his mind. In his own house an hour after his time for arrival at the convent he had strayed into the kitchen, the domain of his sister Martha, who was the only one left in the world who could talk to his Lordship just like any other human being.

"And just what are you doing here?" she asked from her throne above the kitchen table.

"Looking for a drop of tea," he said.

"Well, I never. Why aren't you where you're supposed to be?"

His Lordship, the Bishop of Regiopolis, took out his Waterbury watch. "I have a feeling I intended to do something this morning."

Martha looked at her brother. She was a very punctual and exact woman. "At this moment, my lad, you are giving the habit to Sister Horan at the convent."

"So I am," he said without disturbance. While he did not delay, it had taken him some time to dress and to have the horse harnessed to get over to the convent to clothe Sister Horan, so that she might begin her novitiate.

The Noviceship was not as structured in those days as it was to become in later years. Sister Horan was officially given over to Sister Mary John as Mistress of Novices, but she was trained more by doing than by formal instruction. Devoted as she was, Sister Mary John had little time for the training of the four novices who were placed in her charge. But Sister Horan soon discovered that the other nuns, with whom she worked, gave almost as much shibboleth advice as the Sister in the kitchen had given, and all of them appointed themselves Mistresses of Novices.

From Sister Mary John, Kate absorbed a series of religious principles, clear and unquestionable, and had her reading directed to Thomas a Kempis; the rules, Rodriquez, the pious books of the period. She was sent into annual retreat and days of recollection, given by the Jesuits, who though thoroughly competent in their own Ignatian spirituality, were far from masters of the Spirit of St. Vincent de Paul. Kate Horan never quite succumbed nor did she turn out to be, as many nuns did, a kind of female Jesuit. Some of her sisters, she knew, even thought of themselves as such.

Ideally, as she had been instructed, she could receive counselling in the Confessional, and she read with edification of the hour-long sessions Sister Margaret Mary Alacoque had with Claude de la Columbiere, but she could not quite make it — and having tried once, gave it up and resorted to the formula:

"Father, forgive me for I have sinned. It is a week since my last confession. I am a Novice. Since then I have violated silence on several occasions. I have been slightly uncharitable to my sisters. On two occasions I did not rise promptly with the bell, and I have had distractions in prayer. I am sorry for these and all the sins of my past life."

She had learned that sorrow did not consist in emotion; and if she felt nothing, she knew that the words of absolution would take her sins away. For her penance she usually received three Hail Marys, though there was one French priest, whom the nuns tried to avoid, who always gave the Litany of Loreto and a ferverino on devotion to our Lady.

Since it was conducted by Mother Edward, one area of disciplinary counselling was never omitted. This was the monthly meeting and the bi-annual Manifestation of Conscience to Reverend Mother. Kate prepared for it with greater dedication than she prepared for confession, for she knew it was her duty to lay bare her whole soul to her superior — not only her sins, but her faults, her temptations and her virtues, so that Mother could guide her. In Penance, it would be only your sins you revealed, temptations didn't count; and if you brought up your virtues, Father would be angry with you. And if you mentioned anyone else's faults, woe betide you. But you were supposed to manifest such temptations, as you

93

had observed in others, to Mother Superior.

Kate's intentions were always good — to be open with the superior. It was only when she faced Mother Edward across the grim desk, without the security of the dark confessional box, or the sacred knowledge that the priest could not reveal sins, ever, even under torture, that her courage failed her. Actually, her cowardice began earlier in the very imagination of the scene, and her preparation became more and more, as the months went on, an explanation of the faults she might be accused of, a rebuttal of arguments against her, a denial, where possible or plausible of the peaching of her peers, and readiness for the inevitable moment when the Superior would say: "It has been brought to my attention——"

The fear mounted in the long wait at Mother Superior's door, wondering what the sufferer within was going through; the searching look at the culprit who emerged; sometimes, the dread sight of tears, and next — you.

Time after time she emerged having said only that she was happy, she tried to be good, yes, she liked all the Sisters, had a vocation, kept in good health, would try to improve in prayer and obedience and was sorry that she had whistled in the laundry. No. She knew no evil of the other novices. They edified her very much. As to the accusations made against her, she adopted a philosophy of gratitude that so little of her deep evil came to light, so that she could offer up the false things said against her as penance for the true things that might have been said. For them, she would wait for the Particular Judgment. Or for Chapter.

Chapter, or the Party, as the novices irreverently called it, was an ancient monastic discipline, from which the modern Sensitivity Program has been stolen and that in turn depends on the rediscovery of its value by Mr. Chuck Dieterich of Synanon (where they have produced almost miraculous results). As a bedrock condition for its effectiveness, the Synanon environment is essential, but the religious community commitment is ideal. A prerequisite to its cathartic effect is the certainty of the love of one's peer group, previously proven by action; but to attempt to create an artificial love-unity among random strangers, whether by verbal love statements or by touch, is traumatic.

94

But in 1871, when Kate was introduced to Chapter, nothing remained of it except the empty shell of its structure.

White-faced, Kate knelt in the circle of the nuns who looked to her like avenging demons. She kissed the floor as a sign of humility, knelt upright; and sensationless with panic, she announced her faults. Ideally, this should have been a depth picture of self-awareness of anti-social actions and attitudes; actually, it had degenerated into formulas similar to her Confessions and her Manifestations, only here she must speak only of external faults.

When she had finished with her *Culpa*, each nun in turn, beginning with the lowliest, had the charitable duty of revealing her little sister's external faults.

"Sister Horan knocks into people and doesn't apologize."

"Sister broke a lot of cups and didn't pick up the pieces."

"She has kind of a fawning attitude."

"She walks funny, like on eggs."

"She has an affected way of talking."

"She runs giddily up and down the house, particularly on the stairs, which she has been seen to take two at a time."

"Sister has a very wordly view of chastity, particularly when undressing in the dormitory before lights out. She should be more modest in her unclothing, waiting for complete darkness." That hurt.

From her own sister: "She shows attitudes of contempt toward her elders."

Mother Edward summed everything up and added a few bricks of her own. It was not her fault nor was it intentional if she seemed to be caustic.

Sister Horan kissed the floor again, rose, and in a ritual of love and gratitude to those who out of charity had been most helpful to her in revealing her most hurtful faults, gave them the sororal embrace, the *amplexus*.

One of their most literate candidates was heard to murmur, "So Judas did to Christ." She withdrew from the Community shortly after.

Kate's main reaction to the experience was that she wouldn't have to endure it for another six months. She valiantly and successfully beat down the temptation to think that her attackers would one day be on the floor themselves and from her scrutiny of them, to prepare a neat little pile of stones.

If the decadent practices had little effect on the formation of Sister Horan, the instructions in asceticism minimal, and in mysticism nonexistent, her structuring came mainly from involvement with The Work, into which she plunged, with people, with whom she lived, with constant association with the professed sisters, from whom she absorbed by osmosis attitudes and dedications and values. Add to that the emulation normal to the young, by daily intercourse, and the hero-worship, that had waned from Mother Edward fortunately transferred to her novice-mistress, Sister Mary John, since she was the one chosen by God to receive it.

To Kate the Novice Mistress was not only wise and loving and maternal, but she was mature, even old. Sister Mary John at that time was twenty-three years of age, but her manner was demure, her behavior professionally religious, and her almost emaciated face — her pallor — was made venerable by the garniture.

If her instructions in the spiritual life were neither extensive nor profound, they did have the virtue of clarity and Kate was to abide by them all her life. They were: Duty in all things; The perfecting and dedicating of the present moment; Charity or good will toward all men; and a cheerful, even happy acceptance of whatever God would send. The last was peculiarly apt for sisters dedicated to Divine Providence.

The notes that Sister Horan preserved from Sister Mary John's infrequent conferences are scarcely to be ranked among the relics of the great masters of the ascetic life, but they show that the Mother Mistress had a shrewd understanding of how to get along in her contemporary community. Her practical guide reads:

### How to Be Happy As a Religious

1. Adherence to regular observance.
2. Never interfere in the office of another.
3. Order and cleanliness in apartments.
4. Never take anything from the office of another without permission.

96

5. Respect for own dignity.
6. Discretion in the parlor.
7. Love for Community.
8. Kind words for all.

Somehow through such simplistic tenets Sister Horan, like thousands of her Sisters, managed to attain happiness, remaining in the convent until death.

Truly it was The Work which trained the novices. Kate Horan was sent at once to Regiolopis, which was closed for two years before and in deplorable condition. The old people and the novice moved in together during a cold March, and the girl struggled up three flights of stairs to her charges, tugging a bucket of what had been hot water, but which froze on the floor before she could scrub up the accumulated grime. Then after the warming weeks the frost leaked out of the moldy walls forming pools of its own mucus on the floors. For two years and two winters, the old people huddled together by the only box stove.

The novices washed their own clothing where they could, and hung it to freeze in the alcoves in which they slept. In those two winters Kate sometimes remembered that the kitchen had been warm, but in the summer she thanked God because then, the kitchen had been hot.

Also through these two years the other four novices and the old were her only human companions, and the obligation of silence in addition to the work load kept her from chatting with her other little sisters. Only the old to talk to, to listen to, only the very old.

There was the Rule of Grades, which forbade novices from holding private conversations with the professed except on special and rare holidays. For a time, Sister Horan was naughty. Attracted by the maternal expanse of Sister Mary of the Cross, she sought comfort from her, and Sister Mary of the Cross could not resist the needs of the young, though she confessed her weakness every time she went to confession.

One day they were caught. By Mother Edward, on catlike feet. Sister Mary of the Cross' penance was private and only the novice was obliged to eat her dinner sitting on the floor of the refectory, served by Reverend Mother as a conscious example of humility.

97

A memory of Dickens stirred in Kate's heart. And more, she just wanted to show the superior how much her old penance bothered her. Her voice cut through the dinner reading, "Please, Mother, may I have some more?"

There was a scandal. The reading stopped, Sister Mary of the Cross giggled, but like a mitered abbess Mother Edward literally forked over the remainder of her own meal and remained, after that, in martyred temperance. She said nothing to her subject, but Sister Horan's vows were held up for three months.

Then there was the Sin of the Corn. Older religious eat quickly since there is no conversation you learn not to waste time. Through long before the youngsters the professed sometimes forgot charity sufficiently to stare them out of appetite.

One autumn evening there was abundant corn from the farm. Sister Horan reached for a second piece, but the eye of old Sister Patrick was on her, withering the gesture. At grace, with some distraction to her prayers, the novice slid two ears into her bulge, and though she suffered through chapel visit, she managed to get them safely up to her alcove. That night she had a royal feast, munching her cold and delicious corn under the light of the moon while the others slept. For the first time, with the cobs under the pillow, she went to sleep replete.

Such were her only recorded transgressions, but August came and September, and October and still she was not accepted into the Community. Three newer novices were due for their profession on March 19. If she did not take her vows then, she would be forever disgraced. Was this an indication that she should not be a Sister? Mother Edward's delays seemed to indicate that she was not acceptable, and Sister Patrick, whose attitude implied that no candidates were ever acceptable, kept pointing out to her that a vocation consisted in the Call by superiors to be professed in religion. If you did not receive this Call it was your duty to return to the world.

Kate Horan did not accept this expedient mysticism. By the delay, she was annoyed not discouraged. She had a vocation and if Reverend Mother didn't know it, God did. God and Sister Mary John.

Finally, just before the Vow retreat, to the disapproval of Sister Patrick, God spoke through the voice of Mother Mary Edward. On Vow Day, with a sense of having run through an Indian gamut, Kate pledged herself to God in the presence of her entire Congregation, now numbering twenty-two. She and the other three girls became, as they firmly believed, the Brides of Christ. Her wedding gown, made by her milliner mother, proclaimed it; the ring on her finger testified to it; and, like a bride, she received a new name.

The naming of nuns is naturally important to them. Most of them have no more freedom of choice than an infant in baptism. They select a name, which the wiser Council often turns down, picking out instead some obscure saint under whose patronage the vow-sister is placed for life. Though no doubt their patron saints are admirable examples of holiness, they have rather exotic names. Sometimes, of course, they never existed. To be safe most communities place all their sisters under the protection of the Blessed Virgin, so that most nuns have as their first name, Mary. The second name is the one by which they will be known until death, the name which they have exchanged for their own patronymic.

Kate Horan had asked for Dosithea. As in many other cases she was not given it. But was there a secret admiration for this strong girl in the cloistered bosom of Mother Mary Edward? What pressure was brought to bear by the Mistress of Novices, Mother Mary John? Could it have been a mere slip on the part of his absentminded Lordship, the Bishop of Regiopolis?

Kate Horan emerged from her vow-christening with the name: Sister Mary of Providence. *The* Sister Mary amidst so many others, *of Providence*, the official name of her Congregation, was bestowed on her like an accolade. The Sister Mary of Providence.

Sister Mary of Providence turned and said to God: "Thank you." She had known all the time that God wanted her.

For two years after her profession, there was no change in her occupation, and the only social advantage that profession gave her — legitimate conversation with the older nuns — she avoided. After her indiscretion with Sister Mary of the Cross, she had rigidly practiced the virtue of forgoing particular

99

affections, destroying any individual attractions that she might feel, attempting, as Sister Patrick instructed her, to be "All things to all men," which Sister Mary of the Cross said meant being nothing to anybody.

She had found it hardest to reject the love she had for her mother. She had tried to do the required mother-replacement with Sister Mary John, but her worldliness kept cropping up whenever she wrote a letter home. Whenever she received one, she made the sacrifice of destroying each as soon as it was answered.

Within two years of her profession, God took a hand and called her mother to Heaven. Sister Mary of Providence had tried to make the renunciation of carnal affection, and now she could belong entirely to God and to no creature.

As to her attitude toward the sister of her blood, Mary of the Seven Dolours, it is more discreet to quote Sister Mary of Providence and to let her own incomprehensible account stand exactly as it is:

The axiom "There's no joy without some sorrow", found literal verification in my life that year, for following my Profession — which brought me unbounded happiness — I was visited by a heavy cross . . . . . the death of my beloved mother. The news of her untimely . . . . or shall I say TRAGIC death . . . . was broken to me with kindly sympathy, and permission given me and my Sister, Sr. M. Seven Dolours, to attend the funeral. Sr. M. Seven Dolours however, was not told that my mother was dead — possibly because of her emotional temperament — and so it became my painful duty to tell her. As we neared home, I broke the news to her as gently as possible, knowing that that was the best thing to do. After the funeral obsequies — which filled my heart with sorrow — we returned to the Convent and I resumed my round of duty. In vain did I try to drive away the disconcerting thoughts that harassed me, but the wound was deep and not easily reparable. In order to distract my mind and avert a calamity, I undertook the work of two or three Sisters, hoping in this way to gain merit for the soul of my beloved mother, also to regain my accustomed calm and tranquility. In the religious — as perhaps in no other state of life — life's worries and cares are tempered by the application one must give to duty. This blessed factor preserves us from much of the depression that others experience in time of deep affliction, though at the time it may have the aspect of cruelty. Such indeed was my experience!

# CHAPTER 8

One day two nuns came begging at Father Harkins' door, and they were from Kingston, the ladies he had vowed to defend. After that, Father Harkins wasted no time. He discovered that Sister Elizabeth Clifford's brother was his old professor at Regiopolic College, and he firmly believed that the finger of God was there, by which he meant less mystically that he had a friend at court.

The nuns did not delay either. Although in 1873 their whole congregation had only twenty-six members, some could be spared to establish a post Civil War base in rich America, particularly when there was such great need there.

Father Harkins had shown them Holyoke, the paper, cotton, satin and threadmills getting their power from the Connecticut River, the hordes of Irish and Scotch Catholics who labored in the shops or in construction work on the new dams. The sisters saw his crowded Sunday Masses and were even more edified by the size of the congregation at the Devotions and at the long Sunday Vespers and Benediction, but to their encomuim the Pastor only snorted, "You ought to see the mobs at the mission, or at Easter. Where are they the rest of the year?" He shook his head sadly. He had been taught to leave the ninety and the nine and go after the stray. "That'll be up to you, Sisters," he said, because he knew they would come.

To be fair, he also showed them the houses of the workers, shoddily constructed, without sanitation, pack-jammed with inmates who slept in shifts in the terrifying warrens to which the owners condemned them. In that year as in many years, typhoid fever had decimated them.

He brought the nuns over to the almshouse where the old and sick were relegated when they were of no further use as a commodity. There they stank and sometimes mercifully died. Though Sister Elizabeth breathed fire as she walked among the reeking sick, Sister de Chantal was more delicate, and made her way to the door and the air.

102

"How can they? How can the owners do this to them?"

"They have an answer," the priest replied. "They say they give them clean places to start in, but after three months they have thrown the swill down the stairways and the slops out the window, and the vomit of their drink is on the walls."

Sister de Chantal needed more than air.

He went on, "They say our people have always lived with pigs and they like it this way."

"Mon Dieu," Sister de Chantal prayed.

So, since she was French, Father Harkins consoled her by showing her how — above the charred ruins of the French Church where seventy-three had been burned alive the year before — her people were building again for the love of God. If there had been arson, no one could prove it.

Of his own accomplishment the pastor did not boast. The nuns could see for themselves. He had now acquired practically all the square north of Hampden Street, including the last holdout, for which William Ludden had extorted $14,500, a sum that Father Harkins had cajoled out of the Bishop. On this plot his School for Girls stood proudly. Then, discretely separated, there was St. Jerome's Institute for Boys. Oddly, the nuns noticed, Father Harkins said little about that. He had conditioned the building for $40,000, first as an overflow church for his parishioners then as a school.

"It has only one advantage," he said. "It's in the midst of the Patch." He smiled. "That's what the Yanks call us. Or Tigertown."

He paused. His expression, the nuns saw, was of pain. The Patch. The year before, after a spreading distemper of the cattle, smallpox had broken out in the Patch, and the men pulled wagons full of contagious dead to the common pit where they buried them. He, Doctor Reed and Doctor O'Connor had worked, almost alone among the dying. In the midst of the plague, uncurbed license had broken out in Tigertown, particularly on Sundays after Mass. The decent Irish and the Yankees joined and established vigilantes. Among the dead were some, as only he and the doctors knew, who had death-marks that were not from smallpox.

This, alone, he kept from the sisters. He was only

somewhat careful when he said, "I'd like you to take St. Jerome's Institute, too." His overcaution was not missed by the sharp ears of Sister Elizabeth. Something odd there.

He brought the Sisters into his office-parlour-guest-bedroom, sweeping the papers and debris that had overflowed from the desk, off the cot so that the nuns could sit if they were careful; he extracted some fresh paper from under a jumble, and wrote an official offer to the Kingston Community of the only house on the property that they could use as a convent. He had had his eye on it for a rectory ever since he had wangled this shack in which he lived from Father Sullivan; but, oh well, he could make do.

He handed them the document. "I'm not minimizing the work you'll have to do, it'll break your backs."

"But not our hearts," said Sister de Chantal sententiously.

He smiled at her. Plucky little thing, though she couldn't stand the almshouse.

"What I was going to say was"—he rummaged through the papers and came up with a notice—"though you'll work hard, just take a gander at this!" He handed them the work-sheet for laborers on the canal:

5:00 a.m.: Begin Work.
6:30 am: Breakfast
7:00 am: Resume Work 12:15 pm: Eat
1:00 pm: Resume Work
6:30 pm: Supper
7:15 pm: Resume Work
9:00 pm: Layoff

Sister Elizabeth gasped. "And we work for God!" which irrelevance was perfectly comprehensible to the other two.

"It's a wonder they have strength enough to do what they do on Sundays," Sister de Chantal commented, thinking of the crowded services.

"It is that," the pastor agreed, thinking of far more strenuous activities. "And you know, last year the owners had a sign on the mills that anyone who refused to work on Christmas day would be fired. The Yanks hate Christmas.

Almost in one voice both nuns asked what the workers did.

"Not a man of them worked." He smiled with some hint

104

of personal pride. "Not even the French," he added for fairness.

"And what did the owners do?"

"They couldn't fire them all, could they?"

"Isn't it wonderful how our people stick together," said Sister de Chantal looking very young.

"Sometimes," the priest said wryly, thinking of the Kerrys and the Corks; the Connaughts against both; the Irish versus the Scotch; the Gaels and the Gauls. "Yes, God bless them, in the big things they do."

So all on fire with zeal the sisters returned to Kingston from their begging trip, not exhausted this time, but bent on a new begging from their superiors, to increase their burden. Sister Elizabeth lost no time in enlisting her brother who remembered Father Harkins well. "So Hotspur Harkins is at it again!"

At the same time Father Harkins was writing his old friend Father O'Brien, whom clerical gossip named *episcopabilis*, an almost certain successor to the ailing Bishop Horan. When a speedy invitation to visit reached him, he enlisted Dr. James O'Connor and went on a tour of inspection to Canada.

Doctor O'Connor's report was, "You've got to admit the old people are clean and they're fed."

Father Harkins summarized: "The sisters work hard and they're poor."

In his mind he kept a picture of a little girl, a nun who had charge of the aged. He couldn't remember her name, but when he had found her on the floor mopping up the physical spillings from her old, he had said, "It's not much of a place you've made out of my alma mater." He had intended it as banter, but it must have sounded crusty. The little spitfire turned on him. "If they'd trained you seminarians to work for the poor instead of reading," she groped for something and came up with, "St. Jerome," which hit home, "this place wouldn't be what it is."

Her accusation was unfair to him, but it amused him. He roared with laughter and she looked at him as if she liked him. Pity, he couldn't remember her name. He wanted that one. She had spunk.

He had just about got back to Holyoke before the tables

were turned and two Kingston sisters inspected him. One was a tall icy blond whom he liked because she seemed as one given to command. No wonder she was the General Mother Mary Edward or whatever they called her. Her companion probably just sent along for the ride, was too small-boned for honest work. She looked pious, too. Oh yes, these nuns knew how to choose. Of course, the little one was the Mistress of Novices, Sister Mary John.

These women were marvels! They wormed out of him the Sunday Riots, the Vigilantes, St. Jerome's Institute. After a few days he had to admit that though the big one was a snoop, the little one spotted every fly on the wall, and it was Sister John who under the rhetoric of request demanded that they visit St. Jerome's; when he tried evasion, she smiled meekly and pushed him into a visitation. Oh, my God!

St. Jerome's Institute for Boys. Now that was a pretty kettle of fish. For once he played coward and turned the nuns over to his sister, Grace Harkins, whom he had appointed founding principal two years ago. He slipped out quietly and prayed fast.

The nuns emerged undaunted. "There's a good deal to be done there," Mother Edward remarked, with understatement. "We'll have to give that more thought. But the other works—naturally I will have to take it up with my council."

Of course she would. Father Harkins had attended meetings with bishops, and he could just hear the replies the girls would give to this dominant and efficient woman. "Yes, Mother, yes Mother." So it was practically settled.

The last word came from Sister John. "Don't worry. It is God's work. He will provide."

So God did. With amazing rapidity the Kingston Sisters accepted the mission of Holyoke, under the signature of Mother Mary Edward, General Superior, dated April 23, 1873.

What amazed and terrified Father Harkins was the signature under the next letter, which outlined the conditions of acceptance: The Rule of St. Vincent as adapted by Kingston would be retained; the Motherhouse at Kingston would assume full financial control, and the assignment of personnel went to Holyoke; the question of St. Jerome's Institute

106

would be left in abeyance. But the letter was not signed by Mother Mary Edward but by Mother Mary John, General Superior.

They had ousted that magnificent woman and stuck in the little pious one; they must be out of their minds, he thought. But he had a Machiavellian plan. He would get Sister Edward to found his community, and they could get as pious as they liked in Kingston. He'd show them what a real woman could do in Holyoke.

His plot did not go astray. On November the seventh, 1873 the pioneers arrived: Mother Mary Edward McKinley, Superior; Sister Mary of Mt. Carmel Byrne; Sister Mary of the Cross Keating, and Sister Mary Patrick McKinley who turned out to be a half-sister, and in a kind of faded way she was a half replica of the Superior.

Any less stalwart soul than Mother Edward would have been disarmed and captivated by the warm reception given them by the faithful of Holyoke, but she refused to be overwhelmed. She had come here to a more limited field, and armed with less authority; the thought that historically she would go down as the Foundress of Kingston; now as the Foundress of Holyoke did not console her.

She felt that the welcome of the townspeople and the offered services of Dr. O'Connor, while both sincere, were a bit effusive and perhaps intrusive. Possibly because of blood-affinity, possibly because of their greater restraint, the only ones she fully accepted as they her, were the Scotch girls.

The *Scotch girls*, which was their official name, were a colony which had brought its ancient art of weaving to the Lyman Mills. Schooled at home in the Lowlands by Franciscan Nuns, Mother Edward's dourness tugged at their heartstrings. They poured in their money, their time, their labor in personal aid; they were met by proper and reserved gratitude; they responded with love.

The speedy arrival of the sisters caught Father Harkins in the lurch in only one detail. Their convent was not ready, so he fitted it up as a makeshift hospital and orphanage and quartered the nuns instead across the river at South Hadley Falls. Of course it meant they had to cross back and forth, but at least, their quarters there were better than his, he thought complacently. That was certain. But the crossings would get worse now that winter was coming on, whether they went by ferry or over the trestle.

The celerity with which things happened now, showed the need there was of the sisters. November fifteenth, the first orphan, Edward Riley aged eleven, came to them;December second, they took in their first patient, so that this is the true date of the foundation of Providence Hospital. But need does not explain that only one week after their arrival, they took in their first postulant. They were glad to get her.

Immediately, the City Almoner discovered them and quartered his needy on them for the munificent sum of $7 a week for patients, $6 a month for orphans. The part-time tasks of making and selling altar breads, church linens, vestments and shrouds were an extra source of income as well as an extra work load that was to continue for about fifty years. But it was not enough. They needed full-time begging.

Mother Edward shrewdly knew of her young General's commitment to Holyoke, and she simply outlined the needs of rich America. Out of her own pitiable store of subjects, Mother Mary John sent down two more nuns, one of whom was Sister Mary Dolours.

Sister Dolours was a skilled beggar but, like the Sisters who for years joined and followed her, she experienced little of community life, the conventual ideal, and her dedication was accepted as a necessary evil and at best temporary, and her active ministry of working with people should be terminated as rapidly as possible. It was not easy for Sister Dolours to be tolerated by Mother Edward.

Though the work that Sister Dolours did, in addition to begging, kept her out of cloister, it brought her closer to the people of God. She sat with, soothed, bathed, and medicined the sick poor in their hovels; she spent nights with the dying and washed the dead for burial. When she got back to Hadley Falls she blamed herself for not kneeling in the chapel at Adoration, since her knees were worn-out from scrubbing filthy floors, which she had done with much lye soap and muscle. She also encountered the affluent, whom she called "our betters" and begged from them shamelessly, for her poor.

108

Though she labored under her vow of Obedience, she still confronted the disapproval even of the laity who felt that since she was not living a cloistered life, she was not quite a nun; but it was against her own community that she set up her barriers of self-defense. "Little they know about people,"; "little they know about the poor; little they know about work," she thought, as she confronted the terribly overworked sisters of her convent. But so she thought.

Yet for most of the Sisters that year went by so fast you wouldn't believe it, and mostly in happiness, too, because there wasn't time to brood. Besides, they knew that it would do no good to complain about overwork to Mother Mary John who had told them in her visitation that as St. Patrick had heard the call of the Gael from across the water, so she had heard the cry of the needy in Holyoke. There was no use in manifesting to their General that they found living under Mother Mary Edward difficult, because she kept insisting that the spiritual life came first and would tolerate no absence— except from the extern sisters, from the four hours of communal and rote prayer in the chapel, no matter what might be the needs of the flock. In theory they agreed with her. Besides, Mother John knew their local superior better than they did; and it was Father Harkins whom they should blame for getting her down here, when they had voted her out of command. There was a rumor among them that the Pastor was becoming a little disillusioned with his choice, finding that though Mother Edward always said yes to his demands, nothing was ever changed. As to what the nuns thought of Father Harkins, they admired his spirit of indifference, which kept him living in his shack, but feared that sometimes he imposed it on others, particularly when he moved them back from Hadley Falls to Holyoke and just after they had adapted their time order and had some kind of conventual life at Hadley. In Holyoke he had bought the Parsons property, transferred the sisters to part of the Holyoke House of Providence and moved the orphans to South Hadley, which meant that many of the nuns had the crossings to do again, though from a different direction. Also, to have their convent quarters in a part of an overcrowded hospital and home for the aged, was not quite in accord with

Mother Edward's dream of monastic claustration.

More than that, their pastor would never give up his firm intention to have them take over St. Jerome's Institute. With grim foreboding they knew what that would mean to them.

Their fears about the added burden of the horrible school were not ill-founded. He did not give up. His negotiations with Kingston were coming to fruition as rapidly as his sister's school was collapsing into chaos. He gloated over the fact that the boss-lady in Kingston had had her heart wrung with each of his magnificently rhetorical appeals, therefore neither he nor the Holyoke community was surprised when in August, 1875, six sisters came down while the tiny community in Kingston somehow managed to struggle on.

Father Harkins was not even surprised when he found that the leader of his new battalion was the little fighting wren who had attacked him from the soapy floors of Regiopolis.

"I'm the pastor. Do you remember me?" He went right on. "You're going to run my school. For a year. If you don't make out, I'll get somebody in who can run it. But I'll play fair with you. I'll give you a year. By the way, who are you?"

"Who, me?" Why did they always say that?

"No. St. Catherine of Sienna."

"I am Sister Mary of Providence."

Sister Providence arrived at the so-called convent at a moment of jubilation. The will of a Protestant gentleman was probated, and under Item Seven read: "To apply the annual income of $1,000 for the support and maintenance of the Catholic Orphan Institution on Dwight Street in Holyoke, called the House of Providence." It was their first benefaction in rich America.

She shared her sisters' joy and scarcely noticed that she had to climb three flights, through the sick and the indigent aged, to the square, flat attic that was the convent. Later she noticed that she had to run down three flights every time the doorbell rang, though she did enjoy the mystification that occurred there. Set plunk in the middle of a long stoop, covered by an overhang, were two identical doors, a constant embarrassment to visiting drummers, to whom one door was opened, and Sister Providence would greet and dismiss the callers. Then the callers would go to the second door. They would have no way of knowing that the two doors led into a single hall, and that the nun met as the second door opened was also Sister Providence, who, by the way, loved all drummers.

With the other nuns she also grew adept at ripping up their single rug, whipping it around back room and laying it in another ward when visitors came to see their dear ones. The House of Providence became known for its identical doors and its identical rugs; but though there were truly two doors, there was only one rug.

What no visitor saw was a curious necessity on their third and conventual floor, which had nothing above its flat roof except the weather, so that on rainy days the nuns erected a panorama of umbrellas against the leaks. When one of the sisters needed her umbrella on a rainy day, there was the comforting plop, plop of dripping into a pan. The house had not been quite ready for them.

This condition went on until some interested person manifested the inconveniences to Father Harkins, who promptly evicted Patrick O'Gara and returned the nuns to their makeshift convent in Hadley Falls; and the nuns, their penates and their chattels once more crossed the river and returned daily, once they had installed the less bedridden under their own umbrellas.

These were mere physical inconveniences. There was also St. Jerome's Institute for Boys.

Sister Mary Providence found three hundred lads from the ages of four to sixteen and a couple of hulking louts who must have been eighteen, packed into these six classrooms that were undivided by corridors. But every time there was a mass movement, all other pupils had to scramble through the senior class where seventy-five desks all occupied were scrambled helter-skelter into a space that was ideally designated as a room, by virtue of rough, unpainted board partitions through which three years of wildcatting had driven holes, some of them gaping and splintery ragged.

One aperture in particular was illustrious. Michael, an overgrown fifteen, personally inducted Sister Mary of Providence into its meaning.

"See that, 'Stir?" The Sister saw it all too plainly, and at the same moment realized that 'Stir was to be her title for years to come.

"That's where Fodder Harkins went to kick me in de pants."

"Did he succeed?" the nun asked.

After pausing for a moment to interpret this strange gibberish, Michael said, "Naw. I dodged him, see? His feet went through de board, see?"

There was an admiring roar of laughter from the not inconsiderable mob that had gathered. "Gees, he looked funny with his brogue stuck in there!"

"You would have looked funnier if it had been stuck in you."

Though there was a slight titter, she knew that her humor was a bit too subtle. She went on: "Does he do that sort of thing very often? I mean, kick the boys?"

"Naw. Only me. I get his nanny-goat, see? Naw. I'm the only one."

A contributory voice in a tone of pride added: "He hates us, 'Stir. He's a real bully-boy with the strap."

A chorus of proud assent reached her, and then Michael's voice overtopped all. "Show 'Stir the welts on your sit-me-down. Digger—take your bags down."

One scarlet face revealed the identity of Digger, "Aw, gees," he said.

"I'll take your word for it." Digger was relieved. "Does Father Harkins do this often?"

There was almost a chorus of confirmation from the boys, who to a man, approved of their pastors' strength, agreed that he had to, when they got out of line, had nothing but contempt for the four fragile ladies who had attempted to teach them.

"Item one," Sister Mary Providence thought, "we must change that."

Looking into the reasons for the low regard that her charges had for the lay-teachers who had begun and endured the school from its inception under the Pastor's sister, Grace Harkins, she uncovered other facts.

There were almost no textbooks, and whether remediable or not, each book was repaired as best it could be and pressed

112

into service the next year. Truancy and demanded absentee-ism were taken for granted; short term attendance was a matter of course, since after twenty required weeks of intermittent attendance was over, the boys were expected by all to go to the mill—and in this the youngsters were gladly obedient. Some, too, shifted over from public school to parochial school, in and out, covered by a glad little note from whichever school was delivered from their presence or their menace. Grading was a matter of physical space; records were nonexistent; classroom droning recitations, done collec-tively, were drowned out by singing practice or bedlam beyond the next partition.

Sister Mary Providence began by itemizing the conditions that needed remedying. But after Item Ten, she wrote: "Everything," gave it up, and was ready to begin her first day as a teacher.

# CHAPTER 9

Sister Providence's first day in the classroom was a cold terror. She had not wanted to teach, or she would have applied again to the Sisters of Loreto, but had determined on a life devoted to the poor. She had no teacher training of any kind, had experienced only two memorable teachers, and her own schooling had been woefully inadequate. Today she faced ill-assorted urchins in the partially boarded off area that was her classroom. As she looked down on her charges, she knew that their curiosity about her was sprinkled with roguishness, and that the little imps had every intention of subduing her as they had destroyed the four lay-teachers before her.

On the positive side, she was a woman of twenty-five, not a child of sixteen, such as she had seen pressed into teaching by mother superiors desperately needing subjects. Again, she was a nun, her holy habit an armor; she had the blessing of Obedience so that God would supply that which she personally lacked.

In preparation for this day she had outlined lesson routines that would last her a month, always dreading the nightmare of running out of material. But when the day was over, what with the unusual number of demanded recesses, the pouring through her area of boys from the upper classes, the intercepting of missiles through the cracks in the walls, the unexpected visit of the Pastor, who questioned the boys on Catechism, and called them, to their mystification, "The Theologians of the Schools," she discovered that she had taught nothing at all, and had managed only to get their names and make a rough draft of those who were new to the Institute and those who had been in this same class for a year or two. As to their names, she wished there were not such great devotion to the Apostles and Patrick and Michael, and almost declared a jubilee for one imp whose glorious name was Seth.

When the awesome day was over she was waylaid by a

114

little pixie who fascinatingly had one huge freckle on the very tip of his nose, and whose gibberish made her realize that she would have to learn the local patois and to count among her blessings that her own diction was almost perfect. She laughed out loud when she finally understood what the child was asking her.

"Why do you talk so funny?"

She replied: "Before I get through with you, you'll talk funny too," but as he did not understand her, there was no great harm done.

After she had, in some terror, crossed on railroad ties over the river trestle and then strolled back to the convent, she realized that she was breathing in the fresh September air with new relish, and it came to her that in her absorption she had been unaware of the odor of enclosed and unwashed small boys. It reeks from their clothes, about which something must be done, as well as from their bodies—over which she was powerless. On the credit side then she added that she had wanted to work among the poor, and God knows, her charges were poor. Soap was expensive; water had to be carried up from the river, too precious to be wasted on the bathing of the young.

She must have been in a brown study, for as she entered the convent walk, she came upon Mother Edward quite by surprise.

"How was your first day, Sister?"

"I really don't know. I spent all day getting to know their names."

"That is very good." A unique experience; there was almost an expression of approval in the Superior's eye. "You have made a proper beginning. I myself am always careful to learn strangers' names and use them often. It will influence your classes."

Well, at least I have done something right, Sister Providence thought. But a new panic came to her. What would she do when the class rioted, as it surely would some day? The four new teachers had pledged not to turn their charges over to the strong arm of Father Harkins, but to win them by gentler means. That was before they saw them. How do you quell an uprising? Her experience had been devoid of menace.

I'll let Mother Edward determine that, she thought, blessedly unaware of what was passing through the Superior's mind.

Mother Edward was thinking, in the balmy September peace, I won't have to bother much about the school. The sisters will handle their own problems. She could turn her full attention to structuring her community, and to financing her many enterprises, quite enough, she thought. Her policy continued. Through the first year, though Mother Edward was in nominal charge of St. Jerome's, she left the teachers to themselves, with no supervision of the classrooms, no one to whom the refractory could be sent. It is scarcely remarkable that by spring the school gave every evidence of falling apart.

Long before that though Father Harkins became aware that all was not well. He could not understand how Kingston could send him four utterly untrained girls, and though the laywomen had not made any great success of St. Jerome's, they had at least been professional teachers. Except for his sister Grace, they had dispersed after the coming of the nuns.

His sister was still with him, sometimes locking herself in her room, and he could hear her muttering when he left her tray outside her door. His family was cool toward him, too, for luring Grace from Boston to this western outpost, and then firing her in preference for some foreign nuns who were botching the job. They were right too. He had treated his sister shabbily.

It was a day in November when he caught five brats in the outhouse, plotting some mischief, but certainly skipping class. After he gave them a good tanning he realized that this was the first in two months. The nuns "kept them after," they said. This was an insult to red-blooded boys, and he must inform the sisters of Solomon's injunction: "Spare the rod and spoil the child." Yet the nuns' solution saved him a lot of energy, and there had been no major crisis yet. But he must forestall it and have a trained teacher show these nuns how a school should be run.

It was almost Christmas before he got around to confronting Mother Edward. He couldn't quite warm up to her. She never said no, although she always had to refer major things to Kingston for approval. He suspected that it was the

Superior's way of passing the buck. They were crafty, those submissive ones.

This time, to his surprise, Mother Edward got her back up. She seemed to think that everything was going just fine at the institute; she didn't want Grace Harkins snooping on her nuns.

He let everything go till after the holidays. He had other things to think about since he was planning to split the huge parish and to build a third church, which he would call after the Sacred Heart. That would please the Jesuits and get them to come up to help him sometimes.

But at the Christmas gathering of his clan, the family was chillier than ever, and Grace had got to them with her righteous story. He armed himself and attacked Providence, who seemed to be the boss anyway in all but name.

"And what do you know about teaching?" he asked her.

"Not very much. But I know a great deal more than I did in September."

"My sister is a trained schoolmarm. You could learn something from her if you had any of that humility I hear so much about."

"Humility? The children humiliate me every day." She turned toward her 123 charges. Only three had dropped by the wayside. Her arms went out in an embracing gesture. At the moment of attacking them, a wave of maternity went through her—she must protect them from Grace Harkins.

The Pastor recognized the mother instinct when he saw it; even a small bird could peck out your eyes.

"I would be glad to learn from your sister," the nun answered, "and I'll do it this once. But I'm these children's teacher. God gave them to me. Your sister can only visit my classroom."

Poor God, he thought. He always gets the blame. But he had to admit that Providence was as good as her word and that she did invite Grace over, who, after a week or so of pulling herself together and getting herself up in her schoolteacher's outfit—a black skirt and a white shirtwaist with a collar up to her ears, her hoops and her stays in perfect order, and her hair pulled back in a bun, and her schoolmarm's glasses secured with a sliding chain to a gilt

117

holder that she pinned beneath her collar bone—Grace Harkins went over to the Institute to show the nuns how a trained teacher would act, and looking every inch the part.

At the stroke of the bell, Grace strode into the classroom while 120 pairs of eyes measured her. Two boys were playing hookey that day. Miss Harkins brushed by Sister Providence as if she were not there, rose to the dais, and without even saying the prayer, seated herself at the desk. With her ruler she tapped for order. Sister Providence thought that Seth led them but it might have been Michael or Patrick or James or John. As if the tapping were a signal, the entire class burst into song—if you could call it that—and the howlings grew louder and faster as Miss Harkins' ruler inadvertently kept time.

From the holes in the walls, a barrage of missiles clattered down into the howling mass, and defenders arose, manning the chinks, to return the onslaught. The three other nuns scampered in from their areas, knowing what they had dreaded had come to pass—the revolution was in full swing.

Grace Harkins had risen and was shouting things totally drowned out by the boys. Her face was red, her glasses, released from their moorings, tangled in the chain, her hair streamed down over her distraught eyes. As suddenly as she had risen, she collapsed, sitting woebegone behind the desk.

Sister Providence made her way to the dais, reached into the drawer of the desk, extracted and rang a bell. The unexpected sound stopped the clamor at least long enough so that her voice could be heard over the bedlam.

"Recess time!" The unexpected break in routine stunned the pupils for a moment, long enough for her to say calmly, "Go into the yard. We will ring for you when class is to be resumed. Go quietly."

They went with a whoop, but they went. Two of the nuns supported Miss Harkins. "It's recess," they smiled at her, and very tenderly conducted her back to the rectory.

After the bell had rung again and the pupils had reassembled, Sister Providence looked down upon her flock. There was silence on both sides of the desk, but there was a need for explanation.

It was Michael, I think, who said it: "We don't want that old bitch."

It was certainly the lad with the freckles who added: "We want you."

"I want you, too," Sister Providence replied.

Whatever classes she would teach for the next twenty years, she would want too, but they would never be quite the same as these rapscallions.

She began to teach them then. A teacher is one who enables students to learn. Sister Providence's children always learned.

All the sisters were kind to their pastor; in his presence they never mentioned Grace Harkins' visit. In a week or so, without looking, they knew that Grace was on her way to Boston. The Parish of St. Jerome settled back into its own strenuous progress.

From then on, Father Harkins visited the school more often, demanded written reports of grading and progress and schedules, looked at tests, reviewed the absentee lists each day and was appalled by what he found.

St. Jerome's Institute was a mess.

He waited patiently until the June term was over before summoning Sister Providence to his cottage, a tactic which he reserved for the most serious emergencies.

She found that day an insight she was to use for years to come. The pastor was not dangerous when he was gruff or angry or loud; the bellow was all there was to it. But beware of him when he was sweet and reasonable.

"Sit down, Sister. Let me move those things for you. You must be tired out after the hard time you have with those boys of mine. I've been thinking that perhaps it's too much I've asked of you." He groped under the debris on the desk and came up with a folder. "Now here," he went on, "is a report I made up on the running of the school, and I want you to know how grateful I am to you poor Sisters, without enough help, without any experience at all." He gave her no time to interject a word. "And so I've been thinking that Kingston ought to send me more nuns—maybe some who have taught for a while, since I hear you have teachers up there. Oh, don't bother to look at that report now, later will do, and be sure I know you've done the best you could. I say that in my report to the Mother House. You'll see it all in there. Only I've been wondering if Kingston can't send me real teachers—and then came the bombshell— "if I shouldn't try to relieve you to work with the poor and the sick and get another Congregation in. As a matter of fact I have one in mind."

In a flash of what she hoped was divine inspiration Sister Providence made up her mind. "If you will entrust me to deliver this report—how formal my language is, her consciousness said to her—"I will go to Kingston myself and present it to Mother Mary John. I think I know the solution. Besides," she added, tapping the report, "whatever bad things you have to say in this—you are right."

Oh, he was right, she thought, as she read the summary of their first year. The sisters had made a mistake in not asking that the children be examined before they took them over, so that now there was no way to tell if there was a change for the better, as she thought there had been, since the four professionals were replaced. On the other hand, she realized that with Mother Edward's minimal interest, there had been no supervision at all. The Sisters maintained order on their own; they were left to advance the boys at will or even to dismiss them from the school and pack them off to the pagan public school, if they took a dislike to them.

Then she thought of her own life. Take four hours out of the day for spiritual duties, which came first, as the Lord explained to Martha, add the routine household tasks of cleaning and washing and mending, for was not this God's house, and add to this what she had done, and probably would do, never knowing whether it was because she wanted to, or because it was expected of her, since both were true—and there was simply no time left over for correction or for preparation of classes. During holidays the teaching nuns were supposed to pitch in and help at the hospital, the orphanage, with the poor. But she thought with some misgiving of how, during the teaching week, she had got herself involved in so many ways.

She went with the visiting sisters, Sister Mary Dolours and the others, to the homes of the abandoned: nursed them, laid them out when they were dead. She taught catechism to the children in South Hadley and gave remedies to the sick in the hospital because the night nurse Sister Teresa was ill; and there was no night service. She thought of the many nights when she and the other teachers had made up beds from chairs and tables, giving the beds they had to the patients. And she thought of her most recent involvement of love— the woman with the suppurating cancer. How she had felt great happiness in dressing her wound and every day before classes she would be delayed at South Hadley because of this. Then she would cross by boat if it were available or on foot over the railroad trestle—thus arriving breathless and exhausted to begin class.

These extra labors could scarcely be curtailed, but at least, in the school, there could be some organization, some control, and one head.

Sister Providence went to Kingston, presented and ratified Father Harkins' devastating report and made her request to Mother Mary John. After a day of consideration and prayer the General Superior agreed to the proposal and sent Sister Providence back to Father Harkins.

"I didn't get all you asked for," she told him, "but I want you to give us a year more, and if you don't see that you have a good school at St. Jerome's you can look elsewhere for Sisters. But give us a year more."

"Well, all right." He was mystified. "But I don't get it. What's your mysterious cure-all?"

"Oh—didn't I tell you? I am the new Principal."

"Glory be to God," Father Harkins exclaimed, and he beamed at her and mystified her. "Humility is Truth," he said.

During the year of probation, Sister Providence was so busy that she scarcely noticed that her adopted country was going through significant times. She was informed that it was a disgrace that Mr. Rutherford B. Hayes was elected president, but that he was less of a bigot than the other one. She wondered if there were not more than two mediocre men named to govern so vast a country. She had heard annoyed people talking about the inconvenience of the railroad strike. There were mixed reactions to a new union of workers called the *A.F. of L.* How you thought depended on whom you listened to. Confusing. Her prosperous friend, Mr. Judge of

South Hadley, who was so generous to her in all her causes, told her the unions were instigated by anarchists. The parents of her students were for the unions, provided they would produce better working conditions, but they didn't want them in Holyoke, where they might stir up trouble. The priests were of two schools, they were no help. Even Father Harkins could not decide in conscience whether the strike was a virtue or a mortal sin, and he grumbled that the Vatican should lay down the law one way or the other and not leave busy pastors to come to deep moral conclusions on such a question. Sister Providence had no time for such vexing considerations.

She had produced some kind of organization in the institute by holding meaningful examinations, and without respect for size or age, grading the pupils. The nuns had feared some kind of repercussion from the parents on the demotion of their overgrown louts, but the complaints were minimal and revealed something far worse—the apathy of the families to education: as long as their young were out from under their feet and safely in the care of the Good Sisters.

That desire presented a problem. The overcrowding of the building was caused by the laudable wish of the Catholics to save the souls of their children. As soon as the Pastor would try to cut down the admissions, Mrs. Murphy would arrive with her Dennis, who simply had to be admitted. Mrs. Murphy wept and asked him, did he, who posed as a priest, want her Dinny to lose his soul in the pagan public school, which he was always preaching about, when it wasn't about money?

He ignored the last charge. Since, at the time of the annual report, he made his sole plea for increased collections, and since the weekly donations for working adults averaged seven cents per capita, he did not feel guilty. On the other hand, the pastor believed that a soul was more important than a crowded classroom. Dinny got in.

He made one compromise. The sisters could draw the line on admissions when every last desk was taken. In conspiracy with their Principal, the nuns spirited out one desk whenever a boy left school or was expelled, gradually widening the aisles, but so gradually, you would scarcely notice it.

Now, the Pastor could honestly say, "I know, Mrs. Halligan, but we haven't got another desk for your Matthew in the whole school. Isn't it a shame, though?" Sadly he would see Matthew cross the street to lose his soul.

The lowering of class numbers helped a bit with the textbook problem, but when the nuns recaptured as many of the used books as they could, mended and taped them, there were still not half enough. How often they heard the excuse: "Naw, now how could I do the homework, 'Stir? I ain't got no page in my book."

Which was more valuable? Sister Providence wondered, the feeding of bodies or books, the nutriment of minds? She knew the answer. Without bodies you can't have minds, but throwing her values aside she petitioned Mr. Judge for textbooks. She was flatly refused.

"I'll give you medicine and food and fuel. Use slates. I did. So did Abraham Lincoln. Why, I'll even collect clothes for you——"

She jumped in before he finished. "You will?" And thus was born the Friday *clothes*.

At the end of every week, beginning with the most ragged, four or five boys were outfitted in trousers and shirts sewn by the sisters from castoffs, and some even got shoes, which had to be carried home and were to be worn only in school and at Mass and, of course, bad cess to it in the Winter. At the end of each school year there was a new distribution. Old clothes were collected, restored where possible, only reduced to clean rags when tatters were too shoddy for mending.

Subtly, too, Sister Providence devised a way to get the boys' clothes cleaned once a week. Though the back-breaking laundry already consisted of all the washables from orphans, elderly, patients, Father Harkins and the nuns, she enlisted small boys to trundle water up from the river, turn the clothes-wringers, fill hampers, and lug them by hand to storage. At last Seth came up with the labor-saving device of toting the hampers by long ropes, delightful over ice, but still possible when spring came. For all this, Sister Providence let the word leak out that ample Sister Mary of the Cross would see to it that the wash-crew got pie and bottomless mugs of milk. Also nobody looked to see if these boys picked out shirts and underthings that were closest to their own size.

123

Consequently the wash-crew was the best dressed.

Having reduced the numbers and cleaned up the clothing, Sister Providence introduced a Kingston practice. She insisted that her nuns call every boy, *master*, and always refer to them as *scholars*. It is amazing what it did for the *esprit*. The rumor spread that it was hard to get into St. Jerome's and easy to get put out, and her charges began to feel that they were a cut above the riff-raff at the public school, and yes, even superior to the girls in the Notre Dame School across the way. But that was only after they had organized athletics, which Mother Providence coached herself. Sometimes they won.

Books. That was the problem. She bearded Father Harkins, but he only pointed to his own tomes and said, "They can have all these except my breviaries," and he did not take her seriously.

She compromised. She went to the Superintendent of Public Schools and shamelessly begged books from the wealthy city. She got them too. Of course, for her three teachers it meant not only learning a new text but added hours of expurgating all anti-Catholic slurs, blacking out paragraphs in the History books, inking over the vulgar words that were tolerated by the public and found in so-called literature. Amazing how they poured filth into the innocent ears of the young.

After the textbooks were antiseptic Sister Providence glanced at the remaining pile that did not need vigilance. "Thank God," she said, "there's nothing obscene in arithmetic."

It must not be thought that the Sisters had no other distractions. They had to move with the orphans to South Hadley, but then were no sooner settled when the Bishop designated it as a new parish and chose their convent as the rectory for Father David McGrath. Promptly, Father Harkins cleared the orphans out and perched them in the loft of the institute. The sisters moved back to Holyoke. Though it saved them the trestle crossings, they had to carry food across the yard for sixty orphans and up two flights of stairs three times a day rain or shine. Thank God it was April.

By this time, Mother Edward knew they had to have

property. On the outskirts of the city there was some land for sale, the site of a former hotel; even though Sister Providence had spotted it first, the Superior had to admit that it was desirable. The area was known as Ingleside, but Sister Mary of the Cross, cherubic with optimism, had already rechristened it Mount Saint Vincent, and Sister Leonard had buried a medal of St. Joseph on it.

Unknown to them, Father Harkins had other plans, and he didn't want his nuns to go traipsing off where he couldn't keep his eye on them. They must have their own land. They would buy the original Parsons property for $15,000. There were no ifs or buts about it. With their dreams still on Ingleside, they sent Sister Teresa, not Sister Dolours, on a great western trip, from which she returned with $6,000 in gold and a hacking cough. After a year or so of house-to-house canvassing, they scraped together from the mill-workers another $9,000, paid for the Parsons property, and were legally incorporated, May 31, 1878, as The Sisters of Charity of the House of Providence, Holyoke, Massachusetts.

Then they began their second drive, again from house to house, again from the now rich West, for Mount Saint Vincent's.

One day, in despair, Sister Providence returned from a fruitless trip to South Hadley Falls. As night fell, she was no richer, and only the numbness of fatigue atrophied her body. Never had it been so far to the House of Providence. There was a high curbstone where she stood.

She had a temptation. She wanted to sit down on the curbing. It was dusk, and who would see? No one was about. But if anyone did come by, what would they think of a nun who allowed herself such self-indulgence, sitting there in the gutter? She tottered on like a somnambulist and did not feel the ache until she got home.

She allowed herself some concessions. During the day she crept up to a vacant room and went into what was a coma rather than a sleep, disciplining herself, setting the alarm-clock in her brain, for twenty minutes, after which she swam up from exhaustion.

Her bone-weary fatigue, she knew, was not totally physical. She was young and strong. Something else wanted her to shut out the world.

At first, after her return from Kingston as Principal, Mother Edward, though scarcely enthusiastic, had, as a dutiful religious, accepted the Will of Superiors.

For months now, she had let the school run itself, but in this new arrangement it came to the Superior one day that this young nun showed an attitude of independence, unbecoming to a religious. Sister Providence consulted her on nothing, referred nothing to her, made her own rules and enforced them on the other teachers, who, though agreeing in the main, properly manifested the autocratic sway, to her, as to their true Superior. Mother Edward did a little testing. She made some suggestions to Sister Providence, but the suggestions were ignored, simply brushed aside. No Superior could tolerate such abuse, for it would split any Community.

One day, as she had carefully planned, she accosted Sister Providence, asking her with no show of rancor, "Who is the Superior here, you or I?"

The answer was direct enough. "I think you are the Superior."

"Then what are you?"

"I am the Principal of St. Jerome's Institute, and my appointment comes from the same source as yours does—from Kingston."

In justice to her subject, the Superior admitted that in all things not related to the school, Sister Providence was scrupulously obedient, and even overly generous, but let no one interfere with her own sphere of authority, let no one even try to insinuate that St. Jerome's Institute was not her personal subsidiary. You couldn't let a thing like that go on, could you?

What Mother Edward had not achieved by direct confrontation, she now attempted by constant maneuvers. Though she said no more about the school, she carefully reproved her subject for each infringement of the rule—for nodding at meditation, for returning to the convent after dusk, for having lights on and studying after proper hours, for some carelessness at prompt obedience at meal hours—everything, that, as Mother Superior, certainly came under her jurisdiction.

126

Sister Providence felt it as a part of her fatigue, balancing it off at the end of that first year, against Father Harkins' approval of the school report, and of herself. But she knew she was at the breaking point.

One day she announced, did not ask, that she was going to Kingston, with the permission in writing from the General Superior, Mother Mary John. Mother Edward knew that Sister Providence was going over her head. Well, one would see.

She saw. When Sister Providence returned from the Mother House she presented her Superior with a letter from Mother Mary John. As Principal, she was practically independent, and there was nothing anyone could do about it, though the victory of the subject scarcely endeared her to the Superior.

A very unwise decision had been made in Kingston, Mother Edward knew. The rift in her community was clear, and the teaching nuns would say, "But I can't take on that extra load, Mother. Sister Providence has forbidden it." Sometimes she thought that the younger nuns also were being swayed.

She consulted with Sister Dolours. After all she was Sister Providence's blood sister. Though she received strong moral support, Sister Dolours said, "Oh, that one. Don't try to tell her anything. She won't fight you back—she never would. But she just won't do anything. She's that aggravating. We don't even go to the same cases together any more. She has her own life and I have mine."

The last straw was when Mr. Judge from South Hadley Falls came over and asked to see the Superior. Mother Edward greeted him decorously and engaged in some meaningless conversation. Then Mr. Judge said to her—*to her*—"I wonder now if I could see the Superior for a moment?"

"The Superior?"

"Why yes. Sister Mary of Providence."

"Oh. Oh, I see. Surely. I'll get her."

Who is Superior here, you or I?

And that, too, was shortly decided by Mother Mary John in Kingston, for after a suitable interval following Sister Providence's manifestation at the Mother House, neither of them was Superior. Sister Edward was relieved of office and removed to Ontario. Sister Leonard, pious little, sweet little, terrified little Sister Leonard was made Superior of Holyoke and found herself with the tail end of the debts on the Parsons property, and how it ever happened she would never know, with a firm commitment to purchase the site of a demolished hotel that had a deservedly riverside reputation but had now mercifully burned to the ground, fifty acres of overgrown hill land, and the reasonable debt of ten thousand dollars.

But Sister Providence was not upset. Though it took a little convincing, Father Harkins came over to her side; Kingston promised the loan of $10,000; Divine Providence had scraped up $15,000 for them for the Parsons property and could be counted on again.

She now knew everything about the inner workings of the Holyoke Community, since Sister Leonard never made a move without consulting her; she guided her superior's hand in the signing of the contract for Ingleside. Only one small detail remained—to inform the Bishop.

She was not a bit surprised then when her nominal Superior came shaking into her cell one evening.

"The Bishop has sent for us," she said.

"Us?"

"Well, me. But you know I can't talk to Bishops. So I suppose it's you and me and Father Harkins."

"I think we'd had better go alone."

"Not ask Father Harkins?"

"Perhaps not this time. He just gave the Pastor of the Sacred Heart a check for $3,000 when the split in the parish went through. The Bishop might think he was—well—a little profuse." It was the first hint that the protectorate of Father Harkins was coming to a close.

"What do you suppose the Bishop wants? . . ." Sister Leonard quivered.

"What does he say?"

"Something about not going through proper channels in signing for Ingleside. And he thinks we're bankrupt."

"He's right. Bishops always are. But we'll convince him we have resources he doesn't suspect."

"Oh, yes. Treasures laid up in heaven."

"That, too. But I don't think that will convince His Lordship—I mean, His Excellency."

So the sisters properly met with the Bishop. Sister Leonard said nothing at all. Sister Providence spoke the words in which she had been coached by Sister Mary John, who provided to be not only a good businesswoman but a superb diplomat, which, for all his heroic virtues, could not be said of Father Harkins.

When they met him, the Bishop's handsome old leonine head seemed to have developed a mane, which quite subdued Sister Leonard but did nothing at all to the spirit of her companion.

"How could you foolish women do this?" His Excellency thundered in his richest episcopal voice. "You're head over heels in debt on that Parsons property, and now you've signed a commitment for a disreputable hostelery."

"The hotel burned down, Your Excellency, and what debt are we in?"

"Why, the fifteen thousand for the Parsons property."

"That is all paid, Bishop."

"Paid? What do you mean—I have a note on that property—If it's paid up, you should have sent me the cancelled note. I never saw it."

"Oh, I'm sorry about that, but it was all arranged in Kingston."

"Everything seems to be arranged in Kingston. Not even in our own United States. Canada. Who do they think they are—the Bishop of Springfield?"

"No, Your Excellency. But we thought since we paid for the property we should keep the documents. They are quite safe with us."

"Didn't say they weren't. But they belong to this diocese. How can I keep anything straight around here? Now as to this Ingleside—"

"The Lord will provide, Your Excellency."

"He'd better, because I won't. And every penny you spend on building comes out of your coffers. Just a minute, though. It doesn't. You'll go syphoning off money from the parishes, filching from the Springfield diocese, that's what you'll do.

It was that Harkins trained you—him and wild building."

Yes. She had been right not to bring Father Harkins.

"What are you going to build there anyway?"

"An orphanage. And we'll turn the House of Providence into Providence Hospital. The city and the diocese need it."

"You're right there. But this other scheme—now look you here . . . Don't you women ever do anything like this again without my permission. It's got so your own bishop doesn't dare do anything unless it comes from Canada. We'll have no more of this nonsense."

"No, Your Lordship."

"There you go again—British snobbery. British." He gave one last snort and dismissed them.

Sister Leonard, saddled with new debts, was mute, but Sister Providence said serenely, "He didn't say no to Ingleside, and I think Reverend Mother will agree that since we own the property, we had better hold the deeds."

When she reported to Father Harkins all that he needed to know, all he said was, "God help all poor Bishops when they come up against such as you."

It was no surprise to anyone, then, when within a matter of weeks, another official letter came from Kingston, its contents bringing great relief to Sister Leonard, chuckling amusement to Father Harkins, grunting and admiring defeat to Bishop O'Reilly, a scarcely perceptible shift to the community at large, and a calm acceptance of God's will to the one chiefly concerned.

Mother Mary of Providence was now Superior at Holyoke.

# CHAPTER 10

Then began those ten years in which Mother Mary of Providence was sole Superior of the entire Holyoke operation, and remained as Principal of St. Jerome's Institute.

Also, she built Ingleside. Well, not quite alone. There were workers, of course, but there was also Father Harkins. Father Harkins and she built Ingleside.

The Pastor had obtained proprietary rights by the simple expedient of purchasing the adjoining farm from the Stursbergs and promising it to the sisters outright, as soon as all the renovations were complete. This gave him the right to criticize the blueprints, harry the architects, bully the builders and cajole the workmen.

Because Mother Providence was doing the same thing, it was all a bit confusing because the two bosses had, not infrequently, contradictory ideas. She wished he would concentrate on the plumbing; he wished she would stay away altogether. But he is responsible for the myth that she hauled mortar up ladders, ran across a tightrope of a girder and was hammering in nails as she sat astride the rooftree. She did no such thing. She stayed demurely on the ground. But glory be, she was always around.

Eventually, when she could see the Pastor's buggy way down by the river road, she would find the most inconspicuous spot she could, wait out his visitation, and then follow in his footsteps after he had gone, and say, "Don't worry at all. We'll just go right on the way we planned it." She said it all very sweetly. After it was finished she gave him all the credit; he became quite convinced that if it hadn't been for him, the whole place would have been a mess. The sisters got the Stursberg estate outright.

It was a wonder that he could afford it. He had at last built himself a sizable rectory, after thirteen years in his makeshift cottage. He had watched all the other buildings go up, three churches, a hospital, two schools, an orphanage and convents of sorts, and last of all, when the Bishop threatened to send

131

him curates, a decent house for the priests. You couldn't ask young lads just out of the seminary to live the way he had lived, now could you? It was a reasonable motive. So he built a solid house in which he lived the rest of his life and in which he died.

If Mother Providence resented the intrusions of Father Harkins, she looked forward to the more and more frequent visits of her general superior, Mother Mary John. In fact, her former mistress of novices came so often that once Mother Providence said to her archly, "I think your heart is really here." The Canadiennes, guilty of preferring the mission in the States to their own Motherhouse, smiled knowingly at each other.

The age gap between them had decreased over the years and was eliminated by their shared authority. There were only four years between them, which amazed Mother Providence when she discovered it. They presumed rightly that their younger subjects viewed them as indeed venerable, for these two young women in their thirties had completely assumed the mother-roles that their stations required of them. Far from the intention of their founder and foundress, accustomed to the great-family tradition of Europe, where the status of the head of the family was totally independent of age, the American Superiors of both genders confused themselves with the only thing they knew: the Father and the Mother of the small natural family. They treated all their subjects as if they were immature children.

Everyone accepted it. Their grumbling was good-natured. "You'd think they were the only ones with brains around here," or "I was running a business when those two were in pigtails." But they would submit, because God made the natural law.

To the subjects, the unanimity of their superiors was edifying; to the Superiors it had grown out of a great need. There was no one else to whom they could talk openly. Woe betide the lady in office who made a confidante of one of her subjects. Even if she were too chummy with another nun, Mother was suspect. And if word leaked out that she had betrayed a confidence, let her be anathema.

Sister Mary of the Cross understood all this. When Sister

132

Patrick had said waspishly, at the time when Providence had replaced her Sister Edward, "Now you'd better watch out. She's been gunning for you for years," Sister Mary of the Cross smiled.

"Why do you think that?" she asked.

"It's clear she never liked you."

"Do you really think that? Isn't that funny?"

Sister Mary of the Cross knew that since the noviceship, Mother Providence had liked her. There had been moments securely alone, over a cup of hot chocolate, when Mother had almost—not quite—been intimate. If Mother was a lonely woman, it was because she still thought she was Margaret Mary Aloquoue, being nasty to her friends, for the love of God. Sister Mary of the Cross paraphrased Soeur Rosalie, and said, "Sometimes I wish she didn't like me. Then she'd be nice to me." But you couldn't get Patrick to understand. "Anyway, it doesn't matter. I like her." That closed the conversation, and Sister Mary of the Cross just stood by, waiting, if ever she was needed.

Because of her utter abandonment of involvement, Mother Providence won the confidence of her nuns. And another attribute of hers helped mightily, her innate sense of the *family secret*, which probably did as much to foster a spirit of unity and to give a morale to the various Congregations as their more spiritual commitments.. Mother Providence had a deep conviction that what was planned or even discussed within the family circle should be revealed to no one, certainly not to those outside the Congregation, but not even to subordinates, after the high echelon meetings of the Administration. Mother Mary John had written it in her counsels; Mother Providence had had the same sense of inviolability of family secrets from her girlhood. Thus these two women could talk openly only to each other and they had no wish to have things otherwise.

Consequently her nuns knew that no matter how severe the penances she imposed might be, and at times they were harsh, their faults would never be revealed to others. Since, through the practice of Manifestation, this reticence did not work both ways, and religious knew they had a duty to lay their whole souls open to Reverend Mother, they could and did do so with almost sacramental confidence.

133

No. She had no favorites in those days. She did not dislike anyone, though she had been relieved when Mother Edward's ideal nun, Sister Carmel, had been summoned back to Kingston to be general treasurer. As to her own sister, Dolours, she once admitted to Mother Mary John, "I do not like her," and added quickly and truly, "I do not dislike her; I just don't like her." That settled any bond of blood ties.

There was another and unexpected aspect to her government. She developed what was perhaps not any great sense of humor but rather a sense of fun and by it managed to turn the building of Ingleside into a lark. After a day on duty, teaching, scrubbing corridors, she would gather her children for a hot drink, encourage them to don ridiculous costumes—over their holy habits of course—and do strange, impromptu dances, all the while building up an anticipation of a trip to Ingleside on tomorrow, their free day. When it was well after bedtime, and they felt naughty, she would say, "Now run into chapel, make a quick act of contrition, and pop into bed." Sometimes she would even say, "Make a big sign of the cross while you are getting into your checks and go right off to sleep."

Conditions at Ingleside during construction, and for months afterwards until the water main was connected, were primitive. Their drinking water was pumped from a well, but other than that, they had to haul barrels up the hill from the Connecticut River to the Asylum or trundle the orphans' clothes to the river banks. As she had lured her boys at St. Jerome's to take over the washing, now she lured her sisters into making of it, a Saturday game.

Impatient, even during the week, she conned her teaching sisters into the long trudge to Mt. St. Vincent. They now numbered eight, one for each grade. After school she would get them to pack a supper-lunch and eat it on the way. When they reached the open farm land they would rearrange their habits to look like nuns of other communities; and a new Portress at Ingleside once entertained them for a full ten minutes while Mother Superior chattered in her faultless French, over gingersnaps and yeasty root beer, thinking they were some of the immigrant nuns who were descending upon America. Lured by Bishops and understaffed Mother

134

Generals, the immigres saturated the Catholic public with private lessons in French, music and needlework, after which they found themselves rejected. They were seldom without shelter because other nuns took them in. Mother Providence sounded pathetically like them.

That evening, the barrels from the river did not seem so heavy.

They made only one sad pilgrimage. They buried Sr. Teresa, the night-sister whom Mother Providence had for so long replaced.

On the joyful side, there was the ground-breaking, July 12, 1880. Bishop O'Reilly turned the first sod, and as he contemplated the beribboned spade, said, "This time it took only one generation from shirtsleeves to shirtsleeves. My father was a pick-and-shovel man, and now in my old age you sisters have made me one."

At least—Mother Providence thought—Your Lordship had a life of soft hands. Our own callouses will never weaken off.

Nor did they. The Bishop had no sooner eaten his gingersnaps, and the episcopal crumbs were still there, when Sister Carmel, the treasurer from Kingston, bore down on Mother Providence.

"Do you intend to go on with this building?" she demanded without introduction.

"What else? Didn't we just break ground for it?"

"Turning sod doesn't mean building a building."

"It does to me. The contracts are all out."

"I know that—now. It's a wonder Reverend Mother or you, for that matter, never tell me these things until they're all done."

Silence sometimes has its disadvantages.

"How do you expect me to do my job? Just pay the bills? Out of what? I ask you. Where is the money coming from to meet payment? Can you answer me that?"

"We expect God to provide."

"Very well, then. Because I won't. I'm going right back to Kingston—to make my retreat." Even Sister Carmel knew this was a little farfetched; this was July, the retreat was in August. Maybe the treasurer contemplated a pilgrimage on foot. "So you take charge of things. You and God."

135

She flounced out. Bishops forgot promissory notes. Treasurers never forget.

Beg again, Mother Providence thought, and more callouses.

How Mother Providence ever erected the massive building, Sister Patrick used to say, acidly, was "By bad food and my sweat. We didn't have any problem about actual poverty."

This was not entirely true. It was boomtime in Holyoke. The unions had come, and cotton, wool, paper, silk, alpaca, came bundling forth from the mills. Women and children found fulltime employment; the workers learned about overtime and piecework. Now Seth and Michael, the bright ones, went to High School, and for Dinny, who had not lost his soul and ambitioned the priesthood, there was Holy Cross in Worcester, or for poorer boys, a College on Harrison Avenue in Boston. Even lads who chose other professions were being trained in the Catholic colleges. The older institutions admitted some Catholics but the Irish Quota was tokenism. If you were continental Italian, French or Spanish Catholic, you could get into Harvard or Yale; but your chances were slight if you were American-born Irish.

Catholics accepted their isolation. They built their own increasingly liveable ghettos, erected and staffed their own schools and began to hold firmly that you should trade with your own kind, patronize your own doctors and lawyers, vote for the Democrats, build your own society, and sparked by the literate *Pilot* of Boston, read your own Catholic authors. If the others didn't want you, you could have your own pride and eventually your own power.

Mother Providence plunged into this rising society, making friends of the Mammon of Iniquity, the new moneyed group. Around her the Irish were discovering grandfathers who were poets and schoolmasters before the famine, and even ancestors who defended South Boston against the British during the Revolution. Perhaps now the memory of the poverty of her girlhood faded, and her father's foundries and her mother's millinery increased in reality.

Through these contacts and the self-sacrifice of her nuns, Mother Providence paid off the entire debt within six years. Mother Providence—and God.

The real blow did not fall until two of those years had passed.

It was a beautiful day, that August 16th, 1883, and Mother Providence was filled with joy and triumph. Sifted by the sunlight that fell upon her desk through the open window, came a breeze from the Berkshires that had a recollection of spring, and a hint of the tang of autumn.

She was writing her reply to Mother Mary John of Kingston. Out of their mutuality, out of their love Reverend Mother had proposed that the entire novitiate be moved from Kingston to Mt. Saint Vincent's so that the new little sisters would come under the influence of Mother Mary of Providence; therefore she could shape all the future spirit of the Sisters of Providence of Kingston. As both women knew, it also meant that the seat of government of their rising community would ultimately be shifted from Ontario to Holyoke.

Mother Providence had dreamed of it, but never believed it. She wanted to write just yes-yes-yes, but she began more formally, "Beloved Mother in Christ: Your proposal has filled me with great happiness and thankfulness to God—"

A knock on the door. "Come!" What now? A sister—Sister Mary of the Cross—a pale Sister Mary of the Cross, only her rosary beads chattering, held out a yellow telegram.

Mother Mary John was dead.

Aged thirty-six. In Religion, twenty years. Five years, Mistress of Novices. Eleven years General Superior of the Sisters of Charity of Providence, Kingston. Thirty-six years of age.

Mother Providence tore up her letter bit by bit. The breeze was cold. She closed the window.

After the decent week of mourning, Mother Mary of Providence went to the chapel of the Motherhouse of Kingston from the hall where the superiors and the professed had voted—the *Chapter*, they called them. She made her oblation.

The Chapter and God, had chosen as the new General Superior, Mother Mary Edward.

Through the years while bicycles hazarded life and limb on Dwight Street, while you heard more and more about Andrew Carnegie and Standard Oil and Trusts, while Mother

Mary of Providence gathered the ready money, willingly given because the new Catholics swelled with pride at her convent's bastioned impressiveness, to Mother Edward's credit it must be admitted that she left Holyoke alone. She did not interfere.

Mother Providence did not give herself time to brood. Indeed, there was no time. She put in her formal reports to Kingston, received form acknowledgments. The annual visits of Mother Edward spruced up the conventual life of Holyoke. There were no more dances, hot drinks, funny costumes, or omitted night prayers.

Sister Mary of the Cross confided that she could not talk to Mother General, but remained open with Mother Providence. Gradually she could perceive that the other nuns were less and less communicative. Mother Edward had erected a barrier, enclosing not only herself, but all other Superiors. They had been so free with Mother Providence, so free with Mother Mary John. A dumb devil had got into them all.

The Superior threw herself into the work. To the tune of $22,000 she completed a wing on Mt. St. Vincent's Orphanage, and paid for it by 1887. It was not 'til that year that she received a peremptory summons to Kingston.

Under the aegis of her sins she confessed to Father Beaven, but she did call on Father Harkins. The interview was violent and memorable.

"I have been called back to Kingston," she said.

"Why?"

She sidestepped the question. "Under Holy Obedience."

"Is it that Edward? That chilly old fish you have up there? What does it mean? Did she bounce you as Superior?"

"I don't know, Father."

"But it may be, hey? Then ask her who's to run my school, will you? Does she expect me to raise money for all the fool things you've been building? Does she? Not another penny will you get out of me. She can put that in her pipe and smoke it." The veins were standing out on his forehead. "What are you going to do? Stand there and take it?"

"What can I do?"

"You know what you can do. You can fight her, can't you, the way you fought me? Where's your gumption?"

138

"Mother Edward is my superior."

He did not say damn. He took up a chair and hurled it at an invisible Mother Edward. It shattered against the wall.

"Well, now. Well, now." He looked relieved. "Tell me this. What do you have up your sleeve?"

"I can't tell you that," but she had compassion for him and added, "but I don't think I will be in Kingston long."

"So I have to be satisfied with that? Well, I will be." He smiled at her and tried to reconstruct the chair. "Now you come back to me, do you hear?"

"I will," she said. And she did. She wrote in her journal, "After a brief interval, I returned." No more than that.

Publicly, she came back with only one commission: that the orphans' liberty be reduced so that, according to edict, they would be imprisoned in their house and small play yard. Mother Providence was obedient and announced that due to the dangers of straying, the orphans would be allowed in the future only freedom of the grounds at Ingleside. This gave them the same roaming they always had, but the words satisfied Kingston.

Thus for Father Harkins and the sisters the incident petered out, but it would not die within the heart of Mother Mary of Providence.

Then began her own dark night of the soul.

Now she was alone. In her journal she puts the word in upper case: ALONE.

For the love of God she had cut everyone off. Of her three brothers, one was now dead and the others were in far-off California. Her general superior rejected her; her subjects would not open up to her. With Father Harkins there had been mutual interests; he liked her, she had admired him; but had they ever been friends?

Sister Mary of the Cross stood by.

In the books that Mother Providence had read, her sacrifice of human love should have freed her for union with Christ, but she could not even pray to Him. Once she had grown drowsy at prayer, but often she had found rest in the communal chanting of the nuns. There had even been moments of exaltation and even in her busiest moments she had been aware that God was near her, until she thought that she had learned the secret of the practice of the Presence of God.

All this was gone. Strange doubts shook her. They had taught her that she should find God in the monastery and bring Him forth to the people. It had not worked. She had had no great spiritual experiences in the noviceship. Only through the children she had been given in that first year, only in the old woman dying of cancer, had she found Christ. That was years ago, and it had not been right. So Kempis said.

What shocked her most was not the aridity of vocal prayer, or her failure to attain the ability of frequent aspirations, which her new confessor, Father Beaven, advised, but the meaninglessness of holy Mass. A man was way up there before the altar, muttering meaningless words. The pressure of the Sacred Host on her tongue was routine, and her habitual attitudes of worship were empty gestures.

Along with this she began to realize the inadequacy of her teaching, which she knew had been utterly unpreposed. She was innocent of the slightest training. Did not one tempt God by trespassing proudly into what should be a profession? Was any of this fair to the pupils?

She thought of asking for two years at normal school. She could turn over her responsibilities to the Holyoke facilities to someone else, or rule part time, and mainly *in absentia*.

The conflicting duties oppressed her. Father Beaven ironically advised prayer, but she returned from Chapel more confused than ever.

Very well. She would throw the problem directly on the shoulders of Mother Edward. No. Her superior would be only too happy to send her to normal school and get rid of an encumbrance. Then what of Father Harkins? In two years everything would collapse.

At last, God gave her a grace. She knew by the discernment of spirits that her desire for professionalism had been motivated by dissatisfaction and pride. She saw the tail of the serpent. She would not ask for training.

She was not happy, but she made up her mind. She would stick to her guns, but she would take every opportunity to visit other schools and observe other methods, which she would apply.

140

With grim will she began her incessant trips of observation. What she did not know or ever realize was that for the wrong reasons she had chosen the better part. Her genius was such that she learned from contacts and observation and very little from texts and formal instruction. She became, they say, a great teacher.

Three years passed in this spiritual dryness, in a sense of uncertain compromise. At the end of this period she knew that it had been only a postulancy, a forty-days-in-the-desert preparation for what was to come.

## CHAPTER 11

Early in 1890 there came out of the blue another summons from Bishop O'Reilly. Mother Providence chose her companion with care—Sister Mary of the Cross, whom she knew would be silent as the grave. It was well.

The Bishop hinted broadly that the Community of Holyoke should cede from the Community of Kingston and that the local branch be diocesan, under his own Episcopal See.

"There was no discussion of the subject on the return trip. Mother Mary of Providence said unnecessarily, 'We must not speak of this.' Her companion said nothing but remembered that the Bishop had previously said that he never felt free to ask any special favors of the Sisters, since they were so restricted that they first had to consult Kingston, and that in the interview the bishop said the same thing to Mother Mary of Providence clearly."

"She replied: 'Your Lordship, our Rule does not provide for a separation. It rather forbids it. I would not wish to do anything for which I might be called to account on the Day of Judgment.'"

"The Bishop answered her objection. 'You will not be asked to do so. If Rome should grant a separation, you need have no, scruple.' "

Thus it began, and Mother Providence was left alone to study the proposition and to remain neutral, and could consult no one for months, for nearly two years.

She thought that she understood the Bishop. Like herself, he had hoped that the seat of government would be moved to Holyoke, and had been disappointed. Then too, most Bishops preferred their own diocesan congregations, and just as every pastor wanted to build a church—Father Harkins had built three—so every Bishop wanted to be the founder of a congregation of religious. You got canonized for that, didn't you? Well, not solely, but it helped. And every Bishop thought he knew more about structuring the private lives of

142

women religious than St. Vincent de Paul did. God bless him. Bishop O'Reilly was probably no exception.

On the other side of the picture, there were bishops who already had groups under them, and His Lordship, the Archbishop of Regiopolis would cling fast to his own Community, and Reverend Mother Edward, who now regarded her experience at Holyoke as exile, would regard the cutting off of the American mission as nothing short of civil war.

Logically, Mother Providence knew, Kingston had a very weak case. There, not so long ago, the English had broken off from the French of Montreal; and before that, the Canadians of Montreal had broken off from Paris. In the American South, Mother Seton had severed her ties from her stemgroup, and her own daughters had split, stating their army camps by their uniforms—those who wore the Civil War bonnets, and those whom the clergy called *God's geese*, flying nuns with huge cloth wings on their heads, a garniture that they religiously believed had been instigated by their holy founder, St. Vincent himself, when he threw a piece of linen over a peasant girl's head and said, as one inspired, "There is your habit."

Looking at the history of her order, Mother Providence became convinced that the splintering had been in God's plan. She found precedent among the Franciscans, divided into the blacks and the browns. Directed by Father Beaven, she read about the Benedictines, united by a single spirit and a single rule, but whose far-sighted founder had given local independence to each of the great monastic foundations, wisely knowing that the ministry would differ from place to place; resultantly, she knew right now, that there was as much difference between the English and the German Benedictines in America as there was between the Church of England and the Church of Scotland. Yet they both had the mark—they were sons of St. Benedict. Then Dominic had come along and established a powerful instrument that had something for everybody—ranging from contemplative nuns to friars preachers. Only the Jesuits remained intransigent, for which Mother Providence, as did most of her contemporaries, blamed Ignatius Loyola and his militarism instead of the authoritarian aristocracy of Francis Borgia, Duke of Gandia, or the Iberian legalism of the restorer, Father General Anderledy.

In her planning now, which caused all kinds of distraction to her vocal prayer, she envisioned a congregation in which there would be room for all kinds of needed ministries, possible adaptations to local and temporal needs, a meaningful life for the Sister Mary Dolours of the future as well as for contemplative spirits like Sister Agnella, the little lamb, and where there might be room for delightful extroverts like her own Sister Ursula.

Her ideas about a possible religious community had been dreams; now they were plans; and they came unbidden as she knelt in chapel, saying over and over the meaningless refrain, "Pray for us, pray for us."

Kneeling alone in his church, after he had moved his lips to every word of the Breviary, Dr. Beaven knew that he was praying as he planned the future of Bishop O'Reilly's Sisters of Charity. He remained fully aware of the presence of God; he made explicit petitions for guidance; he did not distract himself by vocal prayer but used the intellect and the will that God had given him, dedicating it to the Divine Service. At the end, he would devote a few moments of colloquy, in direct communication with God.

He knew, and the Bishop knew, that in the diocese he was the one man who was aware of the tendencies in Rome. Cardinal Satolli himself had told him that the Curia was cognizant of the dangers of American independence, liberalism, separatism of Church and State. From such things, all the abuses that had brought on the reformation were fomenting again. To forestall this, the Curia would begin at the easiest level, the structuring of congregations of women, then tackle the freer orders of men, and make the Regulars, regulated.

In Dr. Beaven's prayerful plans he could envision the ideal congregation of nuns securely under the control of the Bishop of the Diocese, who would be their true religious Superior, with their own female General an appointee of the Hierarchy, receiving all power by delegation from the Episcopacy. Next, they should model themselves far more on the cloistered order than on the higgledy-piggledy looseness that they now enjoyed. Though they would not be hampered from their work by strict enclosure, he could see his nuns, women of prayer and silence, separated from the world, virginal, disciplined, and above all, obedient.

Though Dr. Beaven knew that he had Rome behind him and that the laity properly approved of nuns being nuns, separated from them, different, holier and far more ascetic, he faced the difficulty of structuring his envisioned order. The older ones presented the greatest problems, having had no formation to speak of, little professional training (if the truth must come out) and lives that gave lip-service only to prayer and enclosure. Monastic silence, he had heard, was almost nonexistent. Well, he would face out the problem of the older nuns as it arose, stressing obedience. In any case, they would eventually die; therefore his emphasis must be on the young, the Postulants, the novices. Yes. He would increase the period before final vows to several years, during which they would renew their vows annually, and hence, not being fully accepted, they could be truly and fully formed.

In his colloquy he said to his master, honestly, "Forgive me for thinking of them as my nuns, not Bishop O'Reilly's. Forgive my thinking, 'When I am Bishop,' instead of 'If I am Bishop.' If this is the sin of presumption, I am sorry; if it is just foresight You know what my plans are, and I think that You approve of what I will do. Amen."

Dr. Beaven blessed himself and rose, blew out the guttering vigil light before the statue of St. Michael and the dragon, scratched away the dribble of wax that marred the simulated marble, genuflected and left the church, completely at peace.

Mother Providence was not at peace when she left her chapel. Again, she had not truly said her prayers, and as always, her doubts gnawed at her. She wanted to be relieved of the dictatorship of Kingston, to be out from under the scrutiny of Mother Edward, to establish a community more fitting to her freer American spirit. Maybe—oh dear no—she wanted to be a Foundress!

On advice she disciplined herself to regard her worries as distractions and to put off any deep consideration of them until she made her annual Ignatian retreat in August. It was given by a young Jesuit, Father Stanton, who impressed her deeply.

In the study that the sisters had prepared for the Retreat Master, she had a long interview; and facing him across a desk was not hampered by the black box of the confessional. He did not help her much with her prayer life, reiterating what Dr. Beaven had said: "When in dryness, pray longer." She had done that and it had not worked; she was only more bored. But he did help with the reciting of the Latin prayers. "You know the words by heart in Latin. While you recite them, keep your eye on the English translation across on the other page. After a while the languages will begin to come together and make sense." Later, she tried this and it worked. Why had she wasted so many years making noises that meant nothing?

As to her problem about the split, he helped. "Your motives, Mother. You are always reading about having pure motives, and that's a good thing. But I would say as a rule of thumb, just keep your eye on the goal, what you want to accomplish. Is it good or bad? You tell me the split would give your ladies a better apostolate. I think so too. There's nothing the matter with that. Now as to the funny little reasons that creep into your mind, like wanting to be General Superior, just forget them. If the end is good, attain it. For the rest, just practice indifference and thank God if he shows you where you are wrong. It's quite simple."

It was. The words were simple, but the application was not. She prayed longer, and her self-discipline doubtlessly helped her character; but still, half her head and all her heart formed an alliance against her indifference. Her youth and her whipcord body had served her well until now, but she began to notice increasingly that annoying heartburns came after meals, and that even simple fried foods, let alone the grease which had sustained her since her novitiate, caused agony. Baking soda could not alleviate it.

The heartburn increased when Mother Edward made her inevitable descent upon them. They had had a good New England breakfast of fried potatoes that first morning, but except for the heartburn she had no particularly upsetting reactions, when the Bishop, as usual, sent for Reverend

Mother and herself. She supposed it would be about routine matters; it always was.

Her own account of that interview with the Bishop, if reserved, is significant. It reads:

Nearly eighteen years had rolled by since the opening of the Mission, and exclusive of the erection of the Home at Ingleside, little had been done to extend the field for works of Charity. About this time, Rt. Reverend Patrick T. O'Reilly, D.D., Bishop of Springfield, asked for an interview with Reverend Mother Edward. I was her companion on that visit to his residence, and he made known to her his design to open a Mother House for the works of Charity, in the Diocese, and expressed the wish to avail himself of the Sisters of Providence for this service. He stipulated that it would mean a separation from Kingston, and inquired as to what measures he should take, and to whom he should apply for the necessary authority to permit the Sisters to remain. Mother Mary Edward told him that the Archbishop of Kingston, the Most Rev. James Vincent Cleary—our Ecclesiastical Superior would be the authority in the case, to which Bishop O'Reilly replied that, he would submit the proposition to His Grace, and if he received no encouragement, he would refer the matter to Rome. Reverend Mother M. Edward, always self-controlled, made no protest—having placed the responsibility on the Archbishop—so we withdrew. Entering the conveyance awaiting us, we started homeward, neither of us expressing our emotions, though we were both very busy with our thoughts and very much astonished at the Bishop's announcement. Finally, Reverend Mother broke the silence with a single exclamation—"A SEPARATION! VERY UN-LIKELY." I said nothing, but I was indeed deeply grateful that I had received no intimation of the Bishop's object in sending for Reverend Mother. Resolving to say nothing on the subject, to anyone, I resumed my duties—I was then local Superior at the House of Providence and Mt. St. Vincent, with a Sister Assistant at each House, as well as Principal of St. Jerome's School—never making the slightest reference to the matter pending, and endeavoring to maintain a neutral attitude with the powers at variance. This occurred in the Fall of 1890 and extended to August 1892, when choice was

147

given the Sisters to remain in Holyoke, under Diocesan control, or return to Kingston.

After the visitation, Mother Providence had only one hope. Her general superior's term of office would expire in the early summer of 1891, and who could tell what more amenable person would take over the government. There was another possibility that she dreaded. It would be a shrewd diplomatic move of the Council to vote for her, herself, tying her forever to Kingston, cutting her off from Holyoke. She could refuse the office. Could she? There was indifference and God's Will.

Another probability was nipped in the bud. The old and adamant Bishop O'Brien of Kingston passed to his reward, but his successor Bishop Cleary was more strongly in favor of Episcopal control over his sisters than his predecessor had been, and to assert his command, he overrode Mother Edward's deep objections and turned the first two floors of her Motherhouse into a lazarium, shifting the nuns again to the alternately hot or cold third floor attic.

As to housing, Father Harkins reversed the Kingston catastrophe and completed for the community a modern convent on Hampden Street; therefore the ladies no longer needed umbrellas or could envy the adequate housing of Ingleside.

She filled the months up with dyspepsia and building, awaiting the elections.

On that hot and humid day in August, she, and the others of the professed, cast their vote. Then His Lordship, Bishop Cleary of Regiopolis, having glanced at the tally, requested a second vote, proposing for election the return of Mother Edward to office. His suggestion resulted in an almost unanimous shift to the Superior of his choice. Though she had protested, had she not, out of obedience, quartered her nuns under the eaves?

In heartburn and in stupor Mother Providence made her obeisance to Her Divine Majesty in the chapel; then she asked for a concession—that she might go as she had gone as a girl, to the mount where Fort Henry stood, across the river.

She had not stood upon the battlements for many years, and it would be cool there above the thousand islands. Once more she could drink in the glories of its sounds and colors. It might renew in her what she needed now, a sense of the glories of Canada. She would renew herself in the bright air, look up the great river and see below, washed by the distance, the pretty city of Kingston; then glancing northward perhaps she could fancy again that there came, marching from their fortress, the splashing glory of banners and uniforms of the Chevalier de Champlain.

Scarcely noticing the heat, she climbed the hill. At the summit the skies, the thousand islands, the water were the same, though the heat had come up with her, stifling even there.

Around her spread a ruin, a shambles, all that was left of proud Fort Henry.

She went down quickly. She intended to go back as soon as she could, silently to Holyoke, where things were still rising, by Riley's Brook.

At the Kingston Motherhouse she was met by downcast glances and obvious avoidances by her own Holyoke nuns, or when she did catch an eye, she saw sympathy, even pity. She knew the symptoms. They were not rejecting her but manifesting the habit of silence. Something had happened to her.

She climbed resolutely through the wards for the abandoned, to the third floor, and the green baize bulletin board where, each August, superiors tacked the announcements of the Missions for the coming year. She found the heading: "Holyoke Mission." All her nuns were listed. Her name was not there.

She could not find her name. Then under Motherhouse, Kingston, she saw it. Yet it was odd. After her name, there was no assignment to any duty, and looking again at the Holyoke Mission, no one was designated to replace her; Holyoke simply had no Superior.

She had once been tempted to resign. She had smiled knowingly when other sisters had said, "I do not mind being ousted—I only object to the way they did it." She had thought she saw through them; now it was happening to her.

By rule, she could have gone to Mother Edward and, as they called it, represented, that is, asked for an explanation;

but some custom and the spirit of indifference opposed any action. Again, she had smiled when she heard other nuns say, "I won't give them the satisfaction," and thank God, Father Stanton had told her not to bother too much about unworthy motivations. Put them out of your mind.

She left the bulletin board and tried to put them out of her mind. For several days she tried this. Mother Edward did not send for her; she had nothing at all to do. She laughed at herself, thinking, "What a grand time for a rest," but it was bitter humor.

She heard nothing at all. Was the General Superior trying to wear her down so that she would come crawling? She could crawl, she thought, if she had to. But the more virtuous action was submission in silence. On both parts silence, and her mind paraphrased sardonically some obscure poet: "Silence is the cruelest answer."

Though there was silence at Kingston, all was not calm in Holyoke. When the shepherdless flock returned to Holyoke, three knights donned shining armor and went forth to battle dragons. The Bishop of Springfield's letter to His Lordship of Regiopolis lacked any attempt at Roman diplomacy; Father Harkin's epistle to the General Superior of the Sisters of Providence blistered the pages; the letter from the Apostolic Delegate bore more than a trace of the somewhat legalistic prose-style of the Reverend Dr. Thomas Beaven, S. T. D.

Without explanation, in late August she was packed off to Holyoke.

"Better not go away at all," she thought on her return. All the physical and material problems had piled up; but worse, dissatisfaction, discouragement, bickerings over loyalties to the homeland against the mission had sprung up. "At least when you are on the spot things come gradually and you can absorb one shock a day. But now they have all bundled up together." She had to remember that if she had been here, she would not now be thinking that everything was falling to pieces.

Bound by secrecy, she could not cope with the rift in her own previously neatly consolidated community. The Kingston supporters had confidence in the influence of Archbishop Cleary, who had been consecrated by Cardinal

150

Simeoni, whom everybody knew would be the next Pope. The Holyoke-oriented nuns were in a better argumentative position, since Dr. Beaven kept them informed of the negotiations; while in Canada neither the General Superior nor the Archbishop was communicative.

In Holyoke, Sister Mary of the Cross made a novena for the retention of union with Kingston; in Kingston, Sister Ursula made a novena that she could go back to an independent Holyoke.

When her own blood-sister, Sr. Mary Dolours, requested an interview, Mother Providence was not surprised. It would be a relief to both of them if Sister Dolours wanted to go back to Canada—and reasonable too, since it must be hard for her to live under the rule of her blood-sister, of whom she disapproved. And the situation was not edifying to the community.

"I would like a change, Sister." She never called Kate, *Mother*.

"I thought you would." Mother Providence nodded. "As the Bishop said, all those who wish may return to Kingston."

"Kingston? Who said anything about Kingston? Why should I want to go way up there? I've lived here all my life."

"Oh. I never thought of that. But it hasn't been very easy for you with the two of us from the same family, and all that. I thought you'd like some other Superior."

"Between you and Edward? It's a small choice."

Not exactly a compliment, but Mother Providence let it pass.

"I'm not getting any younger," Sister Dolours went on. Mother Providence knew she was not yet fifty, but she had thought old for years. "I'm tired of being an outsider in my own community."

"Oh? I honestly thought it would break your heart if I changed you."

"You would. But it never crossed your mind when you sent Sister Teresa on those western trips, did it? She died under the strain, you know. And you may remember that I was quite healthy; and that when I was assigned to solicit funds, it was I who supported this community."

151

So that was it. But it had been Mother Edward who replaced Sister Dolours with Sister Teresa. She herself had had nothing at all to do with it. Could it be possible that Sister Dolours blamed her for that? Oh well.

"Which of the works would you like to be in?" she asked.

"I'd like to teach school."

"You would?" Amazing. Too old to visit the sick but not too old to begin an entirely new professional career.

"At least I've always kept up with my reading," she said, answering the unspoken objection. The Superior winced. God knows, as superior, she had not had much time for reading. Honesty forced her to admit that she had never liked novels—never liked much reading.

"Yes," she said. "You have kept up with your reading." Probably had time during the night hours while her patients slept and she just sat at vigil. "It will stand you in good stead in the classroom. And it will come in handy." She would be losing some of the Kingston teachers and would need replacements. "Very well," she said, "if that's what you'd like."

"I would."

Sister Dolours began her brief teaching career in the community, at nearly fifty years of age, in the following September. Though she never became a very good teacher, she was an excellent disciplinarian and that helped; besides, for a brief while, it gave her standing in the community.

Mother Providence put her sister's problem out of her mind. The Bishop acted quickly. In early September he appointed a committee to make a formal petition to the Congregation of Bishops and Regulars. It consisted of Thomas D. Beaven, Patrick J. Harkins, now permanent Pastor of St. Jerome's, a brilliant and active young curate, Bernard S. Conaty, and the dark horse—the Italian close to the throne—the New Yorker, Very Reverend Dr. Ferranti, who knew all the passes and bypasses in Rome.

At once the Committee called a meeting at St. Vincent de Paul's convent, announced plans to interview each Sister privately, and to get a signed statement of her choice of communities—Kingston or Holyoke. That the interviews were conducted, and the votes read, by Springfield priests, and that no delegates from Ontario were present to sway the balloting—may have had something to do with the overwhelming vote that Monsignor Ferranti was able to route to the Curia.

This time, perhaps without need, the Sisters were put under professional secrecy not to reveal what occurred in the private interviews, and were informed that professional meant practically confessional.

The silence relieved the Superior. Comment and discussion ceased. At last they could concentrate upon their works.

In November the Committee announced a great victory. Over Cardinal Simeoni, who was aging, and not as interested in the outpost of Kingston as Archbishop Cleary had hoped, the Springfield group obtained rescript of *Status Quo* which meant that until a final disposition was reached by the highest hierarchical authorities in the Vatican, no changes of any kind could be made. It secured Mother Providence in office, and came just in time, as Mother Edward was again considering her recall.

The *Status Quo* backfired only once on Dr. Beaven, its instigator. A Sister, whom the nuns charitably described as being "of turbulent disposition" was recommended for return to the Motherhouse; and Dr. Beaven could not help but smile, recognizing the fine hand of Archbishop Cleary, when over Mother Edward's signature, he received the direction that, due to the Status quo, Holyoke must retain the turbulent sister. From now on Mother Providence could handle her own disciplinary problems.

The Superior of Holyoke fully realized how simple a solution she had previously had—to send all destructive boys over to the public schools and all turbulent sisters back to Kingston. By February she was again in a mood to pray for relief from office.

On February fifteenth, 1892, Mother Edward descended once more upon Holyoke. At once she quartered herself in Mother Providence's private office and summoned her for an interview.

She wasted no words. "Sister," she said—not Mother—"by order of Archbishop Cleary you are to leave this evening for Canada."

Mother Mary of Providence was ready. She had been well coached. "I do not leave until I hear from the Bishop of this diocese that there is to be no separation."

Acidly, Reverend Mother Edward asked her: "Is not the Archbishop of Regiopolis your Ecclesiastical Superior?"

"He is," Mother Providence replied, "but there is also an obedience due to the Bishop of Springfield—and some courtesy too. Besides," she added, testing the thin rumors that trickled in from Kingston, "I am told that though you have appealed against the edict of *Status Quo* you have received no rescript, and that *Status Quo* is still in force."

She correctly interpreted the Reverend Mother's silence as confirmation and plunged on: "Under these conditions I am not free to go. My first obedience is to the Vatican. I am not disobedient in refusing to go." She hoped, she prayed that she was right. She prayed! Yes, she realized with a moment of actual exaltation, she had really prayed!

The Reverend Mother rose, every inch the mitered Abbess. "In that case I am obliged to depose you from the Office of Superior."

Mother Providence, still exultant, smiled. "Most willingly. I care nothing for the office."

To do her credit, Mother Edward almost descended into humanity. She looked long at Mother Providence and said, "I believe it."

The interview was formally over, but Mother Providence paused at the door and turned back. "May I request permission to have an interview with Father Beaven?"

Mother Edward's official manner returned. "I cannot allow it. I anticipated that you would ask this. The Archbishop said that it was not to be granted."

Far from daunted, Mother Providence said, "Then I request to see my confessor."

"Isn't that the same thing? Isn't Father Beaven your confessor?"

"Yes, Mother. But after this ordeal it would seem reasonable that I seek the guidance of my ordinary confessor."

No Superior had the right to refuse this recourse. Trapped, Mother Edward nodded defeat.

154

"Would you send for him then, Mother?"

Mother Edward tried to change the attack. "Sister," she asked, "why do you jeopardize your religious standing?"

"I do not think I am doing that."

The General Superior tried again, desperately. "You and I have always been such good friends." How could she say that? Mother Providence had received one nod of approval, on her first day of school, and that was all in all these years. Yet Mother Providence was convinced that Mother Edward was sincere. Was this what friendship meant in the religious life? Nothing more than this? She could not accept or pretend to such friendship.

"Mother," she said, "I have always been your obedient subject, and when the problem is settled, if it be to the loss of this diocese of Springfield, I shall return to Kingston and be your obedient subject again. But for the present I remain in this house and no force shall remove me."

It was the Superior General who abdicated the private office to the Superior of Holyoke. Mother Mary of Providence sat down at her desk and prayed, prayed until community prayer summoned her; and then, to her peace with her other sisters, she continued to pray, and after Father Beaven had come and gone, after her confession, she stayed alone in the chapel.

The confessor had said: "Where there are two obediences you may choose either, if they are in conflict, but only when they are of equal authority. But in this case, your obedience to Rome supercedes your obedience to Reverend Mother. You have no choice but to remain."

Never before had she had a conflict with obedience. She had as a child never seriously disobeyed her mother—or even her older sister. In religion she had been scrupulous about obeying all commands. Or had she? The Sister in the kitchen, when she was a novice? Others. Many others, she saw now. The Bishop about the promissory note? Mother Edward and the orphans? Outwardly, oh, yes Lord, I have done the outward things. But my heart has not been obedient. If it were sorrow which flooded her, she could not say, for she had such joy in the light of her own shortcomings, which the good Lord sent to her.

155

"I am sorry for my disobedience, Lord." she said to Him, "But I thank you very much for letting me know."

The next day she taught her classes with unusual dedication, even with fervor; and when school was over she was not surprised to find Mother Edward again at St. Vincent de Paul's Convent. The history of the community presents the following procedure with eloquent understatement:

Reverend Mother again came to the Convent, accompanied by Sister Mary of the Sacred Heart, from Kingston. The Sisters were again summoned to the Common Room. They were informed by the Reverend Mother that Sister Mary of Providence, because of her refusal to obey orders of her highest Superiors was to be deposed from her Office as Local Superior, and that her place would be filled by Sister Mary of the Sacred Heart.

The deposed Sister Superior, kneeling in the centre of the room, read a written statement in which she accepted her deposition, exposed her reasons for non-compliance with the orders of her superiors and expressing her belief that she was not acting contrary to obedience because of the existing Status Quo decree, which had precedence over all else in the Community, and with conditions with which all were familiar, but protesting that if later it were to be found that she was acting in a disobedient manner, she would humbly submit to any punishment that might be imposed.

Mother Mary of the Sacred Heart was designated acting Superior. Sister Mary of Providence continued her duties as Principal of St. Jerome's Institute.

Alone in the corridor when they met, Mother Mary of the Sacred Heart, took her little Sister in her arms. There were no words needed.

The two hours which followed would normally have been hectic and trying, but Sister Mary of Providence remained, to the edification of all, completely calm. She knew, while they could not, what a light, what a grace, God had sent her. Even with the threat of actual excommunication from the Archbishop of Kingston, she was not unduly disturbed.

When Doctor Beaven came at once to see her, he visibly put on his thinking cap, more worried than she was, and though the letter sent to Archbishop Cleary is in the holograph of Sister Mary of Providence, the ideas and even the phrases are those of an astute lawyer, Thomas D. Beaven, Priest and Doctor.

House of Providence<br>Holyoke, Mass. 2629/92

Dear Rev. Mother,

I have heard your command, that I prepare within two hours, to return to the Mother House. I understand that this order has been given by you and your General Council approved by His Grace the Archbishop of Kingston, Ecclesiastical Superior of the Sisters of Charity of the House of Providence, Kingston, Ont. of which institute I am a subject. I have also heard, read and fully understand the Mandamus of His grace, and its ecclesiastical censures, with the further threat of possible excommunication in case of refusing to comply with said order. But in view of the fact that the "Status Quo" was imposed on the community at the instance of the Bishop of the Diocese of Springfield, I do most respectfully make appeal to the said Bishop or his representative, and do refuse to comply with that order or to withdraw from the house in which I now reside, until notified by the Ecclesiastical authority of this Diocese, that the "Status Quo" has been removed, in other words, that the petition for a separation has been finally and positively answered by Rome. I do most emphatically assert my willingness to obey without questioning the authorities of my Community in whatever they may command me, as soon as I am officially notified by the authorities of the Springfield Diocese that the "Status Quo" imposed, as we have been informed by the Card. Pref. of Prop. in Rome, has been removed. I do this in the belief that I am acting under the protection which holy Church accords to its children.

I am Rev. Mother, in heart and desire, notwithstanding my appeal from your order, the obedient child of Religion and subject of my Community.

Very Respectfully,<br>Sister Mary of Providence.

# CHAPTER 12

On May 28, 1892, Bishop O'Reilly of Springfield received the communiqué from Rome, which made the Sisters of Providence diocesan and his. From now on the accomplished plans of Father Harkins would be a mere cellar for the structure the Bishop would erect. He would create first-rate hospitals, properly staffed schools, modern orphanages. He would begin with Springfield, but he had his eye to the West, where the rich people were beginning to find the Berkshires.

He worked hard all morning, communicated with his triumphant committee, met with Dr. Beaven and almost got around to informing the nuns. Just before lunch there was a pain in his heart. At noon, the Bishop was dead.

Dr. Beaven assembled the Sisters for Mass the next morning, wearing black vestments, pronouncing a short eulogy for Bishop O'Reilly He kept the announcement for the peroration:

"The final legacy of our beloved Bishop was to you. The last hours of his life were brightened by his hopes for you. Yesterday morning, in the last mail which he opened, Bishop O'Reilly's dream, and I am sure, your dream too, came true. Rome has approved of our mutual plan, that you become the Sisters of Providence of the Springfield Diocese.

"It was his hope, as it is mine, that many of you, because you realize the great work for God to be accomplished in this area, will choose to remain here. It was his last wish, not his command. He left you free. Those of you who elect to do so, may return to Kingston; but to those who remain, I promise in Bishop O'Reilly's name, a great and massive expansion of your work with God, according to the vision of our late beloved Bishop. You will advance under the leadership of your valiant Foundress Mother Mary of Providence.

Dr. Beaven was a little disappointed in the effect he had expected to produce. He gathered correctly that, despite all the secrecy, there was not a nun of them to whom this news was new. Nor could he understand why Mother Mary of

158

Providence was upset. She should have been charmed by the lifting of the threat of excommunication.

She had guarded this secret so carefully. Father Beaven had made it appear that she had been a party, an interested party, in the split. When Sister Mary of the Sacred Heart departed that night for Kingston, Mother Providence knew what report she must bring to Mother Edward, General Superior. Even Sister Mary of the Cross gave her a funny look.

No use crying over spilled milk. She assumed complete authority at once, and in collaboration with Dr. Beaven, began the structuring of her new community according to the most modern ideas that were now taking shape in Rome.

Since the Council of Trent the Church had been attempting to cloisterize all nuns and all the regular clergy. Still remembering the medieval abuses of freer monks and nuns, which produced the Reformation, the Ecclesiastical Fathers were dedicated to enforcing a life-style more suited to contemplatives than to workers in the field. Though most post-reformation groups had been founded as communes of dedicated lay-people, acting under personal direction, engaged in direct work with the needy, they had first been forced, often reluctantly, to live by the Rule, and then, through pressures from the Hierarchy and the laity alike, most of the nuns and not a few congregations of clergy, had been pressured into the second step— semi-claustration for all religious. Though most of the formalization came from the founding Bishops, who left themselves free enough, to be sure, it was not only accepted by the modern Mother foundresses, but was implemented by them and looked upon as the idea to be achieved.

Mother Providence remembered the haphazard nature of her own novitiate. She knew how hard it was for her sister, Mary Dolours, after years outside the cloister, now to submit to a way of life never before experienced; personally the foundress knew from experience how utterly untrained girls had been drafted into professions for which they had no preparation; now, with the coming of total responsibility, she began to learn that in the matter of finances there was a dichotomy between the virtue of depending on divine

159

providence and the virtue of human prudence.

She set herself then to the stern task of cloistering structuring and formalizing her new institute.

For three months she had to work against the handicap o having only the say-so of a local Doctor of Theology to assure her authority; on August 17, she was confirmed in office, from Rome. Her first interest was to weed out the malcontents and to send them packing to Kingston, to strengthen the wavering and keep them in Holyoke. When their formal decisions were made, fourteen elected Kingston and she was left with thirty subjects. Added to these might be some, now in Ontario, who would choose to come to America. Sister Anselm, for instance, though from New York had been caught in Belleville and now refused to renew her temporary vows unless she was returned to the States Ultimately, she had to resign from the Congregation, apply all over again in Holyoke, and spend two more years as a novice. Then there was Sister Philomena, one of Mother Providence's own candidates, now long professed, whose insistence prevailed, so that she simply transferred to Holyoke.

Sister Mary of the Cross was torn. She had made her vows of dedication of her life in Kingston, but that life, from the beginning had been in Holyoke with Mother Mary of Providence. It was hard, but following her conscience, she signed for Kingston. Then she had one look at Mother Providence's face, and she changed her vote to Holyoke.

Mother Providence did not send for her, but waited till they met casually.

"Thank you, dear old friend," she said. "But I can't let you do this. Your conscience tells you to go to Kingston. You must go." Then she confessed, "If I were perfectly sure I was doing the right thing, it would be different. I am just doing what people wiser than I tell me is right. So I can't tell you what to do. Your vows were to Kingston, not to me. Please, don't let that be on my conscience too, that I kept you."

By agreement, when Sister Mary of the Cross departed, there were no farewells.

In exchange, Mother Providence received Sister Augustine,

whose dossier said, "A woman of rather undecided character." Oh well.

Though Sister Augustine was the official exchange, in the matter of devotion, it was the beautiful twenty-two-year-old Sister Ursula, who had been recently, Alice Nixon, and who had returned from Canada for the very simple and uncomplicated reason that she loved Mother Providence. No wonder then that she was so soon First Assistant to the General Superior, confidant, friend.

On November 1 Mother Providence opened her first novitiate, and nineteen admirable subjects now assured of remaining in their homeland, entered as postulants. The Diocesan Community was flourishing.

The very night of Father Beaven's appointment as Bishop of Springfield, which came as no surprise to anyone, losing no time, the Bishop Elect gathered his nuns into the Common Room.

"As you all most certainly know," he began, this time taking their knowledge for granted, "you now have permission—no a command—to establish a Motherhouse and officially dedicate a formal novitiate as a Community of the Diocese of Springfield. To that end and for your governance, I now nominate Mother Mary of Providence as your General Superior, Superior of the House of Providence of Holyoke, of the House for the aged and infirm, as Pricipal of St. Jerome's School, (he never called it institute) and in charge of Mt. St. Vincent's Orphanage, and of the convent for Sisters on Hampden Street. I will grant to her the right to appoint or to delegate such authority as she wishes to confer, in the administration of the aforementioned facilities of the diocese, pending my approval, as your diocesan Superior. All those in favor of accepting Mother Mary of Providence as your General Superior, kindly raise your right hands."

The Sisters acknowledged in their gesture Mother Mary of Providence as their God-given Superior General, and Bishop Beaven as their spiritual and temporal Superior. God ratified the gesture, giving the power of authority to the Superiors, the duty of submission to the Subjects. The first act of His Excellency was explicit.

"The first and fundamental principle in the religious life is

161

obedience. As you will obey your Mother Superior in all things, so she will obey her Bishop. As Shakespeare says, this is the law of nature, as witness the earth and planets in proper subjugation to the reigning Sun. So there can be no true order unless there is true obedience; so it is in the hierarchy of the Church, as Christ founded it; the laity is subject to the Pastor; the Pastor, to the Bishop; the Bishop to the Vicar of Christ; the Pope, to Almighty God, from whom, as from a source, all authority comes. Therefore, having established an order of obedience amongst you, I know that you will give the oblation of complete docility to the authority which I have constituted over you, as she, to whom I have delegated this authority, will render complete obedience to me, your Bishop."

Sister Patrick chafed. She would have voted for Mother Providence. Most of them would have. But to have the Bishop appoint her just out of hand, like that, that was a different story. Is that what it meant to be diocesan—to have a man, even though a Bishop, be their real Superior? In the future would their vote count for nothing? True, they had no constitutions yet, to which they could appeal, but she remembered that Mother Mary John had come here on the condition that the modified rule of St. Vincent be preserved.

Sister Patrick was so disturbed that she could not bring herself to go to the Bishop's consecration on October 18.

Mother Mary of Providence and all the other sisters went for that day, forgetting that the lines of battle had been drawn between their right to vote in free election for their Major Superior and the Bishop's claim of appointive power. Too recently they had seen the dictatorship of His Lordship of Regiololis, and the sheeplike abrogation of the rights of their Sisters of Kingston. But even Mother Mary of Providence put it out of her mind on the day of the consecration, for was not their Confessor now their Bishop? They felt like the nuns in Rome, whose chaplain became the Pope; and it gave them an advantage over other communities.

Bishop Beaven had wisely left them free in one thing, anyway. They were women, and though he asked that there be some significant change in their habits, he had left the design up to them. Clothed in their new uniform, they were

162

to appear for the first time at the Consecration.

The change was not exactly flattering, Mother Providence thought, but she had rejected flattering garments before she had entered religion, and her nuns had ratified the new design. To her amazement they had retained what was basically the costume of the expensive Irish dolls imposed on them by a man years ago. They varied it only by bringing down the points of the headpiece in two broad tails that reached the collarbone. It elongated every long face, doing nothing for those who already looked as though they had posed for El Greco; besides it was harder to wash and starch and shape. Yet her nuns had chosen it, and they would wear it until death—unless, she thought, she could gradually do something about it.

The nuns, in their new ensembles, went gratefully together into the choice seats reserved for them by their young friend, Father Conaty. He must have been distracted this morning because he didn't seem a bit glad to see them. Maybe he didn't like their new garniture.

Father Conaty was a *man*. He hastened down to the sacristy and got a hold of Father Harkins, "Peek out there, Pat—up at the right gallery. Do you see what I see in the picked seats?"

The Pastor of St. Jerome's was a man too. "I see nuns," he said.

"You bet you do. What nuns though? I picked those seats for our nuns, and who do you suppose sneaked in there? The Sisters of St. Anne! Golly, but those French are pushy."

Father Harkins, having no sense of reticence, went out to the chancel and in full view of the Congregation he focused on the right gallery. He returned.

"Your Annies are where they belong," he told the young priest, "way in back of beyond where they can't see at all, only Glory be to God, the Providences have got themselves up a new rig that looks just like the Annies, only with a couple of pendulums hanging down their fronts. Women," he concluded.

The two men glanced at at each other with pitying comprehension.

That night after the great Episcopal Dinner, the new garb

163

struck Mother Providence as funny; she liked it better after that. It looks for all the world like the getups we used to put on when we went to Ingleside, or the way we dressed up in the kitchen. The kitchen? What happened to those parties?

With a twinkle she gathered up her nuns and got them together for a hot drink. There was no Mother Edward now to say her, nay.

At last she said to them, "I can't keep my secret until morning. I've got to tell you what our good Bishop did."

"Tell us, Mother. Go on. Tell us."

"He announced it at dinner—at his own acceptance speech."

"What did he say?"

"Instead of us giving him a gift, he gave us one. That is, he and our old friend the City Almoner—you know—William S. Judge. He gave me clothes for the youngsters once. Well, the Bishop was behind it, and he had Mr. Judge give me this."

She produced a document by sleight of hand. It was a deed of gift of the entire Wilkinson Estate called *Brightside, a* property above Riley's Brook, adjacent to Ingleside; a munificent gift that made Father Harkins' donation of land seem insignificant.

It gave the nuns all the hillside from the crest to the river road.

That night they thought well of the Bishop.

The next morning they approved of what they read in the papers about him.

"Bishop Beaven is of English blood and has in him the best qualities of his race. He is recognized as calm and strong, shrewd without shallowness, a good judge of character, who speaks of the best side of men oftenest; deep and in the concern of high office, a Sphinx; but in hours of recreation with fellow priests, of abundant spirit and good camaraderie, enough to satisfy the soul of the warmest Celt among us.

"Nowhere in the world or at any time will there be a closer or fonder union between a diocesan and his priests, based upon a mutual respect and trust that exists today between Bishop Beaven and those he rules in the Diocese of Springfield.

"The Bishop is a large man, six feet high, broad shouldered

164

ınd strong. Strength is his special quality that comes to one's
nind while observing him, and this characteristic of strength
s in the whole man—mind, will and body. The very calmness
ɔf his manner and the sweet graciousness of his countenance
ɐnhances it. He is a very handsome man, with regular
ɛeatures, scant brown hair and with skin soft and fresh as a
naiden's. His mouth and eyes are particularly expressive of
ıis character, with a singular benignity of expression which
ɑraws people to him wherever he goes.

"His eye is his best feature. It is large and full and open,
nuch like the eyes we see in young Augustus, that kind of
ɐye with which a man looks sideways and back as well as
straight ahead, and which is always an index of strength of
ɛharacter. He looks like a Bishop.

"Father Harkins, an old rector of the diocese and his
ıeighbor in the city where Bishop Beaven was then pastor,
said on the day of his consecration: "He is a Bishop—because
ɟrom the beginning, God made him for a Bishop.""

This was very near to what Mother Mary of Providence saw
ın her Metropolitan that day of glory.

Fortunately he possessed what he saw as he looked at her,
ɥe woman of his choice. Though he does not go into any
ınalysis of her character, his appointing her General, his great
ɡift of Brightside, speak in actions better than words. But this
s what he was; some of it due to the new and elongating
ɡarniture:

"She is little, thin, wan, and she has nervous dyspesia, her
ɟace long and drawn. But she is always energetic—even in her
novements."

The Bishop desired and needed energy.

Mother Mary of Providence was always energetic.

## CHAPTER 13

During the first years, Mother Mary of Providence's diplomacy was at its best. Though she knew that the Bishop was unrealistic in some of his demands on her novices, asking they they be set aside completely from the world, trained, as she thought, rather to be cloistered nuns than for an active apostolate with people, she let Bishop Beaven have his way until expediency and need would move him to a more realistic approach.

She watched with particular interest the new young ladies who came to them on the second of January. Most of them preferred her more people-oriented approach to the Bishop's monasticism; but Mother Providence was realistic enough to know that in their support of her, perhaps her young sisters were motivated more by natural than supernatural reasons. The Bishop's way certainly demanded more abnegation.

Mary Leary, later, with some unintentional irony to become Sister Mary Vincent, was the only one who leaned strongly toward the Bishop's ideals. She was an older woman, thirty-three, when she entered; she knew life and people and her picture of the convent had been and remained an almost total retreat from the World. Like the desert fathers of the early church, she would pray for people but not live among them. Her education, though limited scholastically, had been among the shopgirls of the city and had taught her much that she did not like to know. She was so happy with these young, fresh and pure girls. She wanted to keep them that way always.

Though Sister Vincent longed for the promised days when she would become a real novice, and under the guidance of the Mistress, Mother Jerome, spend all her time in learning the values of silence and of prayer, she accepted the necessities of her first days with good grace, though she did prefer Bishop Beaven's conferences to the more practical instructions given by Reverend Mother Providence. Docilely, she did not even think of Mother's advice as worldly, yet the temptation had crossed her mind.

She knew, though, that the present necessities of involvement were forced upon them, and that at the moment nothing could be done. Brightside had not been ready for habitation, but as usual, Sisters had moved in while workmen were still busy with construction; Sister Vincent had to pitch in with the last minute changes, join the others in carting supplies from the older convents, first for the old men and the children, and then, if there were any left over, for themselves. Inevitably this meant constant association with lay people whom she had already learned to call *externs*. Not quite the life she had dreamed of.

Mother Mary of Providence thought of it quite differently. The necessary involvement of the postulants gave both the Bishop and herself a breathing space. Though she approved of Bishop Beaven's interest in their welfare, she wished sometimes that he would allow her to pattern their own organization. Didn't *she* really know the Spririt of St. Vincent? And as a woman she was certain that she knew more about women than he did. But she granted that the Bishop was zealous. He dropped in on them without notification and at the most ungodly times. He asked questions that demanded answers, even on minor detail of administration, and the questions were not always asked of the administrator. Mother Providence had a hard time straightening Sister Vincent out after the Bishop got through with her. Sometimes she wondered, sometimes she sadly knew, with what unintentional twistings the Bishop's interpretations contorted her true decisions. She thought that the appeal made to Sister Vincent by the Bishop's spiritual conferences, though very spiritual indeed, were fitted more to the needs of male trappists than to women dedicated to the poor, the sick, the orphans and the reality of St. Jerome's Institute.

Most embarrassingly, the Bishop presided at every closed meeting of the Council though he was *de facto* their Religious Superior, he was scarcely a *nun* of the Congregation, and the family could not talk. A stranger was amongst them.

And what was happening to her Council?

Matters came to a head the day when the Bishop met with them and produced the signed confession of Sister Drusilda, the lady of uncertain disposition, whom they had accepted with crossed fingers from Kingston.

The Bishop said, "In view of Sister's admitted irregularity, I urge this Council to decree a suitable and public penance."

To the Reverend Mother's horror, Mother Mistress Jerome replied: "I propose that Sister be refused the right of renewing her vows for three months, and that during that time, she be regarded as a postulant, and that if after that period she seems to have been rehabilitated, we again convene and judge her worthiness."

"I agree one hundred percent," the Bishop said.

"May I respectfully suggest," Mother Providence protested, "that the second part of the recommendation be reconsidered, and that if Sister has done her penance she be received back into the Community with all warmth and rejoicing."

No one rejected her proposal; they simply did nothing at all; and their ratification of the imposed Chinese torture had to go out as her decision, under her own name. What her new subjects would think of her, she knew.

Mother Providence had not anticipated the final indignity heaped on the penitent when she reappeared before them, acknowledged her fault as she knelt in the midst of them, and was then assigned a more public confession of her sins at the Community Dinner, and eight days of silent and solitary retreat, before being permitted again, to renew her vows.

Reverend Mother was wrothy. The legalistic mind had set up its Sanhedrin in this punitive kangaroo court, and then asked her, Mother Providence, to inaugurate a family, to be Mother. Grimly and with wry humor she envisioned the ridiculousness of such a procedure in a true family. Quite openly she herded Sister into her own office where she treated her like a little and hurt child.

They should have killed a fatted calf. They should have brought in a ring and a robe. But that her own Council—her own Council—her own friend, Mother Jerome——

Perhaps she was a little short with Sister Monique, who

168

promised to be a very good nurse, when she informed Reverend Mother that, at her representation to the Bishop, she should in the future be assigned to teach Catechism at South Hadley since religious instruction was more Christ-centered than just nursing.

"Indeed?" was Mother General's only word, but her voice was icy. Sister Monique remained in the hospital. She became a very devoted nurse.

And Mother Providence was firm with Sister Vincent. "Make your work your prayer," she said with perfect orthodoxy.

After Mother Jerome's harsh decision, Mother Providence spent more and more time with the Postulants and the Novices, though she satisfied the Bishop by determining that all new subjects would remain unprofessed for several years, allowed only temporary vows, and as such, be separated from the regular community during the hours of recreation; have additional and exclusive religious exercises and counselling, spend one Sunday a month in complete silent meditation. They would also receive constant exhortation, warning them of the dangers to which they would be exposed in the missions where they would be brought into contact with Seculars, women of the world, possibly even worldly women. And men. Hence they must be constantly on guard and be strictly obedient to the Rule as laid down for their protection.

Bishop Beaven and Sister Vincent were charmed. Mother Providence was not quite so happy about it, though she did it; she knew that the segregation of the young from the old would create a new breed of nuns and a war of the generations. Yet in a few years, the old would die, herself among them; in a few years after that the young would become old, and think that conventual life had always been so formalized, yes, had been so for two thousand years. The church did not change.

Not change? She looked at the older customs inherited from Kingston, modified from Montreal, reformed from Paris and St. Vincent. Well, they were in Holyoke now, in America. Remembering her toppling embarrassment at the kneeling embrace on her first day as a postulant, and the silliness of nuns sitting on the floor during meals, in laughing, she resolved to change that memory of the ridiculous moment when she had been fed by Mother Mary Edward.

In some things she stiffened them up. Sister Vincent had not been entirely wrong, when she piously suggested that there was not as much prayer-life among the nuns as she had expected. Why, in actuality, the so-called half hour of meditation had got itself down to twenty minutes. Reverend Mother remedied that, ordering her overworked nuns to rise at ten minutes to five, instead of five, and give a full half-hour of sleep-sodden adoration. In Kingston too they had divided the recitation of a rosary into three sections, one decade distracting them from the Mass. Now she integrated the rosary, added to their vocal prayer of rule, the Miserere at noon, the Stabat Mater in the evening, seven Paters—and Aves, the Litany of the Saints and the Litany of the Holy Name of Jesus. She replaced the silent meditation at breakfast with spiritual reading. It expedited their getting to their tasks on schedule.

Once she had had such a hard time staying awake at meditation; once she had found vocal prayer meaningless—but she had disciplined herself, and God had rewarded her with sleeplessness and prayer.

In only one thing did the Bishop, wisely, allow her a perfectly free hand. She could reform her women's wearing apparel. She began with the Postulants, and got no further, in view of the opposition of those who had elected the Holy Habit, flatirons and all. The Postulants didn't know any better, so she cancelled their headdress, with its pleated border of very fine net, which took them so many hours to prepare, and exchanged their gown of expensive French merino for any suitable black dress, plain cap and veil. They looked sufficiently monastic and a bit less like Irish dolls.

One command came from the Bishop himself, and alone, and its motivation was so ridiculous that His Excellency, though he wrote it solemnly, dined out on it with clerical guffaws for many a year; for the incident that had prompted it had been recounted to the Bishop about the Mother General herself.

Up to this time there had been no question of the nuns

170

going alone on a mission that prompted them. Mother Mary of Providence did not give it another thought when an unmarried girl had shown up at Brightside and had explained that since everybody knew who was the prominent and married father of her child of love, it would haunt the baby's life forever if he were placed for adoption in the churches of Holyoke.

"Where is your baby now?" Mother Mary asked.

"Outside."

"Well, for heaven sakes, girl, bring him in."

When Reverend Mother had been presented with the swaddled baby, had fondled it, had said the unintelligible things that infants understand, the girl-mother asked, "Where are you going to put it?"

"Now that's a thought," Mother Providence said, "You know what I'll do? I'll take it to New York. I know just the place. And come to think of it, there's a train leaving at eight. I've just time. If we put the baby with the orphans overnight, some busybody would ask questions. Now you run off, and I'll see you when I get home."

One good thing about being the General Superior was that you didn't have to ask any permissions, and no one would question your comings and goings. The baby was well wrapped up and all that had to be done was to get her own shawl and little valise, leave a note for Sister Ursula, and be off.

She trudged to the railroad station and got there well in time. With babe in arms, she discovered at the ticket window that she just didn't happen to think about money. Though the agent was sympathetic, there was a necessity of fare.

Go home, she thought, and miss the train? Put the baby somewhere for the night? Inevitable. But as she hesitated, she heard a mellow voice from behind her, a man's voice, and it said, "I am paying the Sister's fare."

She looked up into soft brown eyes, into a commiserating but perhaps not quite approving sympathy.

"I want the Sister and her baby to travel in a compartment — in as much privacy as possible." He planked down the money, and as she tried to thank him, he disappeared into the not inconsiderable crowd.

Later, as Mother Mary of Providence told the story, she

171

drew a beautiful moral from it for her spiritual children, attributing the timely and almost miraculous help to St. Joseph, until at last, not through her fault, the legend grew that St. Joseph had paid her fare, though all she had done was to encourage her charges to have greater confidence in God, in Whom, if we place our trust, we will never be disappointed.

The story as the nun told it was quite different from the one the Bishop heard. A day or two later the kindly and dignified banker who was an Elder in the Presbyterian Church, assured the Bishop that they were both men of the world, that he quite understood how it was with celibate priests and nuns, and that he was not in the least surprised (having read the exposures of Maria Monk) to find one of the nuns escaping, penniless at the depot, her poor infant in her arms and how he had gladly paid the fare, assuring the poor creature of as much privacy as possible until she reached the Mecca of the lost, New York City. However, the banker added, he would like to alert the Bishop of such unfortunate goings-on, so that perhaps the Bishop could find some way to take care of stray nuns — and their offspring.

Bishop Beaven assured his guest that he would take care of the nuns. He did so at once with the edict that in the future no sister was to go out unaccompanied, and that all of his subjects were to be in their convents by nightfall.

After she had structured the Postulancy and the Novice-ship, and the time order and prayer life of her nuns, her next dream was to professionalize the nursing nuns. She knew nothing about nursing, having been a schoolteacher all her religious life, but now at last she resigned from the Principalship of St. Jerome's Institute, turning over the governance to Sister Gertrude. It was to be some time before she could get deep into the problems of the hospitals because there had been many distractions.

On June 21, 1893, seventy-five boys were transferred to Brightside, and the orphanage known as Holy Family Institute took form; and on the same day she officially named Brightside as the Mother House, which meant a complete uprooting from their central convent on Hampden Street.

In the meantime there had been negotiations from Monsignor Griffin in Worcester, where she was offered the choice of a home for the aged or a hospital. Though she and Monsignor Griffin chose the home, it was the hospital that developed, and from this perhaps came her first deep inkling of where the major work of the foundation would be. Also, on the very day when her first postulants were habited by Bishop Beaven, and he announced to the clergy the well kept secret that he had previously deeded the 127 acres of Brightside to the Sisters of Providence, Father Harkins countered with a declaration of gift of the Doyle property to be used as the site of a new Providence Hospital, and she saw to it that ground was broken almost at once. Hospitals. That was it.

Of course it was just as well, she thought, that she had reluctantly released her beloved school to Sister Gertrude, since she had to go scurrying down to Worcester so often. She reserved Mondays though for Brightside, as she knew that it was important that she share in the drudgery of the clothes-washing and hauling every week. It was a duty of example that she must give, and it was certainly a source of edification to her subjects to see their General Superior toiling with them in the backbreaking and monumental task.

Amazingly, by the eighth of September she had St. Vincent's Hospital in Worcester relatively ready and certainly occupied. There had been many distractions. Among other things, on August 15 they had officially dedicated the new cemetery on the high hill above Brightside and had, for old time's sake, moved the Stations of the Cross from South Hadley to the cemetery. And there had been enough turmoil in Worcester to have taken all her time, if she had let it.

True to pattern, things were not quite ready when the nuns arrived. The house that they were to use had been occupied by a congregation of Brothers, who had vacated and left precious little behind, as the Sisters discovered when they looked about for sleeping quarters. They found a vacant room on the second floor, a couple of iron bedsteads and some cotton mattresses. On these they spread their blankets, rolling the tops of them for pillows; and on these they began their mission life.

173

Their meals were taken either at the Notre Dame Convent or at St. John's Rectory, according to convenience; although sometimes Monsignor Griffin insisted that they have their evening meal in his rectory, particularly when they were downtown, begging food from the storekeepers to whom he had introduced them.

By the eighth of September, 1893 — pleased that the Brothers had left them a chapel, altar and furnishings and that they had been able to install twelve hospital beds, reconstructing the attic for their own use and crowding into it as best they might — they got the Monsignor to celebrate the first Mass, and thus officially to open St. Vincent's Hospital.

Mother Mary of Providence gave them and their new Superior, Sister Ursula, a watchword: "Make the best of things." They did, and she knew that they would, because they had a leader in Sister Ursula. The Reverend Mother had appointed her with some personal sacrifice because now she would have no one to talk to. Her own loss of companionship did not influence her decision. Sister Ursula was young, strong and helpfully beautiful. She faced the hardships with great courage and brought the same kind of gaiety to her struggling community that Mother Mary of Providence had brought to her own in the early days in Holyoke.

With compassion, the General Superior stripped her own convent of the best workers, sending them for a time down to Worcester to help to arrange the furniture, and she slipped in as a bonus, one of the older girls from Mt. St. Vincent's Orphanage to assist in the domestic work, and even one grown boy for general services. But though there were only five nuns regularly assigned to the Mission, the community had 268 devoted women volunteers and a small crew of doctors struggling valiantly to break down the truly deep opposition of the majority of skilled medical practitioners who opposed this wild, twelve-bed, harum-scarum so-called Hospital.

Most of the diplomacy Mother General left to the dimpling charms of Sister Ursula, and she was not surprised when, by the end of October, St. Vincent's had an organized staff of doctors, headed impressively by Dr. Homer Gage, and the

174

several other Protestant surgeons and physicians who joined with the young Irish doctors gave the new venture respectability and above all built up a patronage.

What with Worcester and all, even Bishop Beaven saw the wisdom, no, the necessity of freeing the younger nuns from a strict process of training, to do more meaningful works in the obligations of the community. With Providence Hospital in Holyoke ready to be opened in July, with now growing hopes for expansions in Worcester, he could see that there just were not enough hands among the formed and fully professed sisters. The work simply could not be done.

From his knowledge of tendencies in Rome, Bishop Beaven was twenty years before his time, and he had hoped, now, he knew, his hopes were vain to set up a model community in his own diocese. But though he deplored it he realized that the United States was still a missionary country, that the strict rules of claustration were nowhere enforced; indeed, not required except in the case of a Generalate in direct dependence on Rome, and that he had the right, no, now he had the duty, to grant dispensations.

He did his best to salvage what he could of his original plan, making his own visitation even more strict, demanding that all young nuns have two, not one, annual retreats, and bringing back all sisters to the Mother House for an intensive period of study and instruction just before their profession.

But with reluctance and as a temporary measure, as he wrote in his decree, he would allow novices and nuns with temporary vows to take their place in the works and missions of the Sisters of Providence of Holyoke. This, he pointed out, he only tolerated, and it was to be considered as a temporary measure until they could be replaced by professed Sisters.

It was not he but the Mother General who added the final touch to the new plan; after all, these measures and this more active type of formation was what she had envisioned and quietly worked for. After the deplorings of Bishop Beaven, she added: "One must not be unmindful that according to the workings of Divine Providence, the above-mentioned changes in the training process of our beloved Junior Sisters, is not without its advantages toward the service and glory of God. Toward each occupation which is within the scope of

175

our Institute, each novice will now be exposed, tested, and, where she shows aptitude, trained. It will also expose the younger sisters to the actuality of the practice of the Religious Life, test, and we pray, strengthen, the depth and sincerity of our Divine Vocations."

Without ruffling anybody, she had, under God, meaningfully structured the training of her community. The temporary concession would last long enough to create a spirit and tradition among her daughters.

During this year too she faced her usual problems of financing, discovering by the day of the dedication of the new Providence Hospital, on October 4, that the building had cost the community 60,000 dollars, which was not as easy to come by as it had been before the great Wall Street panic of '93. Luckily, she had one electoral advantage in the person of Mr. Dan Kenney, their great friend, who was to remain city auditor for many years, indeed, until 1934, when he died.

But looking over her actual income it was somewhat appalling. The Hospital Sisters were to receive from the Corporation of Hospitals under their management an annual stipend of fifty dollars. All other expenses, clothing, dentistry, travelling, making retreats, library books, were to be paid by the heavily indebted Mother House, which also was the sole support of the Novitiate. A pittance came in for the support of orphans and destitute children, a trifle per capita for the boys at St. Jerome's Institute. The rest must be procured by begging, or as the General Superior called it *divine providence.*

Looking at the ledger, Mother Mary of Providence came to a, by now, typical decision. They would begin at once to plan for an adequate building, a vast building, to house the Motherhouse Community.

Again, they were helped by Father Harkins. On the original property to which they had migrated, he built and gave them a home for the aged. It was to be his perpetual monument: The Father Harkins Home.

So it was, that by 1896, the great pattern was established; and now, though there were still letters of direction and command from Bishop Beaven, the statements over the signature of the foundress were more frequent. There was little doubt now in the minds of her community, who was at the helm.

Some of the regulations were reiterations of what she had decreed at the very beginning, but others were new. As she herself had been trained by Sister Mary John, she concentrated now, quite largely, on external decorum, but the greater things, she had already taken care of — and it is informative to perceive where her interest in detail lay, which in itself, had some profundity. She would build women of holiness, not of piety, she hoped. She would chop off ridiculous excrescences, but she would insist upon decorum, insist upon great and even physical self-discipline.

Two of her letters read:

March 3, 1896
My very dear Sisters; —
Having noticed that it is becoming a very general custom among the Sisters to wear crosses, medals, and other pious trinkets attached to the watch cord; I beg to remind you of the point of rule which forbids our wearing anything suspended from the neck except the silver cross of our religious profession. You are therefore requested to attach all such emblems of piety to your rosary beads or scapulars that they may be used without being worn as ornaments. I also object to the Sisters being "constituted Promoters of the Sacred Heart League" and having "Diploma" framed without permission of the Mother Superior. The office of Promoter supposes a zealous propagation of the devotion among externs. As the League is under the care of Pastors, our co-operation is not needed; we have authority of local Director for our Institutions, and a Sister so named can gather the intentions and good works without the distinguishing badge of a Promoter's Cross. Our religious habit brings us many privileges and we must beware of admitting any custom that would deviate from the strict letter of the rule. I would suggest that the second Friday of the month be chosen as the day for receiving Holy Communion for the Intention of the Sacred Heart

177

League; when any special feast occurs on that day, that it be taken some other Friday of the month. Let this letter be read in full Community for Novices and Professed Sisters. Praying our Divine Saviour to bless you all with an abundance of grace during this holy Season, I am,

Very affectionately,
Sister Mary of Providence, Superior

August 7, 1896

My very dear Sisters,—

Believing that you will attentively hear, and faithfully observe any counsels given for the maintenance of good order and uniformity in the Community, I make known to you with pleasure some things that have been brought to the attention of the Council as well as some minor details that have come under my own observation.

The Sisters do not incline the head and body in a reverential manner at the Gloria Patri. Consider the Angels adoring the Holy Trinity, and in union with them incline low, as is the custom among religious persons, and in conformity also with the rules of the Church in the divine service.

It is not our custom to prostrate on the prie-dieu as some do after Holy Communion, but all should incline reverently and remain so, for at least five minutes after coming from the Holy Table; instead of that, we find Sisters after Holy Communion, and while others are receiving the Blessed Sacrament, kneeling erect and without any exterior marks of faith that inspires them. Let all, who can do so, kneel at the Sanctus, incline profoundly at the Consecration of the Sacred Host, and remain so inclined until after the elevation of the Chalice.

In some of our small Chapels, the Sisters make quite a noise when they kneel at the Post Communion. If they cannot kneel from the Priest's

Communion to the end of Mass, they should change position silently.

When the Angelus is said standing, the Sisters will bend the right knee to the ground at the words "et Verbum Caro Factum Est." The Sisters are forbidden to put the feet on the kneeling benches or prie-dieu in the Chapel; also to sit with the feet crossed; or to cross them when kneeling, all such postures being unladylike and opposed to religious modesty.

It has been agreed by the Superior and her Council that the custom of sitting on the floor during meditation and examen of conscience be no longer followed in the Community. Any Sister, who cannot kneel during the examen, may sit on a chair. When the meditation is not made in the Chapel, the Sisters may change the position of the chairs and use them, as an easy posture in prayer is an aid to devotion.

The custom of kneeling to embrace each other when Sisters meet after an absence or on any other occasion when such greeting is allowed no longer prevails in the Community from which we have received our customs. It is not generally observed among ourselves because of the inconvenience it occasions and consequently the Sisters may salute each other with the kiss of peace without kneeling unless when they ask mutual forgiveness for a breach of charity. When the kiss of peace is given in friendly greeting it may be done standing. As the subject matter of this letter concerns novices as well as Sisters of the Community, it is to be read in the refectory of all the houses and can be left there a reasonable time so that any one who wishes may have the privilege of reading it a second time.

Finally, I would remind the Sisters that they are not free to employ the time of the Community in private devotions. The daily making of the Way of the Cross is not of rule, although a very praiseworthy devotion. Anyone who wishes to make it daily may do so in her own time, that is, before the morning prayer, or after the night prayer, on Sundays and

Holidays or Conges, in their leisure time, but on working days, special permission must be asked. This does not affect or concern the local Superior, who on account of her many duties and calls at any time and all hours is obliged to attend to her spiritual exercises when opportunity may permit and can therefore anticipate or postpone the time for doing so.

The Sisters are all supposed to go to their (morning) respective duties when the morning exercises are finished and may not linger in the Chapel for private devotions. Earnestly recommending myself to your prayers and hoping that God may bless our labors and preserve in us, to the close of the year, the good resolutions taken at our annual retreat, I am, my dear Sisters

Very sincerely yours,
Sister Mary of Providence

# CHAPTER 14

In his sprawling diocese Bishop Beaven had only four major cities — Springfield, Holyoke, Worcester and Pittsfield. His dream was to establish great Catholic centers in each of them — schools, hospitals and charitable institutions, using his nuns for that purpose. As to hospitals, he now had one flourishing in Holyoke, one promising in Worcester. Pittsfield lay far to the west, in the mountains and forest of the Berkshire Hills; but his own episcopal city, Springfield, was still neglected. True, Holyoke lay not far away, but it was across the river; and though Brightside adjoined West Springfield, it was scarcely the same as having a real hospital in his own city.

He was a bit surprised at the opposition he encountered partially from his priests, but mainly from the local physicians. They harked back to the trial-and-error beginnings at Holyoke, and only Father Harkins seemed to remember and to remind them incessantly that there was no care of the sick at all until the Sisters began their shoddy little place and went from house to house nursing the neglected. Let them say that the Sisters did not know much about what they were doing — but he wondered aloud if the doctors of that day did either. All right for them to laugh at the home remedies the nuns used, but he told them that people fifty years from now would be laughing at the crude medical care they were giving people back in the enlightened year of 1896.

Bishop Beaven was undaunted in his plans. He would have a hospital. And he was spurred on because to his chagrin he learned that his neighbor, Bishop Tierney of Connecticut, was siphoning off some of his school sisters from Lee, Massachusetts, to start a hospital in Hartford. The great Diocesan Cities were all getting hospitals. He would have one despite the opposition, no matter what, and despite the doctors, he would staff it; and if the nuns weren't professional, he would make them so.

The nuns. He certainly had devoted himself to forming

them, but they still were not real nuns in the sense that the most advanced planners in Rome would have them. If these girls were ever to be nuns, they would have to be cured of their modernist and americanist independent ways. They would have to learn the true meaning of obedience yes, and true community living. Though their Mother General was obedient enough and more understanding than a lot of her appointees, he wondered sometimes if she wasn't a slick one, letting things ride for a time, and then while his attention was turned to something else, getting her own way.

He found Mother Mary of Providence willing enough to go along with him, on both his projects — the new hospital and the training of her sisters to be professional nurses (she seemed more enthusiastic about the latter).

"I have been thinking about that, your excellency," she said, "I never was trained as a schoolteacher, and I had to run a school for years. And now I hear the Bishop of Connecticut is doing the miracle of turning his schoolteachers of the Sisters of St. Joseph into professional nurses by the wave of a wand! We do some funny things."

"At least," Bishop Beaven said, in defense of his episcopal rival and friend, Bishop Tierney, "the Bishop of Hartford has one skilled woman to train nurses, which is more than my illustrious predecessor had here. Bishop Tierney sent for a hospital administrator from France — a Mother Valencia."

"Yes. I heard." Emboldened she went on, "And yet Bishop, you ask me to do the same thing Father Harkins asked me to do. He made me principal of St. Jerome's when I knew nothing. And now Your Lordship wants me to head a whole flock of hospitals, when I have never even been a patient in one."

"Touché," he said. "But you learned about schools. You can learn about hospitals, can't you?"

"Yes," she said simply. "I can and I intend to, but I can't ask my sisters to do what I did."

"No, and I don't want you to. Get them trained somehow. And by the way, why didn't you ever ask for training for yourself?"

She smiled, remembering. "I had the temptation once, but I rejected it."

182

Bishop Beaven did not understand, but he nodded, and as she left him, she thought on the way home, without complacency, that the things she had missed and had made up for somehow, she would give to others. She had not had a regular novitiate, so she had structured one for her youngest children; she had had no professional training in anything, so she would dedicate herself to giving all her subjects as rounded opportunities as she could, snipping away at such professional knowledge for herself as she could find and squeeze in.

The first thing she must do, she thought, was to answer in person a letter which she did not inform the Bishop of, but which she had in her reticule. It was a cry for help from the French nun, Mere Valencienne, the lady whose name had come up in the conversation, asking her to help in advising how to go about creating a hospital in the strange American methods of Hartford, and above all, how to turn the Sisters of St. Joseph into nurses.

For the first, she might have some advice, which she would exchange for advice on the second, which was now her own problem. Then she must start thinking about building a great hospital in Springfield. After that she must learn how to be a nurse; and then she must discover how to be a hospital executive. Of course, it helped to trust in Divine Providence, but you could scarcely get expertise by osmosis.

At her first opportunity she scuttled down to Hartford and was met at the station by the stalwart figure of Mother Valencia.

It was not only their mutual French, but something far deeper that made them find trust in each other in that first meeting. They thought the same; they surmounted the same impossible difficulties; they had the same internal fortitude and faith. But above all, Mother Anne Valencia and Mother Mary of Providence found in each other what they both so sorely needed — another woman to whom each could openly talk. Neither had anybody else.

"You will need a trained lay-nurse to teach your nuns. A laywoman of great discipline," Mother Valencia said. "I know of such a one in the Carney Hospital in Boston. She will train your nuns with discipline of great exactitude. You

183

will follow her around, noting and doing and demanding just what she does. Thus you will learn."

"The first thing you will need in building a hospital here, is the support of the men," Mother Providence exchanged. "Go yourself to the businessmen of Hartford. And the Protestant Americans. And get patients into your little red house the first day you open. Americans want to see things done. Do the things before you can, and show them what you need. They will be quite good then."

Mother Valencia smiled with understanding, and said her American words, "I fix."

So Mother Mary of Providence returned to Holyoke with a new motto, thinking that there were plenty of things that she herself had to *fix*.

She plunged at once into both enterprises going at once to Boston and securing Miss Emily Stoney to direct her nurses, beginning the next year, by which time, she knew she would have Mercy Hospital in Springfield as a going concern.

Miss Stoney satisfied her completely. She was an English maiden lady; she had written a book, "Practical Points in Nursing", which was, like its author, eminently down to earth. Miss Stoney abided no nonsense, and as Superintendent of Nurses, preferred brisk efficiency to a cultivated bedside manner. She was a recent convert to the grimmer side of Catholicism, and she had never in her life given in to any of the weaknesses of intimacy. She was perfect and demanded perfection.

For his pet Hospital, Bishop Beaven wasted no time. On February 11, 1896, taking as an occasion the fiftieth jubilee of the first Catholic Church in Springfield, and for the amount of 26,000 dollars, in the midst of ill-concealed mutterings, he presented the Sisters of Providence with the Allis property on Carew Street, and it took Mother Mary of Providence, though not without intervening turmoil, only a year and a half to start replacing the old house, where they quartered patients immediately, with a new and terrifyingly huge hospital building.

The first months, she admitted, were discouraging. Doctors and priests, and most financially important, patients, black-balled them. Their minimal number of beds were rarely fully

184

occupied, and unlike Worcester, her Springfield Sisters had ample places to lay their weary heads and, if they liked variety, could go from empty ward to empty ward.

Mother Mary of Providence did not have it in her heart to burden any of her subjects with the superiorship of this apparently doomed institution across the river. Though she appointed Sister Michael as her assistant there, among her other duties she also assumed control as the Superior of Mercy Hospital. Nor was her action in so doing completely understood by either the Bishop or some of her own subjects.

"Keeping things pretty well in her own hands," the Bishop said, and "Hmmph," said the nuns.

Of the Doctors, she had only one real friend, only one who believed in her, in the Bishop, and in the need for Mercy Hospital. Doctor E. J. Mahoney passing by the empty beds on his daily rounds still withstood the twitting of his fellow practitioners when they asked him about how things were *not* going at "Beaven's Folly."

"Fine," he would say, "just fine. And when are you going to apply for the Staff?"

As the year wore on, Mother Mary of Providence dreaded the Monday washing more and more. On Mondays, with the physical fatigue added to her constant worries, she seemed to develop what she thought was a ravenous appetite, but when she sat down to dinner, a few bites choked her up, and a raging beast began to eat at her inside. She pecked a bit at every dish and learned much from the welcome distraction of the incessant reading at meals. But she was glad when table-time was over and she could wash her own dishes and hasten off to her cell, to writhe alone for a few moments. Some of the younger sisters thought that Mother hastened the meal time so that they never got enough to eat. Maybe she did.

It was nearly the close of the year and she was determined to carry on despite the blood that came from her gaspings and retchings; but God in His mysterious way took a hand. She hurt her knee very badly and while she could disguise her lack of appetite there was nothing she could do about her hobbling.

"It's Mercy Hospital for you, my lady," the doctor told her, and it was no news to her that, when he got her there at

185

last, Dr. Edward Mohoney said, "And you also have bleeding ulcers."

"So I have," the Reverend Mother replied without surprise.

The Bishop was kind to her but furious with her ulcers. The idea of their attacking her just at this moment. Her appointment of Sister Gertrude as acting General Superior was well enough, but Gertrude was not popular with the other nuns, and there were rumors about her, in a different way, as there were about Ursula in Worcester, who was beloved by the laity, but whose personal beauty and charm seem to have been lost to her own community. The Bishop wished with all his heart that he could appoint nuns as Superiors the same way he appointed Pastors. Call them Diocesan nuns, do they? A far cry from Diocesan priests. And it got worse and worse during the months Providence was out of commission; the complaints he had from the young nuns about the way their Superiors brushed them aside! Poor little things. His paternal heart was touched. But Providence must have something, because they all said, "I wish Mother would hurry back."

Mother Mary of Providence tried her best to hurry back, but that was the one thing her doctor told her she must not do. Not that she was idle here. With the eye of a hawk and the memory of an elephant, she was preparing for her nursing course under Miss Stoney. Nothing escaped her.

Just to fill in the time of her incarceration she did then what many a foundress had taken years to accomplish. As a little extra thing she rewrote the Rule for her Sisters. True, she had the pattern of the Rule of St. Vincent, the adaptations of Montreal, the further adaptation of Kingston. But the rule for the Diocesan Sisters of Providence of Kingston, which was approved by the Bishop without alteration and rubber-stamped by the Council, had certain significant and timely changes that would have amazed St. Vincent de Paul and alarmed Mother Emmelie Gamelin. They were strictly in the thinking of a new foundress, Mother Mary of Providence.

The Prologue is significant, throwing light upon her, the times and the modern but no longer contemporary sister-hoods:

# CONSTITUTIONS OF THIS SISTERS OF CHARITY
Servants of the Poor and Sick
called also
## SISTERS OF DIVINE PROVIDENCE
1897 — Holyoke

## CHAPTER 1

### End and Fundamental Virtues of the Institute

*Article I.* The principal end for which God has called and assembled the Sisters of Providence, is to honor our Lord Jesus Christ as the source and model of all charity; serving Him corporally and spiritually in the person of the poor, whether sick, children, aged and infirm, or others who, through shame, dare not make known their wants. This is why, in order to correspond to so holy a vocation, they should strive to live holily, and labor with great care for their own perfection, joining the interior exercises of the spiritual life to the exterior employments of Christian charity toward the poor. Conformably to these Constitutions which they will try to practise faithfully, as the proper means of arriving at this end, they will represent to themselves that although they are not in a Religious Order where solemn vows are made, this state not being compatible with the employments of their vocation, nevertheless, as they are much more exposed than cloistered Religious, having sometimes for monastery but the houses of the sick, for chapel the parish church, for cloister but the streets of the city or the wards of the hospital, for enclosure, obedience; for grate, the fear of God, and for the veil, holy modesty, they are obliged by this consideration to lead as virtuous a life as if they were professed in a Religious Order, and to conduct themselves wherever they may be with as much recollection and purity of body and mind, detachment from creatures, and edification to the neighbor as true Religious in the retirement of their monastery.

There is here the explicit dedication to the work with the poor. There is also however, a noticeable absence of dedication to personal poverty by the members of the Institute, though their work is focused on the immediate needs of the outcasts of society. There is Mother Mary of Providence's truly Vincentian concept that their work did not allow them to be cloistered, which underlies the recognition that their claustration must be one of the spirit, not of place or time order.

The new Constitution rode through magnificently, and if its subtleties were only guessed at by the Bishop, and perhaps not even perceived by the Council, what she preserved and what she changed, were fully and deeply comprehended by the Foundress.

So the months went on and the bleeding ulcers healed themselves, until by April the Doctor knew that the patient's anxiety to be back in harness caused more upset and nerves than any benefit he could inflict on her. So they let her go.

As she wrote to Mother Valencia: "At last I cannot say I was never even a patient in the Hospital, though I fear in the last weeks I was less a Patient than an Impatient. I know a great deal more now, though, than when I went in, and it seems to me that the modern Hospital is conditioned first by the convenience of the staff, second by the ease of the Administration, third by the schedule of the nurses, and then, if there is any stress left over, on the patients. Though this is not ideal, I fear it is inevitable, and I see no way of remedying it during your or my lifetime.

"As for myself, I think my whole upset was simply due to the fact that I was tired. Even a horse gets tired, so I will go back to the reins and try to be a good little horsey."

Mother Valencia had no time to write back, but she scolded her when they next met and gave her a lesson valuable for life. "You must," she said. "Be like me. Do not be scheming so always. When you go to one place from another, say to yourself, 'Now I have nothing — nothing to do, so I will do nothing.' Then feel relaxation in your shoulders. Just in your shoulders. It will creep into the rest."

From then on Mother Mary of Providence was noted for her gaiety and relaxation on her constant journeys, so that they said, "You'd think she didn't have a care in the world," and indeed, through the remainder of her ninety-six years, through strokes and accidents and burdens, her ulcers never bled again, so that when they asked her her secret, and she said, "My shoulders," they smiled at what they thought was a quaint metaphor for strength, not understanding her secret at all.

When she got back, things were in a mess, and she often wished that she were indeed the horse instead of the driver. She held the reins, and she had to pull them tight. She had left enough orders, God knows, but though everyone had had the greatest of good will, nothing had been done.

Most apalling of all was the condition of Mercy Hospital and of that fiasco, the most apalling was the set of blueprints she received from a Mr. Donahue, for the new building. When she showed them to Dr. Mahoney he laughed, and that helped her to relax her shoulders.

Mr. Donahue blamed the Bishop who had not allowed him to confer with anyone who had practical experience in building hospitals, and the Bishop blamed Mr. Donahue because he had no experience.

Dr. Mahoney and Mother Mary of Providence, one of whom knew hospitals, and the other had built buildings that at least stood, combined to insist on indeed, to sketch roughly, a total new set of blueprints for the bewildered contractor. When this set was done, Mother Mary of Providence presented them to the Bishop and his Executive Committee, some of whom unfortunately were experts in architecture and building.

They laughed. They did not mean to laugh at her, only at the plans. But they laughed.

She was not offended. She laughed herself. "Not one of the three of us knows the least thing about it." And I for one, she thought, have never known anything about anything, when I started.

At first, wrapped in her own thoughts, she did not catch the full meaning of what the Bishop was saying, and certainly not the full implication of the unanimous vote of his Executive Committee; when she thought she understood, she was so dazed that she was convinced that she had not understood at all.

189

"After my fiasco with the plans — you gentlemen mean — you mean — " she glanced unbelievingly at the annotation from the minutes of the meeting that they had thrust at her, "that I am authorized by vote of the Board, to serve as a Committee of One, in securing bids and conducting the business of preparing and following the erection of the building, that as Treasurer of the Corporation, said Treasurer — that's me, I suppose — be not submitted to the further direction of the Building Committee."

Stunned she said, "But obviously, I don't know anything about it."

"You'll learn," said the Bishop.

She learned. And she knew that Bishop Beaven had intended to be kind and trusting, and that the thought never crossed his mind that the woman who had just returned from months in the hospital, suffering from overwork, should now be saddled with this new and terrifying responsibility, for he had meant to be kind.

She learned. Before summer she had a professionally drawn architect's plan, had had open bids, to Mr. Donahue's consternation, and had accepted the offer of a Contractor, William J. Burnham, who was not from Springfield, who was not a Catholic, and who was reputed to be an A.P.A.

There was nothing the Bishop or Board could do about it. They had given her all power.

She said to their veiled objections, "Bricks and mortar don't know the hands on them are Catholic or Protestant — Burnham was the lowest bidder."

So they began work with non-religious bricks and agnostic money exactly one year later, in April of '98.

While she and the Doctor were busy over their plans, His Excellency, the Bishop, had also been busy preparing a document for his nuns. While the letter may be regarded as an addendum to the new Rules, it was motivated by his knowledge of the upsets in his community in the last few months. He thought of it, not without justice, as a poor-man's "Letter of Saint Ignatius to the Companions in Coimbra on the Virtue of Obedience," for there was an exact parity of situation, though scarcely of content.

The Bishop wrote officially:

# CIRCULAR LETTER OF OUR RT. REV. BISHOP.

St. Michael's Cathedral
Springfield, Mass.,
April 10, 1897.

My dear Sisters in Christ;—

Some few months since, Mother was relieved of the active duties of her office. At this time it is our pleasure to inform you that her health permits her to return immediately to the work of her position.

We do not wish this occasion to go by, without manifesting our gratefulness for your religious submission to those with whom God has reposed His authority. Our labor is fruitless, if we seek any other way of doing God's work than by submission to Superiors.

Human judgment is of little avail for God's spouse unless it rests on obedience and human judgment never sways the soul with stronger emotions, than when obedience demands its sacrifice in the doing of God's work. It is our fond hope that we shall rarely hear that human judgment influences your actions, rather than obedience. We desire your happiness; we long to hear that you are striving each day to give some new pleasure to your Divine Spouse; we rejoice in the consciousness that your goodness will help us in our manifold solicitudes; but, Sisters, we are sure beyond a doubt that we cannot look for any of these blessings from those of our children in Christ, who are not planting and harvesting in Obedience.

May Obedience guide you in the forbearance which your annoying and arduous duties demand. May Obedience nerve your heart's courage to manifest a sweet and patient charity amid your perplexities of soul and waywardness of nature. May obedience be the lodestone of your religious consecration, which shall draw to itself all the activities of your being; namely, the powers of your soul, the affections of your heart, the resolves of your will and the ministrations of your zeal in labors of charity.

Our little Community is as yet, crowded with crude and undeveloped usefulness. Its ore has not yet been drawn off from its smelting crucible. Almighty God is still separating our spiritual forces from the rugged envelope of nature, by patient and long-suffering charity. He is slowly and painfully separating from the nuggets we have brought from the mine of the world, into the mints of religion, the dross and slag of selfish ways; of complacent excellence; of worldly experience. As yet we are of little value, for we trust too confidingly in our own personal worth; — we seem not yet to know that it is not the natural ore, but the stamp of God's sovereignty that makes the soul's coin current in God's markets.

Sisters, we are therefore helpless and of no avail for God, if the sufficiency of human judgment is the counterfeit coin, with which we are trafficking in God's goods.

We must pour into the mould of obedience, the moulten metal of human endeavor, if we hope to run it off into coins of heavenly value. Of what avail, Sisters, are the tributes of the religious life, offered, if in the silence of your soul He demands "Whose image and inscription is this?" and His awful sentence to your reply is couched in words like unto these; — "GIVE TO CAESAR THE THINGS THAT ARE CAESAR'S: I WANT THEM NOT." To nature, consequently, our crude usefulness, we must in humility and in the spirit of those children, who image the Kingdom of Heaven, apply ourselves to acquire the true religious spirit. This spirit alone is indigenous to obedience. There is no other soil, from which its roots can draw strengthening nourishment.

How earnestly we have besought Heaven to sustain you in your formative period; whilst trials and disturbances crowded in upon you, with the wearying monotony of wave succeeding wave, our Guardian Angels can easily attest. These difficulties came to you from all sides. We recognized that early environment had engrafted upon your natures, habits of thought and forces of heart that found frictions hard to bear in your new and strange home.

We could not close our eyes to the hardships of external associations presented hourly under different conditions in the trying labors of your offices. We knew also the martyrdom of sensitive souls, fearful lest their best endeavors might be swallowed up in the gloom of utter failure, or palsied by encouragement withheld from Superior or elder Sister companion. We were in touch with the gaping wound which thoughtless impatience, unchristian rudeness and intemperate utterance had inflicted upon souls, who were invited to Religion by the hopes of meeting that refinement of heart which the world entwines with esteem about the name of "Sister". We are aware of that excruciating finesse of pain which flays with cruel agony the sensitive soul, who by unreasonable fears, strange misconceptions, or wilful insincerity is exiled from the confidence of her Superior. We have been aware of all these trials, crossing and re-crossing your religious life. We have gone out to you in our silent sympathy, but we recognize that you are all the time in the hands of a heavenly Surgeon, Who, with deft scalpel was separating from your soul's growth unhealthy excrescences, and fashioning your spirit to His own image and while you were suffering, we knew, if faithful to graces given, you would grow into the strength and vigor of soul which form the beauty of the consecrated daughter of the Church.

Upon your generous efforts therefore, we base all our hope. If you respond to the pleadings of grace, who will presume to measure the glory coming to God from your contact with souls in the ministrations of charity!

We can even now, see the horizon of your usefulness widening as the years go on, into the breadth of heavenly expanse, studded with the spiritual constellations of your good works in succoring the miseries of God's creatures.

We can even now glory, if you are faithful to your

religious aspirations, in the exhilarating hope, that you, our children, are trooping along the narrow way to eternity.

We pray that He may keep you in all your ways; may bless you in all your labors; may console you in all your trials and confirm you in your heaven-blest life.

With my blessing, I am, with paternal affection,

Wholly yours in Christ,
Thomas D. Beaven

When the Bishop's letter was officially received and posted, there were many of the community who were angry with the Bishop of Springfield, not because of what he said, which was true enough, but because they believed that he was gunning for Reverend Mother. There were, however, several of them, among whom was Sister Mary Dolours, who believed that at least Bishop Beaven had seen through *that woman* and at last was giving her her just comeuppance.

The former were relieved, the latter disgruntled when the Episcopal action proved that His Excellency was criticizing not Mother Mary of Providence, but the interim government, and perhaps some of her appointed Superiors. But what the Bishop had done left no doubt in anyone's mind of what he thought of their foundress.

He had, they found out, made her a committee of one.

## CHAPTER 15

She was ready to learn from Miss Stoney the nurse from Boston, and unobtrusively managed to be quite near when the professional nurse visited each of the three hospitals two days a week. Her own experience as a patient did not quite compensate for the advances that had been made by her own nuns during her absence, since she had dragooned Dr. Mahoney to organize a series of lectures for them. Already they were assuming a professional attitude, and even Miss Stoney was pleased with the dedication of the nuns and their resolve to learn. She did not realize how their training in external conformity, their shaping themselves to the perfect picture of what a Sister should be, helped them now to look like trained nurses.

When asked later what Miss Stoney taught her, Mother Providence said, "Charts." Other things of course she picked up, but it seemed that even if the patients were neglected, though not much, charts on them, for the Doctors' perusal, was the principal accent. When she told Father Harkins about the charts, he grinned mischievously and said, "Books. It's the same with us. Have the books with the financial reports straight, and when the Bishop makes his visitation he doesn't care how many converts you have — only books. With you it's charts."

Doctor Mahoney reported that the word had leaked out that the newly trained nuns at Mercy kept their charts better than the nurses at City, and it impressed their critics favorably a little bit.

Yet both the Bishop and the Mother General knew, though plans for the building went on apace, that the situation in Springfield was desperate. The priests shook their heads. That woman had talked Himself into putting up a huge pile of brick, for God knows how many empty beds. They couldn't even fill the small house — so she was throwing good money away on a monument.

They talked this way until the malaria epidemic.

The boys came back from the Spanish-American War. Though the nun in white had discovered the mosquito, it had not quite come in time, and the yellow fever, malaria, was in the men. Beds in the City Hospital were all taken, and the overflow came to the nuns. Their facilities were filled and the nuns no longer had a choice of sleeping quarters. Then when the epidemic abated, the news seemed to have leaked out that one got better care at Mercy than at City finally there was never an empty bed at the Bishop's Hospital.

Doctors who had been forced by the epidemic to send their patients to Mercy, seemed now to have got into the habit. Doctor Mahoney said not a word but went around grinning like a Cheshire cat.

Mother Mary of Providence looked at the change with satisfaction, striking while the iron was hot, completing the plans for the now necessary hospital in record time, soliciting for funds with ruthless pressurizing.

She looked at her nuns-as-nurses with delight. They went about crisp and confident, satisfying even the crustiest of physicians with their impeccable charts. Yet, she was pleased to note, they had tempered their mentor's efficiency with a good deal of the traditional kindness of religious sisters, and the kindness was due, not to their technical training as nurses, but to another and perhaps greater professionalism — dedication, charity. She heard them too twitting each other, if one were discovered to be a little overly businesslike with the patients.

"Hello, Stoney," they would say, punning on their former instructor's name, for Miss Stoney, her mission tidily accomplished, had now returned to restore efficiency to Carney Hospital. Mother Mary of Providence did not reprove her daughters.

The plans for the hospital, the new attitudes of her nurses and the filled hospital in Springfield pleased her, but under her happiness and success was a strange wonder, which she thought sometimes was a temptation — a temptation against, of all things, Divine Providence.

She would hear the pious novice, Sister Immaculata say, "Look at Mercy! See how Divine Providence filled our beds!"

She wondered. Malaria, plague, pain and death had filled

their beds. Their hospital had been saved by epidemics. And she remembered from her Kingston history of the Congregation, that plague and agony and death had saved and implemented Mother Gamelin's venture in Montreal. Must the history of the Daughters of St. Vincent always be so? Or was it true of all nuns everywhere? The Sisters of Mercy had bloomed through the Crimean War and cholera in Panama and the gold fields. Persecution in France — the famine in Ireland? Planned by Providence to spread the faith?

Did God really invent the mosquito and instigate American aggression in the Spanish War — to save the face of the Bishop of Springfield and implement the dreams of the Superior General of Holyoke? She could not quite accept that, and the shibboleth of God working in strange ways, His wonders to perform, did not satisfy her.

Her Jesuit extraordinary confessor, Father Stanton, told her to read Job. She did, admired it, but found no answer in it. God spoke magnificently out of the whirlwind, but He gave no solution. She told Father Stanton of her disappointment, and he smiled at her.

"You've got it, Mother. That's what I wanted you to find. God didn't give us the answer."

"You mean it's a mystery?"

"Not quite. We think we can solve it. We're working at it," and that's all she could get out of him. But she looked at the broad piazza on the front of their house, even that in use, now glassed in, now made into a full ward, full of sick. She remained puzzled.

To take her mind off her theological problem and to offset the somewhat less than maternal attitudes of her substitutes during her absence, she redoubled her personal attentions to her nuns. She got into the habit of keeping a bottle of her pet cough-medicine in her office, and if she heard anyone so much as clear her throat, she would pop out at her child, and in they both would go for a spoonful of the infallible elixir. She tempered her corrections of her subjects at this time, delaying them until she could find some minor virtue to praise, and end with, "However, the doctors tell me that the patients brighten every time they see you. So, if you do have lapses in decorum, I suppose it's your buoyancy that causes it."

197

She always laughed and always told of her third encounter with a novice, Sister Mary Mercedes, who, though, she had very mature interests and preferred to associate with the older novices, had a real little imp in her.

When the time came for the third reproof — a serious occasion — in which the novice had led a group at Brightside in dangerous skating across already spring-wrinkled ice, the Superior said, "And what is your explanation this time?"

The novice replied: "Because I am sixteen years old."

Mother Mary of Providence collapsed in laughter. "So you are. Sometimes I forget that. You're usually such an old lady."

So they both laughed. It was better as an ending than the deserved compliment. She did not try to use it by manufacturing occasions, but when the situation arose, she always seized on it. It worked very well. Leave them laughing.

Though there was no need any more for the sisters to make a picnic out of a long walk to Brightside, whenever she had to scurry between her two offices, she would get the Brightside horses trimmed up, bundle a few of the younger nuns into the wagon and trundle them off to a good snack, to a few hours in the country. It was most fun in winter, particularly after Dr. Mahoney had given them a sleigh. Mount St. Vincent had ample warning of Mother's arrival then, hearing the fresh young voices of girls singing "Sleigh Bells" in the clean hilly air.

Now also she could add one thing to Mother Valencia's advice: "When you do go somewhere, never go alone. Relax your shoulders and take some bright young things with you. Make it an outrage." Outing, no doubt.

The months were swift. It scarcely seemed possible to her that by October they had actually laid the cornerstone of Mercy Hospital and that the large building began to rise. But the years were going with equal rapidity. On November 8, 1898, they actually celebrated the first arrival of their nuns in Holyoke, twenty-five years ago. Although she had not been among the pioneer sisters, it was perfectly impossible that a quarter of a century had passed since she had waved goodbye to them from Kingston. So the laity thought that a nun's life was something like a long summer-Sunday afternoon, placid and eternal. Looking back, she could not remember a dull moment.

They had celebrated their anniversary, as was befitting, at St. Jerome's Church, where Father Harkins had celebrated the Mass. Full of the sense of time, on this day, she suddenly realized that the Pastor was old. As it happened, the Bishop could not be there, and so, she realized, for the first time now in many years, as celebrant in his own church, that Patrick Harkins was, as he had been in the early days, the center of their community lives.

Their founder? History, she knew, would rightly turn Bishop Beaven into their founder, as it would replace Mother Edward with herself. And suddenly she felt a pang for them, the founding nun forgotten, the founding priest bypassed. She had not really had as much thought for Father Harkins in the last few years as she should have had — her old friend and adversary.

She was distracted during the Mass, thinking of him. She had thought he would grow crustier and crustier with the years, but it had not been so. Time had mellowed him. And the surest proof of it was the devotion of his curates, whom he never changed until the Bishop removed them, promoted them, though one of them had said in her hearing, "I would rather be an assistant under Pat Harkins than the Archbishop of Boston." And his fellow clergy made his now comfortable rectory their clubhouse. He was a priest's priest.

She had been moved during the Anniversary Mass, but on the eighth of December she did not know whether she was laughing or crying. Father Patrick Harkins on that day presented her community with twenty-thousand dollars as a Jubilee gift to be used for what was to be the Father Harkins Home for the Aged.

The pathos of it struck her along with the humor. The poor man, she thought. Vying with the Bishop. But the Bishop had given them the vast monument of Mercy Hospital, and it was impossible to compete with a Bishop. She wondered too at how many would remember that not so many years ago Father Harkins had no Bishops to compete with in generosity and how many would record that in the beginning he was their sole benefactor, often their sole defender. Also, even though he had almost fired her, had thrown a chair at an imaginary Mother Edward, all through the years, he had put personalities secondary to the cause, and it was merely endearing that he wished to immortalize himself with the Father Harkins Home.

There may have been another reason why her heart warmed toward Father Harkins during this year of '98, in contrast, perhaps, to her feelings about Bishop Beaven. In the constant chess game between the metropolitan and the community founders, she had felt herself out-maneuvered from the beginning of this year, and it had become overt during His Excellency's official visitation on February eleventh.

Unexpectedly he had summoned all the Superiors to a private and closed meeting, and though she had supposed that what went on there would be as confidential and secret as the nuns would have been about their own family affairs, the Bishop had made his statement public to the whole community.

Some of it she did not think was fair. The attack on Superiors had been justified a year ago, but there was a timelag in his criticism now. Nor did it help to procure a spirit of obedience, which he was always stressing, to expose the faults to superiors to their subjects. As to the other part of the pronouncement, she had to concede that His Excellency had simply and effectively out-maneuvered her.

Though she could find no fault with her own maternal attitude, she knew that Bishop Beaven had seen through the fact that she herself had practically taken over as Mistress of Novices and was shaping the young to her own ideas of the spirit of the institute. Truly she had never demanded open manifestation of conscience. But she had set up an aura of social pressure and a fear of being somewhat less than totally dedicated, which had geared her young nuns to a sense of internal pressure to reveal all to her. Also she had condoned the local superiors reading of private letters addressed to herself. She had never openly approved of it, knowing the rights of subjects to direct communication, uncensored, with their confessors, and their provincial or general superiors. Yet, with her dedication to openness as needed in direction, she had seen no great harm in having the local superiors

200

glance at letters before they were sent out. So she had said nothing at all and had carefully avoided finding out about these abuses.

"Caught out," she thought, giving credit to the Bishop.

This is the exact record, as officially noted by the secretary at the Superiors' meeting of what Bishop Beaven commanded. Though the words of the document are as factual as possible, and doubtless contain an accurate summary of His Excellency's statements, since he signed and approved it, the implications, gathered by all dissident subjects that it was totally aimed at Mother Mary of Providence, cannot be ignored.

The account reads:

*SUPERIOR'S MEETING:* At a meeting of the Superiors of the Community, held February eleventh, 1898, the Right Reverend Bishop presiding, His Excellency made known that in his Visitation, he discovered among the Sisters, a certain feeling of nervousness, or uneasiness resulting from the humor or character of the Superior, and he wished each one to take this home to herself as concerning her. He showed the great need of the Superior's maintaining herself in a perfect equilibrium of mind, in order to inspire that confidence which is necessary to the happiness of the Sisters, and he explained that those dependent on authority, are very apt to study the characteristics and moods of those who govern.

He dwelt also on the great need of careful training of the Novices, and the absolute necessity of keeping up, at all times that close relationship between the Novices and their Mistress, that is proper to their state. The Mistress being the Superior of the Novices, the latter should at all times, have unrestricted liberty to communicate with her, and where the Novices cannot see the Mistress once a month, to give an account of their progress, they should be obliged to write, and their letters should be respected, as are those going to the Ordinary and the General Superior. The Novice should present her letter, and the Superior should close it in her presence. His Excellency said that he held in equal esteem, the relation of the Novice to her Mistress, that he does the Religious to her Superior, and while the Church in the matter of spiritual direction, had protected the subject, leaving the Religious free to open her conscience to her Superior, yet hindering the latter from forcing her to make this manifestation, yet the Novice, (this applies to all who belong to the Novitiate) should be at all times encouraged to make known to her Mistress, anything whatsoever she chose to communicate; that as we may hope to retain only a directive influence in the community, the burden naturally falling on the stronger shoulders of the young, it behooves us to form them to the religious spirit, and this can best be done by the Mistress of Novices in the Novitiate; consequently, the local Superiors must bear in mind, that she is only relatively, the Superior of the Novices in her employ, and every facility must be accorded them to be unreserved in their confidence with their proper Superior — The Mistress of Novices.

Approved.          Thomas D. Beaven

There was only one thing that Mother Mary of Providence could do. She must see the Bishop, lay everything on the table, show him the necessity for structuring the growing, the now, by no means infant community, according to the Spirit of St. Vincent, which might indeed, be in opposition to his dreams of a diocesan community according to the spirit of Thomas Beaven, no matter how admirable such a spirit might be. She hoped she might not have to confront the Bishop, but if she must, it would be her duty. She went bravely.

In that interview she had no opportunity to confront His Excellency. Bishop Beaven, always a gentleman, always controlled, was not harsh with her, but he was coldly firm as she had never seen him before, but was later to find him that way frequently. He took matters right out of her hands.

"I'm glad you came, Mother. I was going to send for you. Sit down please." He sat, putting the barrier of his impressive desk between them. "I gather that you have noted that I have elevated your Mistress of Novices to her rightful function. I wish her place to be respected in the future and not interfered with. That, I take it, is clear."

"Now as to further matters, I will expect you to carry out as rapidly as possible, certain reforms in your congregation. I have been very lenient, and I have been very patient, but I fear that the time has come for sterner measures. I really do not think your sisters are developing into real nuns, according to the mind of the Church. I really do not."

He paused for nothing, but went right on. "They have many worldly dedications, left over from their girlhood in a pagan society. I wonder that you have not noticed this yourself. For instance, what are they reading? I think the nursing nuns pick up this trash from the patients — at least I hope they do. Has your congregation no rules about reading?"

He allowed her to reply. "Yes, we have."

"Then enforce those rules."

She would and she promised. She had never had any temptations about secular reading herself. Perhaps that is why she had never noticed what others were doing. She remembered that her only indiscretion had been in hiding from her mother Reeves' Bible History.

The Bishop went on. "Another thing. One thing a nun cannot be and that is self-indulgent. I have seen a good deal of that among you, and some of your subjects have brought to my attention that you encourage such things — condone them, in fact. You will have this abuse pointed out at once. The other areas we shall treat as opportunity arises. I put you under obedience in these matters."

Then he said something that stung. "I can no longer request you, Reverend Mother."

Obediently she wrote the letter:

March 1898

Sisters must be very guarded in their reading. Those in the hospitals are not permitted to peruse matter that may be to them the occasion of any trouble of conscience; and among the subjects that they are forbidden to read is the subject of Obstetrics, as it in

203

no way concerns them. Their own **delicacy** will guide them in this matter; if they keep themselves so free from laxity that they have a correct and careful sense of right and wrong; if they allow themselves undue liberty frightful havoc will be made in their morals, before they realize it. In the matter of secular reading, a great care is to be exercised. No novel, no matter how popular it may be, may be read by any Sisters unless the local Superior has consulted the Mother Superior to know if it be a proper book for religious. The writings of our known Catholic authors, with which we are familiar are not here meant, but in the hospitals, schools, and elsewhere, opportunity for such reading will be found in the periodicals, magazines, and newspapers that find their way to these places. The Sisters must remember that such reading is absolutely forbidden to them. Consult the Rule on this point.

No one at that time would have disagreed very much with such a command given to nuns though how it was to be interpreted by teaching sisters leaves much to the imagination. It did, however, take into account, the growing bulk of relatively well-written books by Catholics, the increase of respectable periodicals, the growth and dedication of Catholic publishers and their bravery.

But then, she looked around for something that could practically point up the need for her subjects to practice self-discipline, to mortify themselves, and her letter on this subject is at best, embarrassing. One wishes one could exclude it from her biography, but Mother Mary of Providence in obedience to her Bishop wrote it and it must stand. Without comment, let it stand.

Temperance....

Of late I have been closely observing a habit gaining among you that threatens your health. It is *INTEMPERANCE* in the use of *tea* and *coffee*. It seems to me a sort of sensuality to take an excessive quantity of any article of diet, simply because we like it. One cup of tea or coffee should be enough at a meal. Less would be better for your health. These beverages are a nerve stimulant, and the use of them as now practiced to a great extent must be immediately stopped. Drink water, milk, broths; let the tea and coffee be not too strong and always diluted with milk. Of course, you understand that it is not to diminish the amount of nourishment that you take that this recommendation is given, but rather to regulate your food and remove that which is hurtful. Sisters, who do night duty in the hospitals, are no exception to the restriction here placed. Let the midnight lunch be taken faithfully but avoid the use of strong tea and coffee.

She tried to be obedient to her Bishop, but she knew he was planning something, and what it was she did not know. In any case he was biding his time, and for more than a year nothing more happened. You cannot hold the sense of suspense that long, and gradually she began to think, erroneously, that Bishop Beaven had abandoned whatever project he had had in mind.

He had not, but he was a patient man, waiting for assurance, upon the proverbial delays of Rome. In the meantime he was laying more subtle grounds.

He had heard from time to time of the interest that Father William Stanton, from his old alma mater, Holy Cross in Worcester, had been manifesting in his nuns. That was good. He would use that, and though no one guessed it, it was the Episcopal hand that had regulated Father Stanton's appointment as Extraordinary Confessor at Brightside.

Father Stanton was just the one he needed to implement his formation of his sisterhood. He was a warm and personal friend. He came from the Boston Dynasty of physicians, the Stanton's, and hence was interested in Hospitals. Above all he was a Jesuit, and what the Bishop confided to him was that his nuns needed a great deal of training in even the concept of the virtue of obedience, prompt, Ignatian, unquestioning, military obedience. He knew he had a supporter in Father Stanton, S. J.

The Bishop also was glad that the nuns liked him, for he was an easy man to like, having great warmth, great personal charm, and above all, a sharp and thoroughly trained mind.

He seemed to have found just the right approach even with Mother Mary of Providence, and the younger nuns, particularly the ones he had personally directed into the novitiate, adored him. They already were calling him their Spiritual Founder, which distressed neither of the actual founders, and shows much about the tact of Father Stanton.

Oh he had a way with him all right and the stories grew and survived about him.

There was the Brady girl, whom he had lured up here from Orange, New Jersey, to become a Providence nun. She had already been rejected by a congregation of teaching sisters, because of inadequate preparation, but Father Stanton thought of the orphans and the patients and knew where he could find a place for her. Miss Brady was charmed, but she asked him a question that showed much about her femininity, and one that never should be put to a mere male.

"What does their habit look like, Father?"

"Well, it's — it's black, you know. And they've sort of a white bonnet on their heads."

"Is there anything distinctive about it?"

"The headgear? Well, yes." He demurred a bit. "It has two flatirons hanging from it."

"Flatirons?"

"Cloth ones, of course. They are kind of hanging from it."

"You don't make it sound very attractive."

"As a matter of fact I don't think it is. But then, I'm only a man."

Miss Brady at least went to see for herself, and the flatirons were as distasteful as Father Stanton had indicated. In her interview, Mother Mary of Providence asked her how she liked the habit.

"I like it very much — that is, the dress part — and most of the headdress. But I can't imagine wearing those flatirons for the rest of my life."

"Oh, you'll get used to them. You may even like them after a while."

When Miss Brady, not discouraged, became Sister Mary of the Assumption, she did not get used to the flatirons. As a Novice they continued to bother her, and as happens to most novices she eventually assumed all kinds of outsize proportions.

Eventually she told Father Stanton about it, blaming him. "If you hadn't said flatirons, I wouldn't see them quite that way. But I just can't face dangling those things about for the rest of my life."

"Then forget about the rest of your life. Take a look at yourself in the coffin, and see if two pieces of cloth are worth that much."

Sister Assumption took a good look at herself in the coffin, flatirons and all, and it made all the difference. She used to say later, "Those flatirons were my greatest temptation — wasn't I lucky?" And she grew rather fond of the flatirons, from the very fact that she had defeated them, and of course, she knew that under God Father Stanton had not only given her her vocation but had also saved it.

So without too much pressure Father Stanton shaped the Sisters to the Ignatian ideal, while Mother Mary of Providence grieved, realizing how many nuns, no matter how different their original spirit had been, had been made into female Ignatians, until the daughters of God in the garden of the King scarcely seemed to present any noticeably infinite variety.

Bishop Beaven still had not made any drastic move throughout 1899, though a change, fundamental in its import, was made. There is no record of who was responsible for it, Mother General and the Council of Holyoke, or the Bishop of Springfield, and the fact of this silence seems to point to tragic unanimity.

At least it was tragic to Sister Mary Dolours. Though she herself had been retired from the work with the poor for some time now, she could not read the new law, abridging the commitment of the Sisters of Providence, without a pang, nor could she stomach the implications, which were a revocation of all the life that had been overflowing with the love of God's poor, had been truly a dedication, a Christlike going out to the needy, yes, and a finding of Christ more among His people, than in the stark pieties of the convent.

How she had turned against Kempis years ago, when she had read that a religious never leaves his cell to go among men, without returning less a follower of Christ. How untrue she had found that to be! And now, how far this new ordering was from the intention of St. Vincent, who worked with his people among the outcasts; or of Mother Gamelin, who searched the alleys for the sick and senile. What was this sister of hers doing to them now?

For it was true, that after many years the practice of nursing and caring for the poor in their own hovels was discontinued, forbidden. Under the guise of cloisterization, a Sister of Providence would no longer go out to nurse the indigent, to clean up their apalling dwellings, to beg for them, to clothe them, and finally to prepare them for the grave. No. From now on, Sister Dolours saw, they may stay piously in their convents and pray for God's poor.

She read what she thought were specious excuses. The Sisters were supplanted in their ministrations by the new visiting nurses. The material needs of the poor were now taken care of by the St. Vincent de Paul Society. The General Superior felt that it would be more efficient to bring the needy, free of charge, to the hospitals and the homes for the aged, no matter what the whimseys of the sick and senile might be. But worst of all — and Sister Dolours was stung — she read: "Furthermore the visiting of sisters on behalf of the poor, can easily degenerate into a social call."

A social call, indeed! Shouldn't it be? Wasn't love — charity, if you liked that word — social? And Sister Dolours wondered how could her sister forget the nature of the social calls she had had with her old lady dying of cancer? Those were the moments, Sister Dolours thought, when she had had some hope for her sister, and really believed that she might save her soul. How could she make such an edict? Social call, indeed? What did they think of herself, as a Visiting Nun, that she had pink tea and lady fingers?

But Sister Dolours was joined by very few in her outrage at the new order. Most of the nuns felt relieved. Trained sisters in the work were aging, retiring, dying; new and more professionalized services were taking up all their time. And, as the more pious among them noted, that this care of one's neighbor was, "outside the sanctuary of the Convent Cloister," though Sister Dolours and her cohorts pointed out, with no effect, that even the new Rule said that they had no cloister and were to bring their spirit of cloister with them into the world. No effect. No effect at all. The banning was a popular decision.

208

And as for the Bishop, he had moved very slowly, but very surely, showing his displeasure openly only once, when his nuns had purchased a new parcel of land adjoining Brightside. They had got twenty-one acres for six thousand dollars, and could not resist the opportunity. But the Bishop signed the agreement with obvious reluctance, deeply opposed to adding to the already monstrous debt that the sisters had incurred. Besides, as he said explicitly, "You have railroaded me into this. I do not like it. But this is the last time. You will know what I mean before the year is out."

On June the twelfth, 1900, they undoubtedly knew. Rome had approved. The Vatican wrote a commendatory note to Bishop Beaven, congratulating him on the spirit of reform, so pleasing to the mind of His Holiness the Pope, in anticipating the standards that soon, it was hoped, the Church would formalize for Religious throughout the world.

At the meeting of the Council, Bishop Beaven presiding, he announced a change in their formula of the vows. Although many of the customs maintained in Montreal and in Kingston may have been admirable for their time and place, they were not suitable for a community in the United States.

Since the Sisters of Providence of Holyoke had themselves abandoned immediate work with the poor, the special fourth vow, adding such a commitment, would now be omitted, and this decision was augmented by a signed document from many of the Community, to the effect that their present avocations now rarely if ever brought them into the immediate services of the poor. This vow was dropped.

The usual vows of poverty, chastity and obedience would be retained, but the vow of obedience must include and be made to the Bishop of the Diocese of Springfield not solely received by the General Superior.

Beginning as of this date, the Postulants would no longer be free to mingle with the older Sisters, preparing them for the new attitudes on Diocesan Obedience, and in the nature of their works, rather than being subjected to the infiltrations of older and now discontinued customs and interpretations.

The new formula of the vows, in its modern interpretation, would be used when the novices made profession, on the 19th of July, and to be adopted by the total community in all renewals of vows, from that date forward.

The Bishop added, by way of homily: "In the taking of these vows, particularly in the vow of obedience to the Bishop, and in the interpretation of the vow of poverty, which frees you from service to any particular class of human beings, opening your ministry to the alleviation of human misery in all your neighbors, at every stage of life, and in every caste of society, you may perceive, in the blessing of Rome upon it, that here is set the seal of heaven's approval on your Institute."

Thus blessed by Heaven, Rome and Bishop Beaven, the Diocesan Sisters of Providence of Holyoke, began their new lives.

# CHAPTER 16

Mother Mary of Providence looked over her situation. Again, she was caught between two duties, and though Father Stanton told her that in such a case she was free to choose either, and that whatever she chose would be virtuous and according to the will of God, it was not easy for her. Her choice was to follow the Rule of St. Vincent, or to be obedient to the Bishop. What he saw for the future of her congregation was, she knew now, diametrically opposed to what she had been dedicated to.

And yet, she must face the changing times. Her certainties about the freer and more people-directed life of the unenclosed nun had recently been shaken severely by a translation of an official letter from the Vatican directed to Cardinal Gibbons, but intended for the whole Church. It was called "De Americanismo" but better called "The Condemnation of the Heresy of Americanism," and it made her aware of the growing spirit of independence and insistence on individuality, as values greater than community. The Church feared the total weakening of authority and discipline.

She could perceive the new spirit among her nuns. And perhaps she had been wrong and had only implemented their looseness of living, festered their spirit of rebellion.

She was aware that Bishop Beaven was in deep touch with Rome and knew, if any prelate in America did, what was in the mind of the Pope in the further strengthening of religious life.

Now too she had a vow of obedience to the Bishop. And she was advised by the other Major Superiors of women, that the times demanded a far more conventual life than they had been trained to, even lived under, in their more docile youth. Mother Valencia had said with regret, "Now I must be stricter."

So the foundress made her decision. She would tighten up the lines of living, accept the present and the will of Rome, and if she could not retain the older spirit of the Vincentians, she would make her congregation as realistically perfect as she could, under the newer and stricter dispensation.

Her regulations to the community, dated March, 1900, show all too clearly, the new attitudes:

March 31, 1900

"It seems necessary to call your attention occasionally to points of discipline that holy Obedience enjoins on us for the maintenance of good order; to this end we wish to remind you that nearly three years ago, Our Right Reverend Bishop, at a meeting of the Council of the Community, ordained that when the Sisters go to different houses of the Congregation, they must ordinarily return to their respective residence in time for supper, thus preventing the unbecoming spectacle of seeing religious on the street or in the cars after dark. On extraordinary occasions, subject to the discretion of the Mother Superior, the hour for returning may be prolonged.

The practical application of this ordinance has shown us that the Bishop is unwilling that the Superiors or Sisters be on the street after dark unless extraordinary circumstances require, and with the permission of the Mother Superior. It has seemed hard to enforce this restriction, and we have thought that it is not fully understood, as the Sisters have had no scruple in returning to their homes an hour or two after their supper-time. Your attention is now called to it in the most emphatic manner, and that we may not be misunderstood, we here enjoin that if the Sisters find themselves from home, on business in any place they will so arrange that they reach their home or temporary stopping place in time for supper. If they be visiting the sick, they will do likewise; if they be at Brightside they will leave the grounds before five-thirty at the latest; the same holds for Mount Saint Vincent. If they be at Springfield they will leave the house in time to take the car at five o'clock. Failing this they must remain in the house where they happen to be, that is in the mission

212

house of the Congregation. Any violation of this ordinance must be reported to the Mother Superior, and the Superiors are asked to enforce the regulation by word and example. It is better to leave some errands undone, than to be found on the street and in crowded cars after six o'clock. Our experience has shown us how wise the provision that saves us from such exposure and we must bear in mind that our Superiors study the matter well before placing a restriction upon us, and we are bound by holy obedience to put such orders into practice.

It is of course, well understood that we are not permitted under any circumstances to travel in public conveyance, such as street cars or steam cars on Sunday. It is better that the Sisters remain home on the Sabbath, and as much as possible on legal holidays; if it is necessary to travel on Sunday it must be in a private carriage. On legal holidays Sisters should start out quite early in the morning or at hours when the cars are not likely to be crowded.

When there is a large number of Sisters at Brightside, they should arrange to go home in small bands; the Superior of every house can either arrange herself or appoint a senior Sister to gather her companions, so that all be done decently, for we can edify the neighbor or we can attract unfavorable attention, according to the care we take to be orderly.

The Sisters should pay great attention to silence on the street and in public places.

### Community Prayers

2. We have adopted the custom of saying together the League Offering of the Sacred Heart every morning after the intention has been read. This offering is made aloud and in concert.

### Reception of Holy Communion

3. Sisters, who do not intend to receive Holy

213

Communion of Rule are required to give notice of their intention to the Superior either the evening before or in the morning before Mass. For every such Holy Communion omitted the Sister must spend one half hour before the Blessed Sacrament in reparation and to console the Sacred Heart for the omission. She may take the time from the evening recreation, and must always give notice to the Superior that she is absent from recreation for this. The Superior henceforth will keep account of those who remain from Communion and to notify the Mother Superior once a month of those who have omitted their Holy Communion; of those who have faithfully and duly reported their omissions and those who have failed to do so. We do not pretend to hinder or force any one to approach the Holy Table, but we wish to know the standing of the Community in this very important matter.

The commands on companions and on prayer certainly went along with the mind of Rome. As to the third edict, insisting that the sisters report and make public their abstaining from the reception of the Eucharist, this was certainly counterindicated in the mind of the Church. Greater than the abuse of demanded manifestation of conscience to women who certainly were not priests, to men who heard the confessions of their subjects outside the secrecy of the Sacrament of Penance, was, what was in fact, an open admission of a disturbed conscience, and was usually interpreted to mean that the religious who abstained thought herself to be in the state of mortal sin. Again, if anything should be a matter of free devotion, it should be the reception of Holy Communion, which Rome taught, was of obligation only once a year.

The General Superior's disclaimer: "We do not hinder or force any one to approach the Holy Table," was at least paradoxical, in a document that effected just such force, and in addition and worse, expressed the state of conscience of the individual to inevitable evil interpretation.

Such commands in various communities were on the increase, and to such an extent that many experienced confessors to nuns were advising the sisters to "Make a good

214

act of contrition, and go right up to Communion, Sister. Tell me about it next time you come to confession. But no one has the right to make you expose yourself."

How common was the practice of forcing the nuns to self-incrimination, how acceptable the abuse had become, is evidenced by Bishop Beaven's passing the regulation without any demurral. But the subject-sisters of the Community of Providence of Holyoke were not so concessive in abdicating their rights of private conscience, and some of them were deeply and tragically disturbed.

The General Superior knew this. What consoled her was the support that she received from two of the most important members of her Council, the Mistress of Novices, Sister Gertrude, and the increasingly important Superior of Worcester, Sister Ursula. If their superior suspected that their vehement approbation was due more to personal devotion to herself than to a conviction of the rightness of her judication, it was consoling to know that at last she had friends who believed in her. She needed them.

The next move came from the Bishop, when he officially presided at a meeting of the Council on the 28th of May, 1901. The secretary's notes record the decision:

In the exercise of supervision, he presided at a meeting of the Council on the 28th of May, 1901, and deliberated with its members, on Hospital matters, fixing their attention upon the need of establishing the profession of nursing on a solid and intelligent basis, and to this end he suggested the wisdom of forming the Sisters, by the study of the duties of nursing, as Professional Nurses, that they might be the better able to meet the opposition which is offered to any one not holding the certificate of a trained nurse.

He expressed the opinion that there should be some one to direct the studies, and act as a Superintendent of Nurses. It should be done by one who would act with the local Superior, without conflicting with her duties. He made known that the Reverend Mother had recently visited Hospitals, with a view to learning the deficiencies that may exist in our own Management. He added that while Divine Providence has wonderfully protected us during the formative period in our work, we should make all haste to reach proficiency, lest God might permit the veil to be removed, and that the public recognize our weakness.

He asked that a ballot be cast for the election of one who might take up the work of Superintendent of the Nursing Corps of Sisters. A ballot was cast and as there was no election, the Bishop asked if the Council would be willing to leave the appointment with him. Ready consent was accorded to this proposition.

The Bishop appointed Mother Mary of Providence, Superior of the Community, to take up the work of directing the studies and regulating the system of nursing in our Hospitals. This appointment, while it occasioned a little surprise, was cheerfully accepted as the best that could be done under the circumstances, and the measure that would best harmonize with existing conditions, since the authority vested in her, would enable her to establish such order as might seem productive of the end in view.

One of the Surgeons had prepared a condensed history or summary of Bacteriology in which he classified the principal types, their form and agency in disease. This was typewritten and carefully studied; blackboard illustrations were used to present the bacteria more commonly found, and these were the first lessons which the Sisters had in the study of bacteria, with which in later years, they have become familiar. It may be safely asserted that new interest was awakened and the movement inaugurated by the Bishop helped to awaken this deeper enthusiasm. As a further stimulus to study and advancement, the Reverend Mother notified the classes that in due time, the Sisters who were pursuing the study and practice of nursing, would be submitted to an examination by two Doctors of the Hospital Staff, representing respectively the Medical and Surgical services. If found satisfactory, the fact would be recorded in a special register of the Community; she would be allowed a certificate of Trained Nurse to which the examining Doctors would affix their signatures, and would be awarded the silver medal duly inscribed with the name and date of Graduation.

With her new dedication to professionalism, Mother Mary of Providence welcomed with joy the advices of the Bishop, and though the strangeness of the situation in which she who had never been trained as a nurse, should be in dictatorial control of the training of nurses, did not escape her; she herself managed to squeeze into enough classes through the years that followed and to manage to take and pass examinations, that at the end of some time she privately wangled a diploma for herself and was somehow or another an official Registered Nurse.

It helped her because she knew that she faced the power struggle between the doctors and the nuns. While the Sisters must recognize what was due to the dignity of the medical profession, they must also, as quietly as was possible, but as firmly as was sometimes necessary, maintain the fact that they, the Sisters, were the owners and the administrators of their own hospitals.

They had particular trouble with the doctors who had worked in public hospitals, and who seemed to have the erroneous notion that they should have some voice in the government of private institutions. They certainly didn't know how to deal with Sisters. They had no idea what the prerogatives of the nuns really were. Gradually, the foundress became convinced that a religious must train the physicians to confine their attention to the care of the sick. Beyond that, doctors must not intrude into administration.

There was another and more subtle problem of which the General Superior was aware, and that was a problem that confronted all the growing Catholic institutions, whether related to health or education or social services, and to remain a problem for many years.

Though the solution was far from simple, the difficulty was obvious. Should they imitate the advances of secular institutions, adapting to and competing with their advances, or should they recognize the difference of their own commitment, and bend all their efforts to build up peculiarly

217

'Catholic standards, making themselves unique? Nearly all institutions chose the latter course, dedicating themselves with all energy to create a system, distinct, and their own. Ultimately Catholic institutions considered themselves not only different, but superior to their secular counterparts.

Bishop Beaven thought, correctly, that his reform program was going along well. Now he could turn his attention again to expansion. He had his eye to the West, to Pittsfield, but before he could accomplish that, two opportunities arose. The first was almost a distraction, and was treated as if it were.

Mr. Bernard Farren, the builder of the Housatonic Tunnel, offered the Bishop and the Sisters some property in Montague City, almost directly in the center of the diocese, scarcely an expansion to the West. But he guaranteed that he would endow the facility, and this was scarcely to be tossed aside. Though the location was isolated and the chances of success seemed slim, the high hopes and promises of Mr. Farren induced the General, though with misgivings, to accept. Almost off-handedly the Bishop became president of a corporation consisting of the residents of Turners Falls and Greenfield, appointed Reverend Mother, as usual, as treasurer, and formalized an executive board. Speedily, and as a gesture of good-will toward the Bishop, the Reverend Mother appointed Sister Vincent, now professed, as Superior, but could spare her only three sisters from her hospital community.

But Mr. Farren made a big touse about it. He gathered an impressive group of the hierarchy at his own home and formally passed over the ownership of the Farren Memorial Hospital property by guaranteed deed to the new corporation, and reiterated his promise of setting up an endowment fund that would yield an annuity of 25,000 dollars per annum.

Though the nuns had no actual money as yet and had to meet their own living expenses—to purchase most of the household goods and supply all the hospital equipment, all from whatever funds they could scrape together from the Motherhouse—neither the Bishop nor the treasurer was totally without hope. Mother Vincent said they would trust

218

in Divine Providence; Bishop Beaven remarked that they had jolly well better trust in Mr. Bernard Farren, as well.

The building had begun at once. Mr. Farren was constantly in attendance, and it seemed to observers that his chief concern was in cutting down expenses, even in cutting corners. That Mother Mary of Providence was there as often as she could be, was not surprising, since, even with the corners cut, the payments must for now, at least, come out of her own funds. She tried to be unobtrusive. She was better at it this time than she had been with Father Harkins. At least there were no open run-ins.

The second opportunity that came to the Bishop in his westernizing plan, could not be ignored. He had a chance to purchase property in Adams for $16,000 and take an adjoining cottage for $6,500. On his own twenty-fifth anniversary he gave this property to the Sisters of Providence, asking that they turn it into a rest home for semi-invalids, and appointed them a chaplain who could influence them and watch over them—Father Joseph Rice.

The Bishop was getting closer to Pittsfield.

With all her material interests and the heaping demands upon her, the foundress continued with her disciplinary structuring of her community, her eye now keen for lapses, her pen quick and strong. Two of her letters may well serve as an example of what she was aware of, and edicts such as these kept pouring forth from the desks of Superiors and Generals in massive numbers, through all these years. The letters indicate that human beings desire to communicate, and that overworked people have tendencies to sleep. Though the first edict could be found reduplicated a hundred fold by all contemporary superiors, the punitive harshness of the second sounds more Gallic than American.

1901

We cannot be too attentive in little things; **uniformity** in all our customs is very desirable. Let us help one another in this.

The Sisters are cautioned against speaking on the street; in street cars; at the church door or delaying unnecessarily to hold conversation in any public place. Strict observance of the rule of silence should be enforced especially in the refectory, dormitories and corridors; also during meals except when recreation is permitted by rule or special permission; exemptions from the rule of silence at meals should not be sought nor too freely granted. Those Sisters, who come to the second table, are held to the observance of silence, even when no lecture is read; the Gospel and the martyrology for the next day should be read at the second table.

## 1902

In our visitations and private interviews with the Sisters we have had reason frequently to deplore and to be humiliated by the tepedity of the Sisters in regard to Meditation, manifested by the frequency with which they fall asleep at this holy exercise. Believing that mortification is a powerful aid to fervour, and that sloth merits punishment, the regulation has been made and is now being enforced, that those who sleep at the morning meditation will ask a penance for it and take their breakfast on their knees. If they sleep at the evening meditation, they will ask a similar penance, and take their supper kneeling. If the Superior notice the fault and the Sister should fail to ask the penance, it is to be imposed. If the fault be committed in the absence of the Superior, the Sister is to perform the penance at the next meal following the fault. If you will be generous and cooperate with us in this effort to overcome a form of tepedity, which is only too general among us, a signal blessing will not fail to be invoked upon yourselves individually and the Congregation in general. It can be exacted from the young but unless all conform generously, the practice will fail of its effects. No means is to be left untried to keep the Sisters in fervour and strongly exercised in religious fidelity.

What deep disturbances and truly traumatic experiences the new laws, the total shift of dedication; the rigid cloisterization were having on some members of the community was not fully perceived either by the Bishop nor by the foundress, for the tragedy, when it happened, left them, as it did all the Sisters of Providence aghast and in a state of shock. This, they had never expected.

One day in 1902, two professed nuns, of previously admirable dedication, simply walked out. In the charity of that moment, their names are not recorded in the annals— disclosures which would be made in the case of later withdrawals. But now the whole episode was spoken of in whispers. And if their sisters were shocked, one can fancy the shock that was sustained by the laity, when inevitably the word got to them. Nuns simply did not leave. Their teacher, their favorite nurse, their confidant and holy model had defected. Had they not been Brides of Christ? Nuns simply did not leave.

To the Bishop, who could have granted dispensations, or got them from Rome, it was not their leaving that appalled him. It was the way they did it. There was no need either, for he would have listened to them, guided them, even sympathised with them. Had he not always been a father, taking sides in the behalf of subjects, even to excoriating superiors? But it hurt that they had ignored him, had secretly let their hair grow for months, showing foresight and planning, and one day, they had without legalization, returned to the world. And—his heart bled for them—they were excommunicated, cut off from the Church and from the Sacraments. These poor, misguided women!

Though Father Stanton was for the only recorded time severe with his proteges and even with Mother Mary of Providence, his statements did not soothe or change them. He said again and again, "These women were not priests! They were not ordained. For a priest to leave—that is a tragedy, because he is ordained forever according to the Order of Melchizedek. But these women only have to go to the Bishop, and he's a good, kind man. He'll fix it up with Rome, and these ex-nuns will become just good, faithful laywomen. You're making too much of this, Sister. They're not priests, I tell you. Besides, priests don't leave. They can't. But remember that you can.

221

These ladies did. That's all there is to it."

His advice was words in the wind. What Mother Mary of Providence, foundress of the Sisters of Providence of Holyoke thought is documented. In it, far deeper than the disapproval that is manifest, is her reaction to rejection, true love, true sorrow—no—deep and maternal pain at the 1902 Defections.

Wishing to draw all profit from special trials and humiliations and to invoke upon the Community the blessing and protection of our Heavenly Father; knowing also that events which become part of our history are soon forgotten I desire to call attention again to the painful experience that so recently afflicted our little family in the unfaithful conduct of two of its professed members and to point out anew the lessons that it teaches.

We have endeavored to make some reparation by the recital of the penitential psalms and other austerities imposed where it seemed to be merited in a greater or less degree. We may hope that this attitude of humility and reparation which we have assumed will console the divine Heart of our Lord for the evil which has been wrought in our midst. We must continue privately to offer expiatory acts for ourselves and those unhappy ones who were of our number.

Doing thus it may happen that the scandal be minimized and mercy may be shown to them and us. For ourselves there is also a warning which should be heeded. Close inquiry revealed that there would have been a chance to avert the blow which brought shame to our Community and grief to our Ecclesiastical Superior if the warning of our Holy Rule and the admonitions so often repeated in retreat Conferences had been heeded; more than one of our Sisters had received sufficient information to arrest the evil, if Superiors had been informed.

It is but just to ourselves to inform you that severe punishment was awarded them for their tardiness in making known the communication received relative to the discontent and the intended departure of one of the misguided members. Religious discipline will be enforced in rigid form and any Sister who may be known to listen to forbidden conversations or to receive any information without making proper use of it will be submitted to rigorous penance. We have had painful experience and convincing proof that much that our Superiors tell us is allowed to make but little impression; that we do not heed the warnings of conscience nor realize the responsibility that fraternal charity imposes. Let us then study our duties to our Community and to each other so that the warning and punishment which has come to us all may not lose their effect; may never be forgotten and need never be repeated. Let us take to heart this truth that when a professed religious has reached the unhappy condition where her obligations become burdensome, she does not rid herself thereof by breaking loose from her rules and leaving religious enclosure. Violation of one's vows does not imply dispensation from them and the condition of such a one is frightful to consider.

Whilst dispensation from vows is the last thing to be desired, it nevertheless enables one to approach the sacraments and hinders grievous scandal and sacrilege. It is the duty of every one of us to do all in our power to keep from our door such awful sins and scandals as we at present deplore; therefore we implore you again most earnestly to be prompt in taking the necessary measures to protect our Sisters and our Community by the means which the rule provides for safeguarding the members of the Congregation. We would like to close this chapter and remember it no more but we cannot. Those unhappy Sisters are dead to us in every sense of the word; those whom death takes from our midst, supported by the Sacraments of Holy Mother the Church are still united with us in the Communion of Saints and we can rejoice even in our grief, because they terminate in death the work of their sanctification which they began at their religious Profession and merit the crown of perseverance. What a lesson we have had to prove the need of craving these great graces for ourselves and for each other. Let us then extend this charity to one another in future and above all let us be so jealous of the good name of our Community that immediate warning will be given when danger threatens. We cannot ask why such a thing could have been allowed in the Providence of God, because, as mentioned above, there are culpable carelessnesses exercised by those who might have been instruments in God's service to avert this trial. Even had their efforts failed, they would have placed the responsibility where it belonged. While bitterly deploring the trouble which those unhappy children of the Community have brought to the Congregation; we must not forget to pray for them as the rule directs that they may see their error and be led to repentance and to the exercises of the virtue of Christian life.

# CHAPTER 17

To the sisters in those years, the accessions of Farren Memorial Hospital and Greylock Rest, which were burdens rather than achievements, ran far behind their joy and pride in what might seem to an outsider, to be far less significant than it did to the nursing nuns. The Bishop had given them the use of an unoccupied house on the Cathedral property, and at once they fitted it up for a maternity hospital, connected with Mercy Hospital in Springfield, but under the capable direction of Drs. Charles F. Kennedy and Charles Downey. Not only was a proficient obstetrics department now set up, completing the efficiency of Mercy Hospital, but the administrators found room to assign a wing for the care of those with nervous diseases. It is significant of their growing professionalism that this rather than the infant facilities caused them their greatest pride.

Yet Greylock Rest meant much to Mother Mary of Providence. She fell in love with the Berkshires, with the paisley shawls they wore in the autumn, the brilliant blue and white dazzling clothing of their brisk, dry winters, the pastels of their protracted spring. And in the summer the Berkshires were cool and odorous with the fragrance of hemlock and larch.

She looked at the cottage, too far away from the main buildings to be efficiently managed by the sisters at the Rest. For a moment she thought of apportioning it as a vacation home for her tired nuns, but it was really too small for that, she thought. So she turned it into a complete little hideaway for Bishop Beaven, where he could and did find peace.

The thought never crossed her mind that she was returning good for evil, because she had never had the temptation to categorize the Bishop as the enemy. They had different ideas. That was all. And she saw no reason for personal emotions to enter an arena of ideologies. Yet it may be that the Bishop's growing coldness concentrated on her, not on her subjects or her cause, subconsciously dictated her great kindness to him in preparing a mountain retreat from his cares. If some of her subjects thought that they too had cares that could be alleviated by a week or two at Loretto Cottage, she indirectly counseled them on the dangers of the spirit of envy.

But then, in the midst of all their expenditures and debts, they purchased Dolan's Farm, a property adjoining Bright-side, and it became clear to the Bishop that they had every intention of purchasing all the smaller farms that adjoined the Wilkinson Estate, and that nothing which he could advise would stop them. The Bishop gave up. Noticeably he retired to Greylock for a week after signing the deed.

Of course things were not all grim in the first decade of the Twentieth Century. Transportation-wise it was much easier for them now that there was a streetcar line stretching all the way out from the center of Holyoke to Brightside. It took a little while to get used to it; and the Sisters who taught at St. Jerome's and commuted back and forth had their problems—none more than Sister Michael who managed to turn all embarrassing experiences into laughter, into tales that would become community legend.

There was the inevitable day when in a packed trolley she was being conveyed to her morning assignment at eight-thirty. All seats were in long rows, from stem to stern of the trolley, and the wide aisle between was for standing. Quickly it too filled up. So she could not help but notice it when a young man across from her was given a seat. In a moment she knew why. It had not been the lurching of the car that unsteadied his gait, but more internal reasons. And at eight o'clock in the morning! Worse, she knew him. He had been one of her pupils. It was Johnny Lynch, very, very drunk.

Sister Michael was an ample woman. She did her best to effect a protective barrier between herself and her pupil, but it was impossible. Of course he saw her, and his glad cry reached her.

"'Stir Michael!"

She was identified to the entire carload. She smiled as demurely as she could and looked away.

Johnny was not only loving, but belligerently loyal. "She's the best teacher in St. Jerome's!" he cried. "There's nobody like that one. She's a good sister." He managed to rise. "I owe everything I am to the nuns. I owe it all to Sister Michael."

226

Clutching the passengers, overcoming the bumping of the trolley, he got himself across the aisle, landing sprawled at her knees. With some fumbling, he extracted a dime. "Here, 'Stir. Here's ten cents. Pay your fare both ways. You're a good sister."

She smiled and took the coin. She said, "But Johnny thanks—but I think it's a little extreme to kneel to me. Why don't you just get up now, like a good boy?"

At the trolley stop, he managed to heave himself to his feet and ultimately with help to disembark.

But whenever she told the story, she added, "Maybe we have as many drunks as the others—but our drunks are nicer. They love us and they give us dimes."

The Sisters to whom she told the story would then chant, "You made me what I am today," and sometimes, add: "I hope you're satisfied."

Then, of course, there was the inevitable day when the winter weather steamed and froze on the panes of the car. Another and more sober former student, Michael Rowan was both conductor and motorman, and when he was on, Sister Michael was always a nickel richer.

One wintry morning Sister Michael was tired. Valiantly she had remained upright during meditation, in compliance with the General Superior's orders, and in dread of the ridiculous penalty. But a little snooze would do no harm now. She had until eight-thirty to get to school.

The trolley jerked over Main Street, up Dwight, where she should have alighted. It stopped for passengers at City Hall and made the big loop over High Street then headed back toward Brightside. Not till then did Sister Michael come to enough to go down and question Michael.

"What's the matter?" she asked. "It seems we're a long time getting into Holyoke this morning."

"Where are you going, Sister?" Michael asked.

"Why, you know very well. You've seen me in my classroom enough mornings."

"It's after nine, Sister. I guess you're late for once. And you're halfway back to Springfield."

"Oh dear," she said, "You are a bad boy. I must have snoozed. Why didn't you wake me?"

227

He grinned at her. "I didn't have the heart, Sister."

So he stopped the next car headed toward Holyoke and transferred her again without charge. To her amazement she found her class in perfect order, and she told them what lovely boys they were, and they all pretended that their deep interest in square root had not developed at the precise moment when they heard her heavy and hurrying footsteps, or that a voice had not cried out, "Cheese it, The "Stir!"

Yet not all the technological advances were as harmless as that. Problems were arising about sisters in crowded cars, squeezed and pushed and jostled, with disturbing necessities of sitting quite close to men. Then too there was a danger in the new telephone, which Bishop Beaven had to face squarely:

Reverend and dear Superior:

Some few echoes reaching me of certain phone conversations between the sisters that grate harshly upon the chivalrous ears of admirers of Sisterly propriety, it seemed to me that centering your attention upon such incidents would convince all our Sisters of the great desire of the Bishop to believe his Religious thoroughly irreprehensible in all religious niceties.

Moral of this Fable: "Don't get too familiar with the 'phone."

Yours sincerely in Xt.,
Thomas D. Beaven
Bishop of Springfield

All was not grim with them. Though they had scarcely noticed it when Father Beaven as one rung on a predictable ladder, had become a Doctor of Theology, they shared in the joy when, at long last, their old friend Father Harkins was made a Monsignor, looking beautiful in his new and brilliant robes. He made no disclaimer about his happiness, as many Monsignors do, claiming that they are unworthy of the honor, making light of their new plumage. He loved it. He admitted to all and sundry that it gave him great pleasure and his joy brought a warmth to the heart of his Bishop, who had worked hard to get the honor for his old

228

and now very dear friend.

However, the years 1906-1907 were tragic for the world as well as for the Sisters of Providence and personally upsetting to their General Superior.

In the larger world, there was the San Francisco earthquake and fire; there was the 1907 great panic of Wall Street, where the collapse of the nation's financial structure was reputedly averted only by the deposits of Mr. Morgan. And to the community, there was the new trial codex of Canon Law, the section for priests and religious, anticipating the full codification of some ten years later, now readied and promulgated.

Rome had spoken. Bishop Beaven was fully vindicated. The liberalizations, of which Mother Mary of Providence had dreamed, were totally counter-indicated by the Vatican itself. Now the priests of the Roman Catholic Church could, had they time, commit five thousand more mortal sins per annum than could a layman, and nuns could read the dread threats that hovered over them for infractions of religious life. And woe betide the women who leaped over the wall!

The General Superior had met defections. She would forestall them now if she could, and if she were made aware of them, as was the duty of her sisters.

She saved one of the younger sisters and was never sorry. Sister Emmanuel, ready for her final profession, did the right thing, and confided in her that she did not think she could face the rigidity of a life that she had not chosen and had not anticipated. Mother Mary of Providence strengthened her—she did more, she appointed her as her own personal secretary and companion, giving of her own strength to the wavering nun. She knew that this girl had come from nothing and would return to a hard world; and she said the right words to Sister Emmanuel for she did not defect but walked up bravely on the morning of her final vows and made her perpetual sacrifice to her divine Master.

Not only this, but Mother Mary of Providence did not inform the Bishop of Sister Emmanuel's vacillation, keeping all these things, as she said, in her heart.

After every triumph, must there be a balancing tragedy? Nonsense. What kind of a diabolic mysticism was that? But in the early spring, when the roads were still choked with snow, and the hydrants frozen, the orphan asylum was burned to the ground. While the nuns herded the babies into protective areas, firemen carried the hoses on their shoulders to the top of the hill while others put shoulders to wheels to help the laboring horses to pull the lightened trucks. They stationed older boys to extinguish embers, lest they fall on other buildings.

In the orphanage—Bethlehem—the sisters had been awakened by the wild barking of the dog, Prince. Accustomed to rising in the night, disciplined by the great silence, they went calmly to their battle stations, so noiseless that some of the little ones were bundled up and taken to safety, without even awakening. Quietly they counseled the older ones to dress warmly, quietly they sat each child on his bed, so that none would be overlooked. And then the sisters, who had so often prayed in unison as they went from the chapel to the refectory, began their chant, and praying in procession, led their toddlers from the smokey building. Not a child was singed. But from safety they saw the flames, as the roof collapsed upon their building—their haven.

So they built again, and by the Bishop's feast day, September 8, 1909, a new Bethlehem was dedicated, and in the new home a much more organized training day was set up for the orphans, who now had precious little time to roam over the massive acreages of Brightside.

Now they rose and assembled for compulsory daily Mass at eight. From there the day was filled with studies, household work, and highly organized and supervised play—with much prayer. Before each meal, after Grace was said, the children remained silent until the supervising Sister rang a little bell. Then, and then only, might their chatter begin, and the length of the silences was proportionate to the excellence of their behavior in the hours before.

There was more than the dedication of Bethlehem on that day of the Bishop's feast, for the Bishop rose at the end of dinner, and in a generous gesture announced that he was presenting the Sisters of Providence with funds for a new and endowed home for the aged, to be known by the surnames of both his parents. No doubt the Bishop was inspired by filial devotion to his mother, but he was a bit tired of the dichotomy his British heritage had set up between him and most of his priests. Hence, the name Beaven-Kelly.

Mother Mary of Providence betrayed herself. She glanced only at the stricken face of Monsignor Harkins. How could his monument, his immortality stand comparison with the munificence of a Bishop? How insignificant now was the Father Harkins Home for the Aged compared with the magnificent Beaven-Kelly Home for the Aged?

Both she and her Bishop knew that her speech of acceptance and thanks were a trifle icy—almost as if she would rather not have received the gift, punctuated by mentions of the bequests of Monsignor Harkins.

The Bishop had not thought of this; it honestly had not crossed his mind. It was perhaps a stung conscience, a sudden awareness of unintended unkindness that produced the witnessed incident that Sister Emmanuel saw and could not understand. A day or two later when the Bishop was visiting them again, it seemed to the Secretary General that His Excellency went out of the way to be kind and gracious to the younger nuns, yes, was even gracious to her, for whom, she knew, he had little time. Then she saw the incident that scarred her.

The Bishop was in his buggy, and the horse was pawing to be off. Mother Mary of Providence, smiling warmly, called goodbye to His Excellency. But the Bishop ignored her; with a flick of his whip, without so much as a glance at her, Bishop Beaven was off and away. The General Superior, keeping her frozen smile on her lips, went back into the Motherhouse.

No one ever had really been happy about affairs at Farren Memorial Hospital, and the original fears that Montague City was too isolated, were being confirmed in most absolute fashion—and no cholera or malaria to save it!

Now increasingly, Mr. Bernard Farren was annoyed. He could not very well fail to perceive that his hospital was a stepchild, that the three other institutions of the diocese were preferred over his venture. What he may not have realized was that to date, his promised endowments had not materialized, and that the General Treasurer of all the institutions was growing desperate. She too had her dream—of a great new and worthy Motherhouse at Brightside, but that seemed far away after the tightened money of 1907, after the new and unexpected financial obligations.

He did not realize how she was attempting to answer his complaints, when she parted with Sister Emmanuel and sent her up to be Superior of Farren Memorial losing thus her friend, her companion. But Mr. Farren was wrothy indeed, when in desperation the Superior General, deciding that she must put the relatively useless and impecunious facility to some practical purpose, sent her novices there, and made it into a novitiate.

Almost immediately a formal complaint came, not from Mr. Farren, but more stingingly from his attorney. It read:

Philadelphia, February 28, 1907

Right Reverend Thomas D. Beaven, D.D.
President of Farren Memorial Hospital,

Right Reverend and dear Sir:-
Mr. B. N. Farren, whom I represent, has directed me to notify you, that, whereas he has recently learned from an authoritative source, that at a special meeting of the Board of Trustees of the Farren Memorial Hospital, lately called and held for the purpose, it was voted to permit certain novices of the order of Providence to occupy a portion of the Hospital and other buildings included in the deed of the hospital; and whereas such use and occupation of said buildings is in violation of the conditions contained in said deed, he therefore enters this, his protest against such use and occupation of the said buildings, whether temporary or permanent.

Yours most truly and respectfully,

Robin MacDonald

232

There were months of unpleasantness after that, though ultimately the Bishop's legal aids won, asserting that these young ladies were in preliminary training to be nurses and thus legally came under the terms of the original **contract**.

But Bishop Beaven was not overly pleased by Mother Mary of Providence's apparently single and unadvised action in founding a novitiate in Montague City. With *noblesse oblige*, he backed and supported her, but his decision was firm from this time on, to take matters legally as well as canonically out of her hands. And there was a more personal thing going on that distressed him to a degree.

As in former days, Mother Mary of Providence constituted herself once more, the actual Mistress of Novices. Now she was constantly at Montague City, directing the formation of the young aspirants. What was she telling them, Bishop Beaven wondered? What kind of spirit was she giving them?

The question was not without pertinence, though the foundress attempted to teach the gentle spirit of St. Vincent by example rather than words, and to retain the more ancient actual poverty of her nuns by necessity rather than by precept.

They had no money. They existed mainly on blackbread and molasses—at least, that is the diet they remembered later. On Sundays they had dessert—an apple or an orange, and during most of the meals they were rushed to finish even their meagre diet, until at last, before the novices were through, the Superior General would signal for the dishwater for the older and more rapid members of the community.

One Sunday there was one orange, and that, at Mother General's plate. In the silence of the meal, broken only by the adenoids of the reader, Reverend Mother peeled and sectioned the lone orange. So each little nun had a section, and that was that.

If she taught discipline to others, she tried very hard to discipline herself in tiny ways that she hoped would not be noticed. Only some were. Her nuns at Brightside caught her out in one such penance, noting that when she returned to Mt. St. Vincent and climbed the hill, she never once paused or looked back until she reached the summit. Then she would stop and gaze on the gorgeous view. When they spoke to her

233

of this habit she said, "Let it be so of life. Do not look back until the work is done." They understood.

Though they had won the Farren suit, it was not until May, 1909, that Mr. Farren to his lasting credit, personally ate humble pie and voluntarily sought an agreement, and so the twenty-first day of May the trustees accepted his requirements as set forth in a second indenture, duly executed by both parties, and the entire arrears of annuity in the sum of nearly ten thousand dollars was paid in full.

As Treasurer, it was a great relief to her. She repaid the Chancery seven hundred dollars for insurance policies and reallocated the rest of the fund toward the once impossible dream of a Motherhouse.

Oh yes, things were better for a little while. But the year had not closed before the Bishop came down with his instruction. It was a far cry from the day when he had appointed Mother Providence as a financial committee of one. For the instruction said that, dissatisfied with the Bylaws of the Corporation of the Sisters of Providence of Holyoke, he now informed them that in the future, under a new legal instrument, perceiving that at present, with the exception of the Bishop of Springfield who ex-officio is President of the Corporation, the ruling Board which now consists solely of the Sisters of the Congregation—from henceforth and hereafter, as is the case with other Corporations of Sisters, an equal number of Diocesan Clergy, to balance the Sisters, would have equal voice on said Board.

So. Once the clergy have financial power, they rapidly assume dictatorial power in all other areas. Mother Mary of Providence knew and infallibly foresaw. No longer would the Sisters really own their own corporations, no longer could they dictate their own policies. In the years to come, she knew this opening wedge would bring laymen and physicians into the true governance of her religious community.

Very well. It was determined. Divine Providence must know what it was doing. And so she would, with all her might, implement every decree of the Bishop. Perhaps at last, he would believe that she practiced the virtue of obedience, no matter what it cost her. He was a good man. He now spent so much time with his aged, and he had already poured into his Home and its grounds over one hundred thousand dollars.

Her obedience and implementation of Bishop Beaven's commands are documented throughout that year; he wrote, and she implemented his decrees.

Chancery Office,
78 Elliott St.,
Springfield, Mass.
March 28, 1910

Rev. Sister M. of Providence,
Rev. and dear Sister:-

Will you take upon yourself to bring to the attention of all the Sisters the following recommendations over our signature.

Sincerely yours in Xt.
Thomas D. Beaven,

Whilst it is not possible for our Communities engaged in the active works of charity to follow the letter of Ecclesiastical Law, in reference to "Cloister" it is within the power of our religious to know the letter and imbibe the spirit of the "Law of Cloister." Consequently, in order that this spirit may be emphasized with our Sisters, we hereby make known our wish to have all our Sisters within "Cloister" before sundown.

We also insist that the Superiors of our respective Houses appoint two Sisters, with the approbation of the Mother Superior, to care for outside "shopping" and that no exception be made to this regulation except through the Mother Superior. It must rest with her conscience and judgment to dispense from or modify this rule.

It is also emphasized that religious decorum and obedience demand, and upon this we must insist, that Sisters visiting any house of the Community must place themselves in obedience to the Superior; report the purpose of their visit and seek from her all permissions that are needed to see persons or visit departments of the house.

There is no exception of persons in this regulation, except the Mother Superior and her representative.

Thos. D. Beaven,
B'p. of Sp'g'd.

## CIRCULAR LETTER OF THE MOTHER SUPERIOR
in reference to the above.

Beaven Kelly Home,
Holyoke, March 31, 1910.

My very dear Sisters:

In submitting for your careful study, the letter of our Right Reverend Bishop, I must endorse its prescriptions by acknowledging that we have well merited the rebuke it contains. The Sisters have not taken seriously the injunctions issued by him several years ago, requiring that all be in their respective houses, *"in time for supper."*

My personal experience has been that they would linger, heedless even of my repeated reminder of approaching nightfall. In the winter season, darkness falls at an early hour; the cars are crowded with workmen and others, and it is unseemly for Sisters to be among them. The order now stands; *"Be within Cloister before sundown."*

Local Superiors are hereby required to see that their Sisters notify the Mother Superior *in writing* of any violation of this ruling. Even in traveling on steam cars, we must bear this in mind.

"Shopping." At our last annual Retreat, warnings were given concerning this subject, but they were not heeded and our Sisters, especially in the immediate vicinity, have been in the shopping districts with unnecessary frequency. A little forethought would prevent these very frequent outings and bring purchases to a fixed period.

Our lack of religious gravity on the street has also attracted very unfavorable criticism.

"Visits." The restrictions placed upon promiscuous

236

visiting of our houses and departments are being gradually disregarded.

The Rule forbids us *to go into the offices of others*, yet some restless and meddlesome spirits habitually disregard this precept; others as soon as they arrive at their destination seek a "particular friend" and have been known to hold private conversations, even during the hour of "Great Silence," and in other cases, they enter and leave a house, without presenting themselves to the Superior, who receives no report from either party and who would deem it unduly severe, if enquiry or complaint were made concerning their visit. Such conduct is a violation of religious courtesy; injures fraternal charity; fosters particular friendships and sows discord in the Community, and it now becomes the duty of the Mother Superior to reprimand those, who may still continue, after the warning given in the Circular letter of our Ecclesiastical Superior. Local Superiors are henceforth under the obligation of seeing that those who come to their house, conform to the regulations herein imposed and kindly remind those who fail.

We must feel grateful to our Right Reverend Bishop for the practical interest and paternal supervision he deigns to exercise over the community and we should eagerly avail ourselves of this assistance in forming customs that will strengthen our religious character.

May 29, 1910—The Cloister Spirit

The work of soliciting donations at Christmas, should be conducted otherwise than by a personal quest; our Institutions should never be placed before the public, as acting in opposition to each other, in seeking charitable aid. Letters or newspaper notices would serve this purpose.

The recommendations of the above articles were accepted and *it was voted* that all such invitations should be referred to the Mother Superior and that all duties that call for visiting the houses of externs, shopping, raising funds, etc. shall be regulated by the

Mother Superior, with the local superior of the house interested.

May 29, 1910—General Chapter Enactments

THE CLOISTER SPIRIT: 1910

[This subject was presented to the Chapter in the following form:]

"We have had an experience of a strong tendency to go out of our convent seclusion without a true necessity. For Commencement Exercises—School Entertainments—Requiem Masses,—similar gatherings, the Sisters manifest a strong desire to go, and while it may be profitable for some to attend, and in other cases the Community should be represented, the Mother Superior is not always free to exercise her judgment, unless she is willing to give displeasure; the mere fact that an invitation has been sent, to a local house, seems to be regarded as an obligation to attend. It also seems unnecessary for the Sisters to supplement the truant officer, by calling at the home, to inquire for absent pupils. It is particularly objectionable to send young Sisters, and no one should be allowed to visit seculars, unless appointed to that duty by the Mother Superior.

It was in the spring that she went, as usual to Farren Memorial, to train her novices. As customary, she went first to Sister Emmanuel's office. It was empty, but that was not strange; the local Superior had many obligations. Yet there was an air of too much cleanness about it, too much order, and she saw, in the middle of the blotter, an envelope addressed to her.

Sister Emmanuel had defected, and by this time she had been legally married by some Justice of the Peace, to a man named Savage.

"Dear God, Have mercy on my child. I tried so to save her. I tried."

The Bishop knew all. Even that Sister Emmanuel had been unstable before her profession, and that, without his knowledge, she had been sent of all places, into the troubled waters of Farren Memorial. He did not attempt to hide his fury.

"You had a duty to tell me," he said. "A grave and moral duty. For neglect of it, you are profoundly censurable."

"I know," she said. "You are quite right. I was wrong." He was not placated.

She was wrong, she knew, but priests are protected from betraying those who confide in them by the silence of the confessional. There was nothing to protect religious women. Nothing.

It was not long after that.

The Community Chapter held its elections. The nuns were unanimous for Mother Providence's re-election, and the vote left no doubt.

"You will adjourn for a week. After that, and after a period of reconsideration, you will return . . . ." The Bishop spoke.

They assembled again. The Sisters of Providence of Holyoke, voted unanimously for Mother Providence's re-election.

The Bishop looked at the returns on the ballot. "I will now give you a choice. It will be between Sister Fidelis and Sister Vincent only."

Mother Mary of Providence would never forget the glances she received from her two loyal friends—the Mistress of Novices, Sister Genevieve, and the Superior of Worcester, Sister Ursula. She knew, when the votes were counted, that they represented the abstentions.

Mother Mary Vincent was the new Superior General.

Bishop Beaven did not mind when his remark was overheard by Sister Ursula. He said: "Now at last I have a spiritual woman who will do whatever I tell her to do." He was correct. Mother Mary Vincent's great virtue was meekness.

Back in her own office, cleaning it up forever, Mother Mary of Providence knew what she must do, and quickly. She must save the community. She must fight for those who loved her.

A knock came at the door, to test her, she knew. She met the two maenads who had been Sisters Genevieve and Ursula.

"We won't allow it," they said.

"Oh yes. You must. The Congregation is more important."

"It isn't the Congregation we entered, and you know that."

"Sisters," their Reverend Mother commanded, "I forbid you to support me. I forbid you."

239

Sister Genevieve said, "I wouldn't respect you if you didn't take the attitude you are taking. But we cannot obey."

Sister Ursula said, "We can't obey you in this. You see—you have no authority. Oh Mother. Mother." They were weeping in each other's arms.

Yes. She knew what she must do. The quicker the better. And she was on her way before her stunned community was well aware.

She left them a letter and on reading it even some of her daughters who had been disaffected by her realized her greatness. They said and continued to say, "We admired her before, but on that day we discovered Joan of Arc."

She wrote them:

Farren Memorial Hospital June 11, 1910.

My dear Children,

I left you very abruptly yesterday, but thought it better to do so, than indulge the feelings that were struggling for utterance. I wish however to say a word of encouragement and commend you for your generosity, your attention to your religious duties and your bravery, even when your spirits may have been low. This is the time when you all will have an opportunity to do credit to me; not by a sentimental expression of grief, at changes that may be painful to your natural feelings, but by showing your supernatural strength. You have counsels and advice stored up in memories of the past conferences; you are sufficiently educated in all that concerns the religious life to be able to meet the present emergency and to look at it all from God's point of view, and the accomplishment of His Will. Let it be in the power of our good Bishop to say, that if I lived close to you, it was only to bind you more closely to your vocation. Although our relations may be somewhat changed, I shall carry every one of you in my heart, and shall give you any help, individually or collectively, that you may seek.

We have all reason to be grateful for the material help extended to us by Divine Providence, in our late undertaking. . . the Lawn party. Now let us turn our attention to ourselves and regulate our affairs, and even though you may not be called upon to render to me an account of your spiritual duties, remember that for this very reason, I shall expect you to be more exact.

We had a pleasant journey. I read steadily except for a few minutes when I dozed off, and we reached Greenfield at four o'clock. I was pleased to find Sister Mary Agatha waiting for us; she called a taxi cab and hurried us home, for which I was thankful because the air was heavy with dampness. It has been raining all morning. I did not rise with the others, for it seemed better to limber up somewhat; now I am rattling this off, as there will be few spare moments when I reach Brightside— for I can scarcely call it "HOME," for there is enough nonsense in my makeup to feel things that need affect only a sensitive young woman.

Now once again, if I have hidden from you all, any evidence of an aching heart, I wish you also to purify your affections and encourage one another; by rising to the occasion; looking on the bright side; and consider the many things that I can do to help, and the great relief it is for me to be exempt from the multitude of calls that a Mother Superior cannot shirk. I am happy but not heartless and if I am sometimes under the control of natural feelings it is rather for your sake than my own.

Perhaps I should not write thus to you, but some apology is due for the way in which I left, and I did not dare to trust myself to bring you together. My duties will bring me to you from time to time and even as I have always trusted you to do your best, in my absence as when I was present, I am so satisfied that what has been done is for your good and I look to you for help to bring about the results the Bishop and I expect. I hope that you have not neglected to offer thanksgiving for the good weather given us on Thursday, and now that the distracting duties of that affair are nearly over, it is your duty to draw into your cloister and not continue unnecessarily the acquaintances formed. We must use creatures only in so far as they help God's glory and turn from them when they have served that purpose, otherwise they will bring us down to their own level.

I expect the help of your prayers, to the end, that having advised others, I may not myself, fall into a pit.

As ever, Sister Mary of Providence.

# CHAPTER 18

From her retreat in Montague City, where the news traveled fast, there was nothing that she could do to counteract the loyalty to herself that was undermining her community. Sister Ursula and Sister Genevieve, first assistant and mistress of novices, had informed their incumbent Superior General that they were going to see the Apostolic Delegate in Washington to represent the illegalities of the last election.

How could Mother Vincent stop them? She was new, inexperienced in government; as far as she could see those two women knew more about protocol and rights of appeal than she did. If she did try to interfere, it would certainly appear as if she were hanging on to her own new position, and as if she clung to the honor, which she did not. She was never conscious that she gave them any permission, and was distressed because she knew that the Bishop had given none. Technically, she had simply not said *no*.

Sister Genevieve and Sister Ursula's money lasted them as far as New York. St. Joseph did not appear in Pennsylvania Station to help them further. Stranded and freeloading at St. Leo's House, which always takes in abandoned priests and nuns, they took stock of their situation.

Sister Ursula had the bright idea. "Cardinal Hayes," she cried. "The Cardinal of the poor! He'll send us on our way!" Sister Genevieve agreed.

They walked the long way up to Madison Avenue, carefully avoiding the danger areas east of Third Avenue to the river, where anything is liable to happen to you from the foreigners who existed there, and the ugly ditch above Grand Central, which they had heard about and did not know was now turned into a great mall known as Park Avenue, with the railroad under it.

They paid a little visit in St. Patrick's Cathedral, noting how significantly its spires soared above all the buildings in its neighborhood, as the spires of a cathedral should; and now rather wearily they wended their way to an interminable wait in the Chancery offices on Madison Avenue.

But the Cardinal saw them personally. If Cardinal Hayes was not as strikingly handsome close to as he seemed from the distance, clothed in his beautiful robes, way up in the sanctuary, he was just as kindly as they had heard he would be. He listened to them as a father should.

Then he said, "I think I quite understand your problem. The only trouble is that we Bishops are bound by laws too. I know that Bishop Beaven would do everything he could for you. He is my very dear friend. And a very kind man. I'm sure he listened to you when you presented your case to him." The nuns kept their poise; they only squirmed inwardly. "Now, as to his justice. If the Apostolic Delegate decides in your favor, I'm sure your Bishop will hold nothing against you for representing. Didn't he tell you this?"

The nuns mumbled, and the bishop went on. "Now as to your present Reverend Mother — I don't think I know her. I do know Mother Mary, of course. Magnificent woman. But it isn't good to stay in office too long. I'm sure it was just that. I'm sure that was what the Bishop had in mind. He thinks with Rome — a very good thing to think with Rome. But what did your mother—what'shername—say when she give you permission to come?"

Sister Genevieve tried. She said, "Well you see, Your Grace, I mean Your Eminence, if you know what I mean, we, well, I think you understand that we, well in a way, we thought that if we were going to see the Apostolic Delegate, if I'm not mistaken, simply we're going to a, you know, higher superior, and that we didn't need anybody else's permission."

"Oh dear," His Eminence sighed. Then he brightened. "Oh. Of course. The Apostolic Delegate gave you permission to leave your convent. I see."

It was Sister Ursula's turn. She looked beautiful in her confusion. "We're awfully sorry, Your Eminence. We didn't know we had to tell anyone."

"My, my. I'm sure that you didn't. But you really did, you know. Now in that case, you won't mind a bit, will you, if I call dear Bishop Beaven. He must be so worried about you,

244

and it will be better if he knows you are here with me. Besides, it's only fair I know what he thinks. I'm sure you can see that."

He personally reached for his brand new telephone, got central and she got Springfield before you would believe it. All he said to Bishop Beaven was, "Yes . . . No . . . Is that so? . . . Oh dear . . . I see." Bishop Beaven talked a great deal. When the conversation was quite over Cardinal Hayes, looking very benign, said, "I'm so sorry but your Bishop would like you, Sister, ah, Genevieve, to return as soon as you can to Springfield. He will receive you back very gladly, you may be sure. But now, Sister Ursula, I'm sure you understand, your Bishop feels that—" He tried to put it in kindly fashion "that you would perhaps be of greater service to God in the world. He advises you to seek a proper dispensation from your vows at the earliest opportunity so that you may again legitimately receive the Holy Eucharist."

The nuns were stunned, but it was sister Genevieve who recovered first. "I can't do that," she said with brave imprudence. "We both came for the same reason. We both should get the same treatment." Sister Ursula, speechless, caught her sister's hand and held it tightly.

"That is your own decision, my dear. Only be sure that you do not go to Holy Communion until this is settled. "And, his last words to them were full of compassion; "Be sure the two of you get enough money from our funds so that you are taken care of."

Sister Ursula as quickly as she could got herself regularized in the lay state and took up the life of the world. Sister Genevieve held out as long as she could, but her separation from her Lord in communion was too much for her, and she went back to the convent and to the community in Brightside. On April twenty-eighth, she made her submission for the twelve long days of her exclaustration, valiantly did her penance for over a year, but on August 25, 1911, this woman who was in her sixties, who had spent forty of these years in the convent, returned, with complete dispensation, to the world.

Mother Mary of Providence wept for her sisters.

For there were fewer and fewer of them now who

245

remembered Kingston and the spirit of the pioneers at Holyoke. The modern nuns admired the heroisms of the early days, but she found few who would be willing to live such a life. More and more, her nuns were finding joy and meaning in the intensely regulated routine of their cloister. Man finds happiness in pattern.

It was almost better when, after her isolation in Montague City, she returned to Beaven Kelly to take up residence and to be retained as General treasurer. However Bishop Beaven may have worried about the debts of the Sisters, he had approved of her retention in that office. Somehow, miraculously, that woman could get money.

At first she was embarrassed by the daily encounters with the Bishop, not only meeting on business matters but because His Excellency spent more and more time playing checkers with his beloved senior citizens. Gradually neither of them seemed to mind meeting. They were both quite civilized people.

She distracted herself by devotion to her task, laughing when she remembered what had been her fears and now were her advantage; that the ones who controlled the purse strings, controlled the administrative decisions. Also, she had now more time for the little things that she had always valued and even to rediscover her own natural family.

She had three growing nieces now — two in distant California, but one whom she had grown very fond of, one who lived here in the East. This was her surviving brother's daughter, her namesake, Katherine. She had met her when the girl was a child, and the little girl had called her "Aunt Kate." How odd! She had forgotten that name, as if it had never been her own.

She had said: "That will never do! Call me Aunty Providence." So the sisters became Aunty Providence and Aunty Dolours.

But now, definitely, except in Community, she was losing her religious name. To the world she was clearly Mother Mary. And in the Community she was now no longer Mother, but Sister Providence. Carefully she always identified herself as Sister, and she could not help it if her old subjects and novices slipped into the more familiar Mother. Only Mother

246

Vincent always, without any slips ever, called her Sister. Oh well, What's in a name? A rose by any other name. And she hoped that at least one of her three nieces would have another name some day, a religious name. She prayed every day that God would give one of them a vocation.

And then, the little things. She proved she could use a saw as well as a carpenter when they built the booths for the annual Brightside lawn party, a project of hers for raising funds for the dream motherhouse. She coached the young boys in the annual fund-raising minstrel shows, big projects that were put on to good profit in a big local theatre. One day she taught them how to dance to a tambourine, getting up on the practice stage, banging and shaking the instrument, and jigging to a fare-thee-well. Boy, could she dance!

Of course. She had seen people do it.

When the plans were on the table for St. Anthony's building at Brightside, she put a third story on it, and though the architect told her that the foundations could not support three stories, the building stood and did not topple over. Though it was something of an eyesore, the foundations supported it.

On the feasts of Corpus Christi, she built the outdoor altars and decorated them. And, by example, she could still teach, as on the day when she saw an unaccompanied sister, against the Bishop's orders, and her own, boarding a streetcar. She grabbed her cloak, sprinted down the hill, waving to Sister Michael's friend, the motorman, and scarcely delaying the car at all, leaped aboard to cheers. The Sister had a companion to and from Springfield. And why shouldn't she be able to run? As a girl she had at least raced her brothers. And she was only in her sixties now.

There was only one disadvantage in remaining young while everyone else grew old. Your friends died.

Each time she had seen him, she knew that he was allowing himself to get old. He was spry and vigorous, but mellowness and splendor did not seem to go well with Monsignor Harkins. There was no shock then when she heard.

She sat with the huge crowd on December 10, 1910, hearing the Bishop intone the High Mass, hearing the eulogy given by Father Ivers, one of Patrick Harkins' old and beloved boys, his former curates, joining with Father Harkins' close friends, all the city officials, most of the business leaders of the city, an aisle of Clergy and nuns, and where they could squeeze into the unreserved seats — the poor, the old, the needy, the loved ones.

She memorized, without trying, the Statement of Mayor Nathan P. Avery, "He has been one of Holyoke's greatest citizens. It would be very difficult to estimate the influence for good which he has exerted on the growth and development of the city and in the form and character of the men and women with whom he has come in contact. Holyoke and its citizens owe him a great debt of gratitude, and the only way that it can be repaid is by the reverence of his memory and the emulation of his sturdy and splendid virtues."

As the Mass progressed to the communion of the Priests, for none of the faithful would dream of communicating at so splendid a ceremony as a High Pontifical Mass, Mother Mary found that she had ceased to pray for Father Harkins, but was praying to him.

"Old friend," she said, "now that you are there, ask Our Lord and His Mother to make me love the Bishop of Springfield as now, at last, I love you. He is a good man, like yourself. I know it — but I do not feel it yet. Please."

Then she continued to talk to him, telling him, as if he did not know, about the great turnout, the mighty pageantry, the splendor of their laying him away. She knew he would have loved this. At her next confession to Father Stanton she confessed distraction in prayer during Holy Mass.

Monsignor Harkins was their friend, their first great friend, perhaps truly their founder. And the sisters knew how greatly he loved them when his will was probated, and they received $2,000 for the erection of a nurses' home on Dwight and Chestnut, where the old chestnut tree had stood, under which had been said the first Mass in Holyoke — the property on which the Sisters of Charity of Kingston had first set foot.

She never was given much time for mourning or for living in the past because within a month she was given the additional assignment of being supervisor of the new, highly respectable training school for nurses. She clutched the certificate as a trained nurse to herself, comforted herself by

248

the knowledge that there was scarcely a hospital in the East that she had not visited, or from which she had not pilfered knowledge and techniques, and threw herself into a whirlwind modernization of nurses' training. Her schools might be different, but they would be better.

The full realization of her dedication to the hospitals did not really reach the level of awareness, though, until she learned, without a pang, that a diocesan appointee, a Monsignor Madden, in a good gesture of efficiency, was concentrating all the primary education under Diocesan control with the Sisters of St. Joseph, and making the Sisters of Providence into exclusively hospital nuns.

She agreed that was better. As the older teachers died off, there would no longer be a dichotomy in the community — the learned teachers against the hospital workers. In the meantime, there would be heartaches to those who had given their lives to St. Jerome's, and must relinquish their life-work. How would Sister Michael take it? Well, she herself had had that wrench and had made two lives for herself without trauma. How many years as teacher and principal of St. Jerome's? And then the Superior had decreed that she make the hospitals her career, and the humor of it was that she herself had made the decree to herself, when she was Superior General.

She did not need to worry about Sister Michael, their greatest teacher. Sister Michael laughed louder, talked more constantly and turned her hand with joy to whatever tasks were assigned her, acting on the cry that she had a vocation to be a sister, not a school-teacher, and that it didn't matter to the Lord what you did, as long as you did it well. She was delighted that she could still work hard and wasn't on the shelf yet.

It was Sister Mary of the Seven Dolours whom Mother Mary should have worried about. She had not been a teacher at St. Jerome's for very long, but the teaching role was now her self-picture. And here she was, drudging in the kitchen.

She knew that her sister would not have dared so to degrade her. Kate always had some pride. But she would not put it past her to have put a flea in Vincent's ear. She began to fancy that perhaps Kate had whispered something about her having been a millhand. And she knew it was true, knew it when trying to be consoling, thinking only of the heroic work her sister had done with the poor, not for a moment reverting to the early days that she scarcely remembered, Mother Mary had said, "Oh Dolours, you have done far more lowly jobs than this! Christ and His apostles were working men."

Sister Dolours knew that she meant she had been a millhand. Round and round in her head, like a squirrel in the cage, as she did meaningless things like scrubbing and peeling potatoes, went the thought, until she could hear the very tone of voice her sister had used when she had said, "Who are you to complain? You were only a millhand." She heard her distinctly. She remembered it.

Sister Dolours' teaching career at St. Jerome's became the important thing in her life. And was it not Kate who had shifted them all over into nursing — educating and training herself and the others into hospital work, and never giving her any chance, she who had been a good nurse to the sick-poor, when there were no hospitals, deluding her with a taste of grandeur and removing her from the classroom? To this!

Surreptitiously she kept up with her reading. Who was it who had forbidden them to be literate? Besides, what was wrong with these books? She certainly enjoyed and got profit out of the works of Booth Tarkington.

Sister Mary of the Seven Dolours was almost unique in her reactions to the former Reverend Mother. Embarassingly her old subjects came constantly to Mother Mary. It was the only thing that rankled in the meek bosom of Mother Vincent. She couldn't help it if she was formidable looking, could she? She didn't feel formidable inside.

Yet what could Mother Mary do? Christ would not have turned them away.

They came with the question of names. She loved her own name, but now, to the public, she had lost it. She certainly knew what a name meant and what hair meant.

An experience with one little girl had summed it up. She had encountered this little redhead when she was helping out at a bazaar at St. Vincent's Hospital.

The girl had been attracted by the nun, who was fetching and carrying goods to the booths. The girl asked her name.

"Sister Mary of Providence. And I want you to come to Brightside. See what we are and what we are doing." Mother Mary was shameless in what she called "encouraging vocations."

Helen was both shy and confused, but her pastor said, "Mother Mary? Why, she's a wonderful woman. She could run a parish better than the pastors." Or a diocese, for that matter, he thought. "Go over to see her."

Helen went to Beaven Kelly. She was given the grand tour, the orphanage, a happy hour for the aged, the sweet-faced novices. She was introduced to a nurse from Mercy who had a vocation. On her second visit she was informed that she would enter the postulancy, that she had a vocation and must not trifle with it and that there was a class entering on the eighth of September.

"But I haven't even told my own mother," Helen cried.

"The sisters will pray for you," Mother Mary said.

The sisters did, and though Helen tried very hard to avoid her vocation and did not enter on the eighth, the Sisters' prayers won, and it was only the twenty-third before Helen arrived and offered her life.

All Mother Mary said was, "I see you got lonesome and came back."

When it came to naming her, Mother Mary said, "Oh, keep your own name. Helen is a nice name for a sister," and then, fitting her hair to be hidden under the postulant's cap, preparatory to be shorn for a lifetime, Mother Mary held it lovingly in her hands, and said, "Oh how am I ever going to hide all your beautiful hair under this little old cap?"

Helen had never liked her red hair before. Now she did. And when it came time to cut it, she could make a real sacrifice.

But as for the naming, there was a moment of terror. There was another Sister Helen among the postulants! Yet when they learned that Mother Mary had named her, our Helen was conceded the name, and the other poor little girl changed hers to something more esoteric and early-martyrish.

She kept Helen until vow time came, when she had to

submit three names to the great and authoritative Council. They rejected them all. Helen tried again and was told to take Gonzales. It repulsed her. She felt neither like a Gonzales nor a Pancho.

So of course she ran to Mother Mary.

"Well, all right. I can see that you can't have Helen — so what is next?"

"I have great devotion to St. Anthony. I asked for Antonita."

Mother Mary laughed. "Ita?" she said. "You're no more the type for a diminutive than I am or Mother Vincent. Can you imagine calling her 'Vinny?' We're women. We don't want 'ita' on the end of our names. Take Hildegarde. You look strong enough to be a Hildegarde."

Dutifully, it became Hildegarde. But writing about it fifty-four years later, Helen admitted that she never could identify with Hildegarde, though she tried, and she still thought of herself as Helen.

Yet as for her womanliness, she proved it soon. In the novitiate, constantly being shifted from place to place, at that moment the novices slept over the nursery. One night she heard the screams of a baby, stole down to the ward, and saw a big rat in the crib with the infant while their guardian nurse, a laywoman, slept serenely with her mouth open.

The rat turned on Helen-Hildegarde, but she got the rat out of the crib, drove it with a broom down its hole, blocked the hole up with the baby's toys.

Naturally, after breakfast she told Mother Mary.

"How good God was to send you the inspiration to go to that baby." Then she improved the shining hour in giving a lesson in the family secrets of the Sisters of Providence. "If that woman woke up and saw a rat, she'd scream it all over the place. God found you, a brave woman, and I know, a silent one."

Though stuck with the name Hildegarde for life, it did not interfere with the sister's devotion to Mother Mary.

There were so many other warm, personal things that Mother Mary could allow herself now. She liked to wander through the dormitories still used in the House of Providence. In other convents the nuns had their own cells, small, neat

252

and adequate. But here even the older sisters lived in a long dormitory, and Mother Mary, with perhaps a touch of nostalgia, loved them for their poverty and privation.

It was a large, well-ventilated room on the fourth floor, where the fifteen nuns quartered. She walked between the two rows of cots arranged lengthwise, and noted with pleasure the sparkling of the many windows. Each sister had her own washstand, a pitcher and basin of heavy crockery, and a screen that she opened at night, for privacy and for a clothes rack to hang her habit and unmentionables. Mother Mary smiled, knowing what it looked like at night and at the memory of the tale they told of the one night that a bat got in, thinking of how funny they must have looked scampering about in their checks and caps, and of the tall, brave one who captured the bat.

She knew too that sometimes the ventilation was extreme, as there were those who confused fresh with cold air and of how the screens would be blown over, and a ghostly figure would silently rise and replace them.

She knew also of the care of this dormitory, the Friday turning up of bedspreads, all blue and white, the chair upside down with the screen on the bed and how then each sister laundered her own curtain and vied with the others in the number of pleats she could succeed in making.

Mother Mary counted the pleats and congratulated the victor.

It was a very simple thing, but she had time for it now. And when she found that two of her young daughters danced a jig before an admiring public, she was glad with them and wanted to join, as she had in the old days in the kitchen on Dwight Street.

They were not unhappy years for her, though she felt sometimes that her deeper usefulness was curtailed, and also wished that she had the power to stop some of the abuses she felt were occurring. One of them, which hurt her, was what the laity called "The Slave Market." On certain Sundays of the year her orphans were taken to the larger churches, announcements about their qualifications were made from the pulpit, and the children were lined up for adoption. Sometimes some of the more attractive ones were taken immediately from the church, but the ugly ducklings went the rounds, Sunday after Sunday, church after church.

"Barbarous," she said of it. And her comment did not sit well with the powers.

On the other hand she was pleased that the Bishop approved of Father Tully's arrangement for assigning priests to cover the sessions of the Juvenile Courts and that he made recommendations for neglected children, truants and delinquents. Many a child who might have been ruined in the reform school was sent to the nuns at Brightside, and when some of the Sisters objected, Mother Mary was really angry.

"Where else do you want them to go, Sisters? Don't you really think they are better with us? And if they aren't, aren't you ashamed?"

Then she would go over and play ball with the youngsters, particularly with the naughty ones, walking back to their haven with one small black hand clutched in her right, one grubby white hand clasped in her left.

All in all, it was a happy time, until another of the Bishop's letters came. It was addressed solely to her, and it forbade her to visit the houses of her community, because it had been asserted that she was encouraging the confidences of the sisters and upsetting the proper order of subjects to their duly authorized superiors.

She was imprisoned at Brightside with her books and her ledgers, and no longer could she twit the local treasurer, looking at what she called "pigs in the basket" — her pet name for the all-covering *sundries*. During this time the pigs in the basket multiplied.

It was safe for her, the Bishop thought, to go to Boston to the State House and bring in the financial report. Then, and then only, could she take, as companion, one of the minor treasurers, and they witnessed of her visits, that the State House people said, "Here she comes! Now for our good time during business hours!" Actually, there was no loss of time. The companions noted that the Sisters' reports were approved as submitted. There is no evidence that they were in error or padded.

In 1916 World War I came, but it affected her own life very slightly. She could empathize with the younger nuns

254

though, and the days of the American Civil War and her **brother John's involvement,** John who had been killed in a snowslide way back in the California gold rush.

The year did mean something to her, though, something deep and hurtful.

It was the year of their elections. As before, Bishop Beaven presided. Silently, the nuns voted, and the recorder, in their presence, counted the ballots. There were two or three small heaps, and one was overwhelmingly large. Silently the Bishop looked at the result.

He brushed aside the large heap of votes. He looked at the second largest — a small number indeed.

"Sisters of the Diocese of Holyoke," he said, "I exercise my power of veto, over your first choice, and declare that Sister Mary Immaculata is your Superior General."

They all filed into chapel and were resigned to the will of God. Only Sister Mary Vincent was overjoyed. Mother Immaculata remained gentle and pious.

Mother Mary continued to sign all checks for the next two years. Always as Sister Mary of Providence. Never once, as "Mother."

As for the Bishop, his final dream of expansion to the West had come true. Father Charles Boylan of Pittsfield had died, and his will bequeathed 20,000 dollars to the diocese, for a hospital in that city — the Boylan Memorial. As usual, the sisters moved in before it was quite complete, and since there was already an adequate city hospital they made it into a maternity hospital — though again, not for long.

Cholera. Malaria. Influenza.

It was influenza this time that filled their hospital or rather forced them into the necessity of converting the Boylan Memorial Maternity Facility into a complete hospital. Within a year, for 35,000 dollars, the Allen estate was purchased, and a complete St. Luke's Hospital was begun, covering over the memory of Boylan by the end of a single decade with an ultimate merger.

Everything had progressed with relative smoothness in Pittsfield until the epidemic. There had been a gradual but encouraging increase in the admission of patients. Alterations were being made in the carriage house to provide quarters for

255

the sisters and the student nurses. It was expected that all would be in neat readiness by the close of the year.

Then the City Fathers descended upon them demanding that St. Luke's be placed at the disposition of the Board of Health for the care of influenza patients.

The nuns flatly refused. There were obstetric patients in residence. It would be evil to expose them to infection. And since other hospitals were crowded, since corpses were literally stacked up in graveyards, they must preserve some place for children to be born.

Their Board of Management agreed — for a more utilitarian reason. The Maternity hospital had been costly, and it was new and they did not want their admirable facilities cluttered up with the plague-stricken.

They came to a compromise. What was dangerous for the patients, would be adequate for the nuns. They allowed the influenza patients to be quartered with the nuns, in the renovated carriage house. The decision was made on Saturday. The workmen came on Monday. By Wednesday temporary stairways, doors, steam and plumbing fixtures had been installed, twenty beds were set up, and twenty patients were admitted. Bishop Beaven himself came up to assist, to give permission for some ameliorations of the rule; the Superior herself did the laundry work.

That year three of their nuns died of influenza.

Now with the war and the epidemic over, Mother Mary, as treasurer, dreamed more dreams of a true Motherhouse at Brightside, and when she was driven to Mt. St. Vincent, still in her old buggy, but now with a driver, Mr. O'Brien, holding the reins on old Nell, she could see her motherhouse from her blueprints, standing there already, majestic and impressive.

But it was still in the dream world of blueprints. For then she had to get $150,000 for a new wing on St. Vincent's, which of course, she did.

Then 1920 waxed into October. The coachman Mr. O'Brien became the last, as he had been the first, to pass over Chicopee Bridge.

Then on the fifth they received word of Bishop Beaven's death, and they knew very shortly that he had nothing left to give them in his will, having in his estate — he had given everything away while he was alive, and so much of it to them — less than five thousand dollars.

Mother Mary was sitting in her office in Beaven Kelly.

It was one of the last sisters from Kingston who found her there, knowing not quite what to say, but in her heart realizing that Mother Mary's early friend and her latest enemy was dead.

She was at a loss what to say, so she made her announcement simply and bluntly, without really looking at Mother Mary, whose head was down.

"Did you hear that the Bishop is dead?"

Mother Mary raised her head. No one ever had seen her weep before. Her eyes were full of tears.

"Our founder," she said. "My friend. And now I have no one left to tell me my faults."

## CHAPTER 19

Bishop Beaven had had only one day of immediate preparation for death. He had dated his experience of fatigue only from the time, three years before, when he had labored night and day during the influenza epidemic. But, though his doctors warned him, he would not give up.

He had read in a modern Catholic Poet, "A short life in the saddle, Lord, not a long life by the fire," but he had had a long and active life, and for his last years adopted the verses as his motto. Actually, he was preparing for another of his fatiguing trips to a confirmation in a distant town, when suddenly he had to sit down. He knew, and it was not necessary for the doctor to tell him that it had been a severe stroke.

"Thank God," he said. "Only my body. My mind is clear."

It remained clear for the twenty-four hours that remained to him, and it is noticeable and touching that he gathered his daughters about him, the Sisters of Providence answering the responses of the viaticum, praying with him, comforting him until he died. Loving him as he loved them.

There is no way of knowing if Bishop Beaven observed one necessary absence, for because of the last years, Mother Mary of Providence's presence would scarcely have been in good taste. If he thought of her then, he could not have had any qualms. He had done what he had to do, had lived to see his foresight approved by the stringent Canon Law, with the total Code approved in 1917, made public in 1918. Everything he had tried to do for his own Congregation, had been codified into law by Rome. And, as with all his contemporaries, he was proud that after all these centuries the massive task of study of traditional cases, the unwieldy body of laws that had previously governed the Church had at last been codified. Truly, such codification had been a monumental achievement, and the legal and the judicial mind had good cause to feel that this was one of the great moments in the history of law.

To have been one of the first to anticipate and then to expedite such a law, was sufficient achievement for one lifetime. If the Bishop's choice had been with Creon against Antigone in the tragic muthos, there must always be some who will sacrifice the person for the Great Good, and so he had been forced to do. For Bishop Beaven, no other decision had been possible. His devotion to the Church was his entire life; and he actualized that devotion in his paternal labors with his flock. That is why they loved him.

The nuns who were now at his bedside had never known other days. They wrote of his achievement as their founder; words that would make any reader of the chronicle gasp in wonderment, at how much they did not know of the labors before their coming.

Their account reads: "At the beginning of Bishop Beaven's Episcopacy, our institutions were limited to the little Hospital in the City of Holyoke and the Orphanage at Ingleside where boys and girls were domiciled. The House of Providence had small claim to the title, being little more than a refuge for the sick, where the Sisters gave such care as kindness and willing service could render.

"In the eighteen years of its existence no progress was possible in its limited condition, meantime the medical profession had made rapid strides and the Hospitals had taken up new methods; surgery had been completely changed in its procedure; Bacteriology in its relation to disease, especially surgical wounds; the sterilization of dressings and everything used in surgery were part of the Hospital service, and called for an equipment that demanded space together with a special training and knowledge of theories governing the Nurses' technique."

As the foregoing witnesses, the process of professionalism had achieved its result. But one may still remember that there had been work with the people of God, intimate, deep and holy; before these necessary, inevitable technical advances had supplanted the more intimate apostleship.

Though Mother Mary had not been with the Bishop in his last hours, she sat unobtrusively in the cathedral and felt, as she had at the funeral of Father Harkins, the wave of love that responded to her old friend, and she thanked Father Harkins for herself that the prayer to him had been answered.

259

As to their total dedication to nursing, Mother Mary now focused her whole life upon it, and the dedication was bearing fruit. It was a great honor when the American College of Surgeons chose to hold its annual meeting at Mercy Hospital in Springfield.

She had only one moment with Mother Valencia, who had attained with St. Francis what she had accomplished with Mercy.

Mother Valencia looked around at the impressive gathering. She asked in French, "How did you achieve it?" and Mother Mary replied "I fix." But Mother Valencia smiled the smile of one knowing that there had been a pleasantry, but no more. She did not remember. She was growing old.

But Mother Mary was not impressed, at least not favorably impressed, with everything. Particularly with that old humbug.

The old humbug was one of those terribly handsome and courtly Irishmen, who gave the impression that he came from a long line of fox-hunting squires. He had done the rather banal thing, of losing the faith at a Catholic college—for him, Holy Cross. Thank God he hadn't written a book about it yet.

Also, he was broadminded. He adored though did not agree with religious. In fact he was just about to take his sister, a nun, to her convent.

Mother Mary was standing at the top of the stairs, beaming goodbyes, when the Doctor spied her. And then, Glory be to God, he dropped to his knees before her with somewhat more grace than Sister Michael's friend in the streetcar, and attempted to seize her hand, to kiss her hand!

She managed to draw her hands under her sleeves, and then, with the projection of a Duse, she said, "Get off your knees, you old goat!"

The last thing she heard was the hearty, obese laughter of Mother Valencia, who had never in her life been impressed with anyone. She got this joke, anyway, and she would tell it with relish all over Hartford. The humor hit Mother Mary, and she had to leave, she was laughing so hard at herself and the Doctor.

More seriously, she knew from all that was going on, that another great advance was in the offing. She knew that

260

planning was in progress to have amalgamated to the larger organization of doctors a New England conference of Catholic hospitals. It would be a great forward step, and she was a leader in the long and careful planning that would make it meaningful.

All other things were of course only a distraction to the Providence Sisters compared with the rumors of who would be their new Bishop and, consequently, their appointed Superior. Most of them had never lived under anyone but Bishop Beaven, and as one of them said, "To the majority of the nuns, Bishop Beaven had been God."

They were happy, in the main, when Thomas Mary O'Leary was appointed from Rome. He was not a tall, commanding man, like their late Bishop, but he had great suavity, the fresh complexion of a child, and he covered a slight lisp by a deep and totally episcopal *basso profundo*. Of course, most of all, he was known to be for them indeed partial to the Sisters of Providence. His great personal friend was Sister Mary Consilii, a very able woman indeed.

Their hopes for his interest in them were confirmed and continued. He celebrated his appointment by saying Mass for them at Mercy Hospital and breakfasting with the Sisters. After that, the local superiors paid their formal obeisance. The nuns went en masse to his consecration and held a special feast on the following day. On September 15, 1921, he professed a class of five Sisters of Providence, and on November first blessed the new wing at Mt. St. Vincent and formally dedicated the new wing at St. Vincent Hospital on the last day of November.

Mother Mary of Providence alone knew what the new wing cost. Four hundred thousand dollars. For a wing! So this was what they meant by the H. C. of L. — the high cost of living. Because of all these debts, the Motherhouse still appeared as a blueprint.

Though the rise in prices was scandalous, still there was more money around than Mother Mary could ever remember. Now that, incredibly, her fiftieth jubilee in religion was about to occur, she looked back a little more often at the poverty she had found in Holyoke, compared with the wealth that the Irish Catholics had amassed so rapidly. There were many

261

of them now who were very, very rich and had moved out even to Longmeadow, building "castles and palaces." Also, and she rightfully took pride in her own race, they had attained along with their money, an easy and real culture; their taste was good; they were well read; they had artistic and civic interests; and above all, they were charitable, as she well knew. In one generation the Catholic Colleges for men and women had raised the cultural and educational level from a minimal sixth grade reading-writing-and-rithmatic standard to a huge professional caste, and, in not a few cases, into the baroneties of big business and colossal wealth.

With some exceptions, the Catholic fortunes were not old enough yet, secure enough, to justify the huge legacies that old American families could appropriate to educational and hospital institutions. Catholic facilities did not have massive endowments as yet. But the sisters had paid four hundred thousand for just a wing. Boston College had moved out from its firetrap on Harrison Avenue and was building great Gothic buildings above the twin reservoirs of Brighton, becoming the Oxford of America. Holy Cross, on the hill of Pleasant Springs, had first added Beaven Hall, a great red-brick building, attached to, but dominating Old Fenwick, for years, their only building. And now modern dormitories were rising. She saw clearly, in that sign, another thing that was happening. Holy Cross was developing into the rich man's College, having sons of its alumni now; Boston College was still the poor man's College, a day school without boarding facilities with the great majority of its students being still first generation college people. Well—she sighed and regretted it — her own nuns had no poor man's Hospital any more. Inevitable. It was the times.

True, the Church's law, now more stringent than ever, made amalgamation of the religious cultures almost impossible because it forbade marriage among Christians of different denominations, a law of which Mother Mary, along with her contemporaries, thoroughly approved, though as a nun it scarcely affected her personal life. The stringent interpretations of the Tridentine Tametsi decree declared that, though admittedly the Sacrament was between the two contracting parties who administered it to each other, yet by a strange paradox the Church declared that this central contract was invalid—not illicit, mind you—unless the main witness was a Catholic Priest. Hence the faithful always said, "Father So-and-so married us," and only the most careful and pedantic of clergymen did not say, "There's a couple I married." The insinuations, for a celibate, were a cliche and standing joke.

The bars were as strict as the laws against the miscegenation in the South. Some few broke the barriers and were cast out; many wangled a dispensation, which could only be granted to slipshod Catholics, whom the priest suspected would run to a justice of the peace if he did not marry them. A few defied everything and went to a Protestant Minister.

Of those who had properly married by way of legitimate dispensation, Mother Mary was most attracted to Mrs. Virginia Creighton, now of Longmeadow, who had married into the Protestant branch of the Woolworth family, married a much older widower whose sons were embarrassingly as old as their stepmother. But the young Mrs. Creighton loved her husband. Her sacramental life, her prayer life Mother Mary felt was like that of the canonized princesses in the Ages of Faith. That Mrs. Creighton was closer to Sister Consilii than to any of the other nuns, was all right. But Mother Mary felt happy in her presence, and was not unaffected by her subtle and delicate perfumes, the texture of her chinchillas and minks. She knew, truly, that it was not vanity that kept the beautiful Virginia Creighton careful of her beauty, but because it pleased her husband. Mother Mary had read in a moral book that this was a motivation that a good and pious woman might follow, to the glory of God. Mother Mary liked Virginia for another reason beyond her beauty and piety. She was of her own background, of the Canadian McGills, and Mother Mary rejoiced to hear her speak, with that perfection of easy enunciation, which her own ear had captured in Kingston, and which now made her acceptable to the new ladies of culture.

In addition to her perfect speech, Mother Mary found that the new ladies, even of the St. Agnes Guild of Worcester, accepted her for another reason. The ladies were all conversant with Wall Street. They were always comparing the market with each other, now, getting and giving tips, authorities on bears and bulls, cutting coupons. And Mother Mary knew more about tips on the market. Actually, and shrewdly, she got tips from them, and knew, sometimes, before the men, when a merger was in the offing. The social acceptance of the General Treasurer was used only to help the General Treasury.

That Bishop O'Leary rushed to identify himself with the Community and with Mother Mary caused the nuns great happiness. His Excellency himself celebrated a pontifical Mass for her fiftieth anniversary. He had not known her in the days of her pioneering or in the years of her power, and he found her to be a reserved little woman, now at last a bit on the plump side, like a mother hen, making a little clucking sound that served for a laugh, her face round, and, having lost its sallowness with the loss of her dyspepsia, now in her old age, ruddy as it had never been in youth. But it was the straight, level glance of her gray eyes, penetrating, that Bishop O'Leary remembered; they went so oddly with her words and voice, which was gentle and musical. But he knew she saw him. Her eyes saw through you.

Quite noticeable to all were the numbers of drummers who paid their respects to her on her jubilee. She had never learned to treat their visits as if they were business; no more than when she was a girl, could she resist the romance of these far-travelling men.

For herself, she asked the Community for a jubilee gift, the not uncommon one of a little trip, though Mother Mary combined it with an official visit, as Delegate to the unveiling of the cenotaph before the Cathedral of St. Matthew in Washington. Also, of course, she could pay a visit to her favorite niece, Katherine, who lived in Washington.

The cenotaph honored the various orders of Sisters who had served as nurses in the War Between the States, so it was only fitting that her now almost exclusively nursing congregation should be represented. And then, from her niece she asked as a really personal favor, a self-indulgence, if Katherine could take her to the museum where the figures of the Presidents' wives, garbed in the dresses they wore at the inaugural balls, could be seen.

Charmed, her niece brought her there and wanted to hug her for being so human and feminine after so many years in her black and ugly dress.

Somehow, to Mother Mary, the dresses seemed to make up to her for the oblation of the gown and furbelows she had sacrificed just before she entered the novitiate. But her taste had improved through the years, and now it was the simple and rich off-red velvet of Mrs. James Buchanan that she admired, and in her own fancy, clothed herself in. As Katherine saw her aunt, here so totally a woman, she laughed at a secret joke, which she would not share, remembering a priest who had meant to be complimentary, saying that her Aunty Providence should have been a man. Really! He should get a glimpse of her that day.

On the way home, Mother Mary and her companion stopped off at New York on a little buying trip, just to make their excursion more business like. It was not for gowns, however, that they shopped; as General Treasurer she bought innumerable bedlamps for the patients.

"Bedlamps, indeed," Sister Dolours sniffed, as she peeled her onions.

But the nun to whom she said it retorted, "But she got them for half price!" And that ought to be rebuttal enough, though truly, the half-priced bedlamps overflowed the storage closets for a very long time to come.

Though her jubilee had been a great joy, it was only a year later that the amazing honor came to her.

She was not the Superior General, had not been for years. She was not even a local Superior. She was not the administrator of any great hospital. She scarcely had a valid diploma as a registered nurse. She was officially not Mother, but Sister Mary of Providence.

But when the New England Conference of Catholic Hospitals was begun on May 14, 1923, it was not one of the other officially great women, but Mother Mary who was, almost unanimously, elected as its first president and founder, and kept being elected till she resigned, not till seven years later, structuring it, forming it, making it respected and meaningful, in all its infant years. It showed, with all too great clarity, what her professional peers thought of her.

Emotionally, the honor did not make her glad but sorrowful. Why, she thought, must externs think so highly of me and those who know me best, put me on the shelf? What weaknesses do my sisters see in me that I can hide from others?

It made her try the harder not to take things personally, to overlook faults. When the boy, Al Logan, was to pick her and her companion up in Holyoke, and went instead to Springfield, she waited with her companion, offering up the lost afternoon, until five o'clock, and then, in obedience, took the before-supper streetcar. When Al came sheepishly in at six-thirty, she had a plate ready for him warm on the back of the stove and used up another half-hour sitting with him. And when she joined the orphans coasting on their sleds down the snowy hill and tore her habit, Al got up a collection amounting to fifty cents to repair it.

She thanked and laughed at them, bundling them into the kitchen of Beaven-Kelly where she made them taffy candy.

They had so little, she thought—so little childhood—and she could do nothing but be silent now, about the grimness of their time-schedule even now in the years of the new freedom.

True, she forgot that she had demanded that her nuns get up ten minutes earlier because they were so sleepy; she only remembered that she had let the children roam—and saw that now they had no time to roam. With distress she looked at their crowded horarium:

| | |
|---|---|
| 5:30 a.m. | Rising bell |
| 6:30 a.m. | Mass |
| 7:00 a.m. | Breakfast |
| 8:30 a.m. | School bell |
| 11:00 a.m. | Dinner |
| 1:00 p.m. | School bell |
| 3:30-4:30 p.m. | Recreation |
| 5:00 p.m. | Supper |
| 6:30 p.m. | Preparation |
| 7:00 p.m. | Prayer at bedside. Sleep. |

Neither exercise nor air. Not much time for fun, for being

266

boys. But there was nothing she could do except tear her habit on their sleds, play baseball with them during the spring.

Her nuns though were at last being allowed vacations, and though they were strictly among themselves, there was a freedom from the wasting routine and a change of view from the month by month, sometimes year after year, monotony of their missions. In 1928 the Community sent a few at a time to the Beach at Westerley, and for the first time in many years, Mother Mary among the others, though clothed in a Mother Hubbard bathing costume, apparently designed by the late Queen Victoria, felt the tingle of salt water. Thank God, they kept up the custom of sending the nuns off, after that, for a whole week every summer.

And now, elections were coming up again, the first under the new Bishop, and the Community grew tense with wondering what would happen this time, so that the Sisters scarcely had more than a passing and approving comment on how the impressive and modern cozy hospital was coming along in Pittsfield, for the new St. Luke's was rising rapidly, to house everything, to replace poor old Boylan Memorial. And Pittsfield now, and the Berkshires were at the height of their glory. Very cleverly, timed to the moment of the opening of the new St. Luke's, Mother General Immaculata, the gentle one who had never reproved her for being Mother Mary, never bothered the nuns who cared to consult her, in anticipation of what she must have suspected would happen at the Elections, raised Mother Mary again, gave her the sanction of her own Congregation, and appointed her, at the age of 76, to be Superior of Pittsfield.

## CHAPTER 21

The Sisters of Providence of Holyoke did the right and the prudent thing, and elected as their General Superior, the Bishop's great friend, Mother Mary Consilii. In turn, the new General healed an old sore through the first decision of the Chapter, that the term Mother might be bestowed on all members of the Council, the Mistress of Novices, and all former General Superiors. Though it did not affect Mother Mary significantly at this moment, since she was again a Superior, the gesture was kindly, and all hopes ran high.

Mother Mary had always loved the Berkshires, which at that moment were at the height of their social glory. The great palaces had been built some years before, and now there had been time to draw the clear lines of social demarcation, which did not depend on the massiveness of one's fortune, but on a host of subtle things that only the denizens understood. There were those rich families who would never be invited anywhere; there were those who would be invited to large dinners; to small, more intimate dinners; and there were the highest caste of diners—those who were asked to lunch. Above these towered the sacred circle of house guests, those who stayed overnight, though one must be careful here, since even artists and musicians and Ethel Barrymore might occasionally be given hospitality. These transients could scarcely be counted. And of course there was always the horrid possibility of the momentary acceptance of politicians, if they happened to be Governors or Senators. But they came and went.

The curse of the Berkshires at that time was, "They are horrible people. They should have gone to Bar Harbor. No—they are so unacceptable, they should have gone to Newport." Such barbarians were never seen at intimate luncheons, but they wanted to violently. Some lived to see their children accepted; some succumbed to trauma and rejection. Some survived into the era of the Berkshires Musical Festival and the social collapse that accompanied it, which the Old Guard summed up: "Less enjoyment for more people."

268

As for the clergy, though their professional services were sought, they had about the same standing as politicians—their acceptance went temporarily with their assignments, save in rare circumstances where severe tests proved that they were in themselves gentlemen.

The Jesuits, against great opposition, had purchased the most magnificent of the Berkshire palaces, Shadowbrook, built by Anson Phelps Stokes, made to magnificence by Andrew Carnegie, from whose widow it was bought, though not easily. A petition to keep them out was eventually defeated by a counter petition to let them in, and since it was headed by Count Robert von Metz of Fernbrook, whose wife had been no other than Nancy Gates Ross and therefore unimpeachable—a Jesuit novitiate took over the most gorgeous estate in America.

Then the Jesuits behaved with great shrewdness, appointing as the first head, no other than J. Harding Fisher S.J., not only a saintly man and a brilliant man, but a great and easy gentleman. He in turn somehow got from the provincial of Maryland and New York no other than W. Coleman Nevils himself, former dean of the perfectly acceptable Georgetown University, as his Dean of Studies, and Father Nevils was not only a gentleman of the southern gentry but was also a strikingly handsome man. They carefully selected their staff, and a single year was the extent of tenure of anyone who did not measure up to the rigid acceptances of the luncheon groups.

Nearly everybody had received the Jesuits by this time—except for Mrs. Anson Phelps Stokes who had settled her family at the bottom of the hill and came into contact mainly with the Brothers who had charge of the farm. Her standards were not exactly the same as that of these good men.

As to nuns, you rarely saw them and never socially, unless they had positions such as Robert Metz described as Abbesses such as Mother Mary.

She was accepted. It was not quite certain whether she was French or Canadian Scotch-Irish, both legitimate, but her speech was perfect, and her inflections recognizable to the upper classes, both in French and English. Her manners in public meetings, even at banquets, were recognizable, and she commited no gaucheries. As to her clothing, well, she wore a uniform and all nuns looked perfectly alike, but then, the great ladies of the Berkshires looked perfectly dowdy all day long and blossomed out only into magnificence for dinner, and the evening. Overdressing was a Bar Harborism.

Mother Mary's acceptance had been helped by the Jesuits. They carefully dropped little comments like, "Mother Mary? Oh, she's a very great lady." Then on encountering her, Berkshire society discovered its own enconium for her, "She is gracious." She was.

As she tried to train her nuns in her own community, some of them were surprised at her values, when she said, "Be a lady, first." Everybody else had told them to be a perfect religious first, and that then all things would be added unto them.

So it was that Kate Horan of Belleville was accepted in the highest society of America and was asked to luncheons, invitations that she had to decline. It is no wonder then that in the dimming memories of her seventies, her father became more and more the owner of foundries, and her mother, at least, a fashionable milliner, and that her own postschool education seemed to imply private tutoring. Also anyone could now check on the fact that her California relatives were doing very well in Stockton and Long Beach, and that her nieces from Syracuse were Sacred Heart girls.

Socially, Mother Mary had the best of all worlds. No one else, she thought, could have the experience of being so close to people of all conditions of life. Berkshire society had walled itself in; admirable middle-class America could not go up or down for their friendships; the laborers could only hope that their children would rise into the professional class and be ashamed of their parents. But she could know everyone. Fortunately she was already a buddy of the workers of the building, for she had stood beside them admiring their skills as bricklayers, the precision of their carpentry, when St. Luke's had been in the building stage. Now, not deliberately, but because she liked them particularly, she had fastened on Pasquale Paduano (Patsy) and made him into total custodian of grounds and buildings, so that

270

really next to herself Patsy had all power. That he loved it as he loved her, whom he called "The Mud," led to a joyous intimacy, so that sometimes Patsy alone could tell the Mud, her faults.

He was only shocked with her once. His Italian Church, Mt. Carmel, was putting on a minstrel and wanted to repeat it for the nuns and patients, but Patsy had heard some of the jokes. He told the Mud not to let the holy ears of the Sisters listen to such things. Mother Mary overruled him, and the minstrel came, jokes and all. He was really disedified when the Mud laughed at one he thought was off color, and then the Sisters followed suit with a titter. But he supposed—and hoped—that they did not get the point.

Perhaps Bishop Beaven had been right and that they must maintain the myth that the laity invented, that even nuns engaged in the most somatic areas of hospital work, should know nothing about life or could not laugh at the things that were as funny. In any case, Patsy represented a multitude of others who could not make the distinction between ignorance and innocence. They were always amazed when a nun revealed an elementary knowledge of human frailty; and they constantly assured priests that they were totally ignorant of carnality.

This disapproval did not destroy Patsy's devotion. When he got a big sliver in his thumb, he went to her like a child, and she gave him a slip for Emergency, but they put a massive bandage on it, so he went back again to the Head Lady and wagged it at her. She took one look at it and said, "They're wrong. We don't have shares in the bandage industries," and she removed the windings and repacked the bandage, throwing most of the material away.

"Thanks, Mud," he said, "now a I do a my work."

As for her other great friend, she dragooned him into her household. She had her eye on a mechanic at the City Garage, Ed Broderick, whom, she knew, was getting the exorbitant pay of 54 dollars a week. Naturally, he turned down her offer of 30 dollars for the job of ambulance driver and community chauffeur. She raised the offer to 35 dollars plus free hospitalization for Ed and his family. He never could understand why he accepted and put it down to the

271

power of nuns' prayer; but he took the job, and with some raises, he kept it until 1955, just about thirty years.

At first he could not quite understand her. The hospital had been given a Cadillac by a rich man in North Adams, and Ed Broderick knew it was intended mainly for Mother Mary when she had to hobnob with the rich. Yet she would not ride in it, and he had to get out his own old open Dodge, even in the dry cold of the winter. One day, he fooled her though, bringing up the Cadillac for her, and when she asked him he tried to say that the Dodge was wheezing and grunting, and he was afraid of her.

She saw through him, though, and she said, "You're the most cheerful liar I ever met," but she did get into the Cadillac. Once in a while after that he could get her into the Cadillac, until the Dodge died one day with a wheeze, and the Cadillac was old enough anyway to transport a lady who was poor.

For her own daughters of St. Luke's Community she reinstated the old warmth she had maintained at Dwight Street. Fortunately, she was far enough away from the Bishop and Mother General not to have the cocoa parties reported in detail, and though she had a note or two from Mother Consilii, advising her not to be too liberal, she was not expressly forbidden to send a tired looking nun up to the roof for a breathing spell or from saying to the one who broke the expensive glassware, "Little Sister, glass breaks." But with each note from the General Superior, she hesitated a moment before opening it, afraid that she would find a command to stop her from allowing the nuns to dress up in funny clothes and have a little party by themselves. "I just love a parade," she said. The ingenious things they could put on over their habits were a caution!

It was not, of course, all fun and frolic. She had, as Mother General, started an educational program for her teaching sisters, but now she knew that anyone capable of further education should get a college degree with a Nursing Major. She did not find any great warmth in Mother Consilii's replies, but she did get three or four of her nuns during the latter years down to Boston College during the summers. Shrewdly, and almost on her own, she sent three of her subjects at a time, for instruction in Spoken French, which would help them, she was sure.

She startled the nuns one day at conference. "I wish I were General again," she said. One was certainly not supposed to say a thing like that, since it lacked humility. After they had gasped inaudibly, she went on "to undo some things I did then. You know, I actually forbade them to drink too much coffee! I just want to tell you that the coffee pot is on every battle station at all times. There were other things too."

She went on to enumerate a few of Bishop Beaven's rigidities. She made them very funny, and never once implied that they were not exactly originated with her. Only some of the older nuns smiled knowingly.

Her old habit of calling the nuns into her office continued, only now she would say "I have something nice to show you," and pray that she would find something.

The coffee was not only for the nuns. On cold days, mail carriers knew enough to make a beeline for Sister Sebastian's office where the coffee steamed. It was there also that the traveling salesmen sipped, chattered, and went away with an order. To her they all still smelled of the spices of Araby.

Of course too there was the day when the young nuns got caught in their prank. Some one of them, a more erudite one, must have met with the Merry Wives of Windsor, for somehow she lured a fine fat Falstaff of a young nun to hide in the linen basket, and of course, Mother Mary came along. She was always being helpful, so she tried to push the covered basket into the elevator. Naturally it would not budge, and naturally she uncovered the Krupps Works nun.

"Oh," she said, "if it isn't Mother's little vixen." The fact that the vixen was Sister Mary Mechtilde, ten years later the terror of probationers, only added to the glamor of her myth.

A year had gone, but for the great joy that finally came to all of them, many a year had gone.

How long had it been since there had been any *rapprochement* with Kingston? Half a century? The Sisters of Charity of Kingston and of Montreal had reconciled within three years. But it was not until 1927 that the first warmth between the mother community and its revolutionary stepchild of Holyoke was manifested. Though the actual visitation to

Holyoke came on the part of the Canadian sisters, the role played in the reconciliation by Mother Consilii must not be underestimated, for it was she who paved the way and she who invited the delegates from Canada. God bless them, they came.

Nor must one discount the diplomacy of Mother Consilii. The first return visit, the first delegate, was the foundress, the revolutionary separatist, the rebel, Mother Mary of Providence who was sent to Montreal—and to Kingston, symbolically declaring the roots of the Sisters of Providence of Holyoke. It was Mother Consilii who planned this.

Mother Mary could go home at last. How many years had it been since she had suffered from nostalgia? Ever? Or forgotten. Yet she must have, she returned with such joy.

It is Ed Broderick's account of the trip, which survives.

After the visit of Mother Mary Clement and Sister Mary Immaculate Conception of Kingston, Mother Mary of Providence and Sister Mary de Chantal, Providence Sisters (Diocesan) of Holyoke returned the visitation.

As Ed Broderick tells it, Mother Mary lost no time, though she did go in the Cadillac. First she stopped at the England Brothers, and when she came out on the arm of Mr. England himself, Ed said, "Where did you get the boyfriend?"

She said, "I just gave him an order for 1,000 sheets. I already owe $450,000 on the hospital. But that will be paid within eighteen years. As for Mr. England's sheets, he knows he will get the order quicker if he takes my arm." Now, she might allow chivalrous gentlemen to kiss her hands.

Actually she had got Ed out of an authentic sick bed. He had the flu when she called him about a little trip to Montreal. The fact that he went and felt better with each mile, contributed to his later belief in her miraculous powers. When they got to Montreal and the old lady insisted on carrying their bags in, he knew she was holy; but when she got him a good pint and told him not to see them till Thursday, he knew she was a saint.

He also saw the power of the woman. The body of the Bishop who had baptised her—from Ed's highly improbable account, since such a Bishop would have been well over a century old—but a Bishop, in any case, was in a locked room,

but he got it unlocked for her, and in she went—the last to
see him until he was on display in his casket in the Cathedral.

According to Ed's account of the trip, it must have been a
slow one because they stopped at every Church they passed
to say a prayer, but perhaps if we discount *every* church, we
get some idea of the peregrination. Time was saved,
however, by her thermoses of coffee and tea and her box of
crackers, which served for lunch. To skip a bit, the return
journey was not without incident. In the States, there was
Prohibition, and, as it happened, the pharmacy was out of
alcohol. Eddie got five gallons of it cheap in Canada, and the
nuns wrapped a blanket about it and put it at their feet.
Actually, they were waved through Customs. But then a car
started to follow them, just beyond the border of New York
State. If Ed speeded up, the car did. If he slowed down—the
car did. It was the bootlegging, no doubt. Well, they must
face it. Ed stopped, and the car stopped beside them.

It was a man from the Berkshires, a Mr. Courtland Bishop,
looking as usual, remarkably like an amiable walrus. He had
recognized Mother Mary. They passed the time of day, and
went on. Glory be to God!

Between her going and her return, Mother Mary had a
beautiful time. At Kingston they had humanized the old
novitiate, putting large verandas around it, making the
internal military court into a garden hung with flowers. Ed
drove her to her hill so that she could walk about the
restored Fort Henry and stay for the pageantry that preceded
the furling of the colors. She stood on the hill in the sunset,
looking again at the thousand islands, seeing once more,
Champlain and his chevaliers coming down the river.

For the first—and last—time she went to Belleville. It had
not changed much through the years, but both her houses
were gone as well as the little school, but it still was no
Kingston. Better, however, than places, one old friend
remained, indeed her only real school friend, the girl whom
she had put between her and the boy, as they walked home.
Emma was now Mrs. Pickett, hale, hearty, and a greatgrand-
mother, and gloriously still as young as Mother Mary. Odd,
she thought, there were no years between their meetings, and
she told her old friend her two ambitions—to see herself

275

safely in the coffin with her habit on, assured of perseverance, and an old whimsey, to know the little girl, still in the world, who would later bear her name—Sister Mary of Providence. Emma, wanted only to keep her senses until the end—and to go quickly.

Had they been superstitious, the women would have attached some significance to their discussion of death and the news which reached them.

One day the old lady, Sister Mary Dolours, had finished her kitchen duties at Beaven Kelly, leaving everything spotless for the morning, as became the house of God. She made her visit to the Blessed Sacrament, went to her cell, and after she undressed and got into her checks, she folded her holy habit carefully, arranged her rosary in the form of an M, made an act of contrition and the sign of the cross, and went to bed. As always she offered her fatigue from her kitchen work and the rejection which it symbolized, to her Divine Spouse, and, for comfort, touched and held her symbolic wedding ring.

Sister Mary of the Seven Dolours went to sleep. She did not awaken.

Mother Providence received the word. Odd lives they had led! She herself had spent a year of postulancy in the kitchen while her sister had been glamorous by traveling about. Mother Mary had not been assigned to scullery duty, but to the Berkshires while her sister——.

God was good to her, Mother Mary thought, taking her sister while she was at Belleville, where the past was brighter than the present. She envied Elizabeth too. She was with her mother and had left her here to wait.

She wept for her sister. Not for Sister Mary Dolours, but for the beautiful girl who had gone proudly to the mills, who had found joy and meaning in Kingston, for the young nun whose tales had inspired little Kate.

Sister Mary of Providence wept for Elizabeth Horan.

When she returned to Pittsfield in September, she had her hands full, because as President of the Catholic Hospital Association, she had planned a series of conventions at various institutions and now had to inaugurate them. Organizing a convention was child's play to her, and the kind of thing that, as a great show-woman she enjoyed. At St.

Luke's she chuckled when she overheard one of the pompous delegates say, "What can that old lady know about hospitals?" She did not hear the sequel, when, as they were leaving, the same delegate said, "She knows more than the rest of us put together." By some miraculous means, by this time, it was true.

In 1928, poor old Farren Memorial had a new wing, and as usual, Farren was overshadowed by the great significance of the breaking of sod at Brightside, for Mother Mary's dream—the Motherhouse. How long that had lain on the boards at the drawing table! Now it was to be a reality. The actual Motherhouse, she knew, would rise not even under her guidance as Treasurer. Credit for the actual building, the great, overpowering building, would go to Mother Consilii.

Mother Mary's interests seem to have been more personal and individual than the more massive commitments she had had until now.

"I know one person at a time," she said then. "I do not know ten thousand." Her individual interests were symbolized in Helen.

She had met the little girl once when Helen was in the play the orphans put on at Brightside, and Helen, in character, had stamped her foot, to which Mother Mary reacted audibly from the audience, "And that's that." But her real decision came when she heard from her old friend, Mother Visitation, that some horrible people had decided to take Helen into their home, but not to let her eat with them, not to allow her to go to school.

With that, Mother Mary decided to take her. She interviewed the girl, found out about her other orphaned siblings, asked her if she could darn her stockings and put in patches, and the too-quick affirmations of proficiency did not fool her a bit. Mother Mary accepted her, but not quite as she was. Cootie-garages had been bad enough, but now, as the twenties progressed, you could not tell the boys from the girls, the way the girls were bobbing their hair, wearing stockings rolled while the boys wore long fur coats and great baggy pants that made them look like suffragettes. What Mother Mary said was, "When you come to be my little girl, you'll have to let your hair grow." Then, turning at the door, she asked, "What are you going to be when you grow up?"

Helen said promptly "A Carmelite." Mother Mary chuckled, thinking that in that improbable case she would have to cut her hair off again.

On July 28, 1928, Helen arrived at St. Luke's in the Cadillac, bringing with her all the worldly possessions that Sister Mary Damian had given her, and that bulked large to Mr. Broderick. "You brought everything but the kitchen sink," he said. But Mother Mary took one look at the dresses, and knew that they would never do, at least not in the Berkshires. The dresses were numerous and could not very well be thrown out, but Mother Mary prayed that Helen would outgrow them quickly. They had hand-me-downs, had orphan asylum stamped upon them, and they were certainly not the thing when Helen took over the switchboard and was practically the receptionist at St. Luke's.

During Helen's stay at St. Luke's, through her courses at High School, Mother Mary showed interest, concern, and gave guidance to the girl—it could not be said that she ever lacked warmth. But though Helen saw her as a mother figure, there is no noticeable sign in their relationship of any deep or exclusive intimacy. What Mother Mary did for Helen she also did for many others. In fact, her attitudes seemed to be more on the disciplinary side, teaching Helen how to scrape a platter, catching her out with a great heap of unwashed and unmended stockings, checking her on her enunciation and making her open her mouth and not mumble. Yet in really feminine ways, she made her affection clear, with Christmas clothes ready and a little crinkly gray hat made of broadtail—but countering these special favors by crossing the chapel in the sight of all, and giving Helen her own prayer book, when she saw the girl dawdling, and checking her on her somewhat unworshipful posture. Yet when she found that Helen's fatigue was due to anemia, she was deeply concerned and put all the hospital staff and facilities at the disposal of her girl.

Wisely too she did not stress the idea of vocation, in fact rather ran it down, saying such things as, "When you go housekeeping you will have to——" And when at last a discussion on Helen's future became necessary, Mother Mary asked with sincerity, "It isn't to please me, is it?" She sent

278

her to Monsignor Conaty for guidance, in this case not trusting herself. Afterwards, Mother Mary took an even deeper interest in the girl's education, watching her success in school, getting a sister to tutor her when she lost time due to rather frequent attacks of illness and advising her to get a French girl to teach her French in exchange for English, as she had done herself in Watertown. The system worked quite well with Helen too.

The greatest kindness of all, and one which cost her something, was in her attempt to modify the increasingly exclusive love that the girl appeared to have for her—by bringing her brother to live at St. Luke's. It gave the girl a somewhat more expanded sense of family and of familial affection. She took every occasion to have Helen visit her sister Alice's home. Yet one act by Mother Mary gave Helen that sense of acceptance that she needed, and, like most awarenesses, the occasion was simple.

Just before her graduation from High School, Mother Mary called the girl into her office and spoke sharply. "When you came here, I told you to let your hair grow, and for a while you did. Then you went and chopped it off again. Now, young lady if you don't have long hair for your graduation, I'll not attend the exercises."

The rebuke had not only the effect of growing hair, but it did far more. Helen writes: "Up till now I hadn't realized that my graduation would mean anything to anybody else besides myself. *Mother was on my side.*"

The lateness of this awareness shows much about the care that Mother Mary took to keep the mother-daughter relationship at a healthy and cool distance, but that her interest in the graduation was personal was manifested in more ways than one. She demanded to see Helen's Graduation address, found it a little too informal, rewrote it in more classical eighteenth-century rhetoric, climbed three flights of stairs to hear it, and was glad that her daughter had learned to speak with her mouth open. And also that her hair was long and that the new white dress looked quite becoming on her.

Then after that, the Mother Superior gave the girl a rather straightforward talk, beginning it by saying that Helen had been too sheltered and that there was a fifteen year old girl here in the obstetrics department, in a private room, as it turned out, and, in some detail, explained to Helen how it came about that the father of the child of the fifteen year old was her own brother. "As you see," she concluded, "she hasn't been sheltered. So I want you to get to know her." The acquaintanceship revealed a great deal to Helen.

In the midst of Helen's education, the whole world changed, and the nuns' world with it, or so it felt, though the postwar era had only consisted of a decade, which ended suddenly with The Depression. The building of the Mother-house ceased and only the boarded-over foundation marred the hillside.

Mother Mary had had just time to make the transition from a large area of social betterment to the more Christ-like involvement with individuals, and she was ready again, doing more of the things she and her peers had done when she was a young nun.

The soup kitchen in the basement, with the constant line of the hungry who were never to be sent empty away, was a constant reminder of their old vow, now discarded, of service to God's poor. The closed and deserted mansions in the countryside, announcing the new poor, the parvenus who had not survived. Among her own nurses and probationers, there was, for the first time, a moment when those young people could remember real need.

The stories of her constant awareness of those needs and her tact in handling each case are testified to by five packed pages of anecdotes, and nothing is better documented in the whole long life of Mother Mary than this history of delicate charities.

There was the student nurse with holes in her shoes, who got ten dollars and was told not to tell—and who was informed a day later that she need not worry because someone had given Mother Mary twenty-five dollars, showing how God paid you back. Twenty-five dollars. A few months ago the benefactions ran into hundreds of thousands.

The student nurse did not have enough money to go to Boston to take her state boards, so a job at the switchboard suddenly opened, and that of course, meant just enough extra pay.

The applicant for the postulancy delayed her entrance, had to go home to arrange some domestic matters—and found two dresses waiting for her, black dresses, just right for postulants, so that she could pack immediately and leave for Brightside. And so the stories go.

But now she knew, in her own way, that the very rich were poor too. At least, they had no available money to give to the sick and the poor. She heard some inside stories from the society doctors, the Wickham Brothers from Lee, about surprising things happening behind the great facades.

Of the Doctors, it was Doctor Criscietello who silently, confidentially, worked best with her and told her most. As a boy he had known poverty and in maturity was affluent and a friend of the massively rich. She had found him here already established, when she came, and had relied strongly on his judgments in framing her policies; it also made her happy to realize that Dr. Criscietello never made an important decision without consulting her.

His patient, Courtland Field Bishop, he knew was friendly to the Jesuits and was an admirer of Mother Mary's, though he had used more illustrious hospitals for the care and treatment of himself and his family than little St. Luke's. The good Doctor took a Machievellian method of involving Mr. Bishop. He sent him to St. Luke's for a routine blood test, scarcely worth a trip to the great centers of Boston or New York. Then he advised Mother Mary not to send a bill. She went him one better, who with the report (negative) sent a nice little note thanking Mr. Bishop for his call on her. Well, he had called—a pleasant little social call in her office.

She got a check from him for 500 dollars, the largest benefaction of 1930. But more. During all her term of office, the Courtland Bishop hothouses provided fresh flowers on a weekly basis for St. Luke's patients; the Metzes followed suit with hothouse fruit; Kate Buckingham, who charged the Jesuits for her apple crop, is said to have sent a caged bird around for the solarium, though that may have been apocryphal, since Miss Buckingham was a bit strapped that year, having just paid $65,000 to get a ventriloquist on the stage of the Metropolitan for one performance, they say. That may have been just a story too, but as they said, if it

281

was not true, it should have been.

Oh yes. Suddenly the times were changed. When Mother Mary, who never grew angry nowadays, though she could still be sharp, firmly disagreed with the analysis she heard from all quarters.

Her conservative contemporaries knew that the depression was an act of God to stop the license of the younger generation. The New Freedom, they had called it, had just gone too far. The young flouted the law of the land patronized bootleggers, frequented speakeasies, lost their eyesight and their locomotion from rotten alcohol, filled their bathtubs with gin, particularly in colleges. Immorality was rampant, and having discovered the romantic usages of the auto, they had invented parking, and you know what that meant. The very young were using condoms thus thwarting the divine sanction. Perhaps most obvious of all was the wild and orgiastic music and dancing that they had created, with contortions of the human body and terribly stimulating rhythms. Law, morality and faith had been bought away by too much prosperity. It had produced what it boasted of—the Lost Generation. And as for the new books and plays, something simply would have to be done. The less said about Hollywood morality, the better.

So God, in the attribute of Divine Providence, took a hand. The hand was that of Mr. Hoover [said the Democrats] and the depression [said all the godly].

Except Mother Mary. At what moment of her years she had solved the doubts she had had about God sending epidemics to help the nuns' hospitals, she could not quite recall, but she had definitely made up her mind.

When they proposed the retributive theory, she simply said, "Rubbish."

Yet when they remarked that things were more orderly now that youth had learned the discipline of poverty, she had to admit it, because it was true, but she secretly thought, "They're cowards. They're scared." Her attitudes put a gap between her and the generation in their forties and fifties. Except for Doctor Criscietello, she could not take their language. It was far easier to talk to the young and far easier for the young to talk to her than to their parents, who simply would not understand.

She sympathized, though she did not agree, with the middle-aged. "I was at my worst in my forties," she said. But the trouble with those of middle age, she knew, was that they did not remember, as she did, the generation that had rejected the phoniness of Victorian and Edwardian evil—and then lost their cause through fright, through the First World War. Nor had they ever known the structuring, the curtailing, the cloisterization of religious women that had followed her far freer, and perhaps, more Christian dedication. Mother Mary, at eighty, had lived long enough to be kind. That is why she had always encouraged Helen to go to the new dances, though she herself was physically tortured by this horrible jazz. Only once she had counseled her not to go. To see if the girl had discipline. To test her vocation. Helen had not gone. Good.

Somehow she had the feeling that her concessive attitudes, perhaps even her popularity, were not recognized with the now fully entrenched powers that be in Holyoke and in Springfield, that is, with Mother Consilii and with Bishop O'Leary. The only time that the Bishop had ever visited Shadowbrook—and St. Luke's—he had seemed a bit chilly, but that, perhaps, was because a Jesuit novice had knocked his herringbone biretta into the soup. By accident.

Yet the only ukase that she was bound to enforce, the only sign of rigidity was an edict demanding that if nuns were ill in the hospital, the attendant doctor must always be accompanied by another sister. Sometimes that could be embarrassing for all three people. Yet even Dr. Criscietello abided by it and painstakingly guessed at the symptoms.

Among her other dedications to individuals was that no matter what the conditions, she never missed the religious professions of the girls she had sent into the convent.

It was a bitter day, that January of 1931, when she got into the now ancient Cadillac and waved good-bye to Helen, happy in having her brother Albin beside her, happy in a new blue hat—valued in that order, she hoped. They went through the winter blues of the Mohawk Trail, as blue as Helen's hat. She and Mr. Broderick—everyone was Mr. except Patsy—reminisced about a visit they had made on Long Island, about the tremendous reception given her by Mrs. Brady, who had a

283

church of her own in her palace, and Ed Broderick twitted her about how at so many convents everybody would come out, throw their arms around her and kiss her.

He asked her how she knew so many people.

"Oh, I bought them," she said. "When they didn't have any money I got them some. Money speaks louder than words," she laughed. "Now that I don't have any, I wonder who'll be kissing me." Then, for old times sake they sang, wondering who was kissing her now, and so singing, they arrived at beloved Brightside, where she was kissed, though penniless.

The bright day had turned stormy in the Connecticut valley, and Mother Mary was glad she had come, there were so pitifully few people there for her children's great day. Glad she had arrived, she was bustling into the Chapel to pay her visit when she slipped. Thank God, there was no one around to see her. She rose and tucked her arm under her shawl.

Her arm ached like fury, it throbbed. But if she let on about it, it would ruin the day for her girls. After that moment, they thought she was acting rather gingerly when she gave the sororal embrace, still hiding one arm.

Finally she got Mother Consilii alone and exposed her hand, blue now and swollen.

"I think there is something the matter with this," she said.

It did not take the trained eye of Mother Consilii to see that the arm was broken.

"You'll have to get that tended to."

"Yes, yes, I know. But let's not upset the little sisters. We could ruin their day with this silly thing."

"What will you do?"

"Ship me down to Providence Hospital—get Dr. Brady in. He knows how to set a bone. Have him fix it up, and I'll be back for the profession."

It was done exactly like that, and without any anesthetic because Mother Mary said an anesthetic would make her dopey through the rest of the day. She was at the Profession, with a neat splint in a neat sling and wore a neat if rather manufactured smile.

She regretted only one thing that day. She had noted that

284

work on the Motherhouse had been resumed, but she could not climb up the hill to look at it, not with the weather and her disabled arm. Pity. But she could foresee that as usual, by Spring the sisters would be following in the train of the workmen, preparing the rooms for occupancy, inhabiting it before it was quite ready.

Back at St. Luke's Mother Mary was aggravated because she could not dress herself. She compromised and got a nun to help her. She didn't like to have people fussing over her, but as she said to the sister: "I don't mind you so much. You seem to have a reverence for the human body." Also it was disturbing to note how long it takes old bones to mend.

The arm was usable at last; and she and a companion could set off on a purchasing voyage once more, stopping at Winsted to pick up the gift of St. Luke's to the Mother-house—a candlestick holder. She looked at the exorbitant price they had put on it, but against which she was armed with a document.

She thrust a letter at the somewhat amazed proprietor.

"If you read that, sir, you'll see that you really want to charge me half the price."

Baffled, the man read his own commitment to sell candlesticks at this ridiculous bargan. Then he found the catch. "But this letter is dated twenty years ago, Mother."

"I know. But I haven't purchased one since. And there's your letter saying I can have it for such and such a price. I'm sure you are a man of your word."

"I suppose I am," the proprietor said, defeated. "But I'll give you the candlestick in exchange for the letter." They concluded the bargain.

At the end of the journey, in the heart of New York, she learned what it meant to be a nun during the depression, when so many religious went even about the streets begging. No different from the old days. She and her companion were rather gruffly told to sit, when they asked to see the manager. They sat. And sat. She did penance for the numbers of subjects she had kept waiting for her.

Since patience is a virtue the nuns sat. They had time for several rosaries.

It was nearly lunchtime when a giant of a man came

bustling out of the inner office, slapping on a derby. Mother Mary rose modestly to attract his attention, and she succeeded. The man was not unkindly—he was just busy, handing her something and hurrying off. In her hand he had pressed a quarter.

The nuns waited again, through the lunch hour.

The man must have been hungry, it took him so long, but at last he came back. Like a comic actor he did a doubletake at the nuns. All nuns look alike, but he was sure, as he said, "Aren't you the same Sisters that were here before? I thought I gave you something already."

Mother Mary held up the quarter somewhat gingerly. "You didn't give me time to say thank you for it."

"You're welcome." There was a prolonged silence. The man remembered his derby and took it off. "Anything else I can do for you?"

"Why, yes. I'd like to see the manager."

"That's me."

"Fine. In that case I would like you to sell me three ambulances."

"Three—did you say three—I mean I heard you. In that case—in that case come into my office!"

It is authentically reported that Mother Mary kept the twenty-five cents in addition to the ambulances.

She arrived home in time for her sixtieth jubilee. Usually the jubilarians were invited to the Motherhouse where a great fuss was made over them. For survival, Mother Mary thought.

There was no invitation on her desk. By the actual date, no note of any kind had arrived. After Mass and breakfast, she sat at her office desk and consigned the impromptu speech she had prepared to the wastebasket. When her mail arrived she received a pious picture signed by Helen. Emerging for lunch, she was yelled at in joy by Patsy, and as a rare privilege, she had Benediction that afternoon. The rest of the day was spent at busy-work in her office.

The congregation made more of a fuss over Reverend Mother Consilii's feast day on April twenty-sixth.

Anyway, the community had had other things to think about. At last they had moved into the Motherhouse, in precisely the way Mother Mary had anticipated—beds and bundles in on May 2, just before it was really ready for occupancy. After that, the whole congregation was engrossed in only one thing. The elections were coming up, and they had memories of very interesting elections indeed. Lately, also, though she had many loyal supporters, the incumbent General was facing some rather deep criticism, and as more of a symbol than anything else, the fact that she had barred off and made out of bounds, the very center of the Motherhouse, a suite, consisting of a bedroom, large parlor and study sumptuously furnished, and across from it a private dining room and two smaller bedrooms, all reserved for the exclusive use of the Bishop and his entourage.

When Mother Mary heard of the arrangement she chuckled. "I can scarcely throw stones," she said. "I gave Bishop Beaven a vacation house at Greylock and the sisters had to wait for years till they got a week off in the summer. I'd be the last one to talk."

"But Mother, that was different."

"Everything is different."

"Yes—but you know what this setup means? It means we have to walk outside the house through the outdoors cloister walk to get from one wing to another! No matter what the weather! Even when he isn't there, we can't go through the Bishop's sacred precincts."

"Oh, you poor things," Mother Mary said. "You have to go all that way! And if it's bad weather you couldn't go over the second floor, or down through the basement, could you? My heart aches for you."

Though she laughed at them, they did not mind it now; but on the other hand, they did not change their minds.

Yet on July 26 everything went smoothly, and with Bishop O'Leary presiding, his good friend Mother Mary Consilii was voted back into office.

There was so little fuss about the procedure that Mother Mary took Ed Broderick and her slight fever from a cold, which she had not cared to reveal, back to Pittsfield and her own little corner of domain. She made a great concession to nature and went to bed early that night.

The next morning she rose, not feeling any too well, but it was only a cold, and she had a job to do and nothing in the world to worry about. If there were to be any changes of mission or subordinate superiors, they were informed by letter some days before. Anyway she had seen and talked to the General Superior just the day before; although the list of changes for missions was always posted on the general Community tablet on the day after elections, it was only curiosity about where others might be stationed or who would be sent to her, which led her to the bulletin board.

Her name led all the rest—Mother Mary of Providence: Brightside Motherhouse. Sister Mary Ciaran, Superior, St. Luke's.

CHAPTER 21

Her sixtieth jubilee had been, indeed, Mother Mary thought, somewhat delayed. Puttering around the Mother-house, trying to make jobs for herself, gave her ample time to think. "I will not brood," she counseled herself. "I simply will not brood." Yet she had the fear that all old nuns have, after a lifetime of activity and of contribution, that they will be on the shelf, a burden to everybody, a burden to themselves.

She must find something meaningful to do. Years ago she had been delicate, but now she was as robust as an ox. She couldn't even look forward to easeful death.

They gave her, with deliberate kindness, something to look forward to, but it struck her as ironic. Why must everything important in her life come after great delay? It was not punishment for her own balancing sins, since she was always punctilious about doing things on time. Then why was it? The waiting in the world, after her first refusal; her interminable postulancy, the long wait for the holy habit; the waiting for her vows, until the other novices caught up with her; even the long waiting in the chapel when the Bishop forgot to come; the years of waiting between being the General Superior and being Superior of St. Luke's. And now, the long delay and the waiting. What they seemed to suppose would be a childish excitement of a girl waiting for a party. Always the delays and the waiting. Why?

In her search for a balance in the universe, the impinge-ment of design on the divine chaos, one thought, which might have satisfied her, never crossed her mind. Though she had been blessed with the noblesse of kings—always to be on time—might she not occasionally have been impatient? Might she not sometimes have been financially rash, plunging into obligations when the funds were not in hand nor foreseeably forthcoming? So Mother Consilii thought; but Mother Mary's search for balance never revealed to her this possibility.

Another thing she might have thought of, but no religious woman of her time or of her commitment would have viewed it with anything but disapproval, as of a hersey. Perhaps God had precious little to do with the delays. Her postulancy and novice experiences had been due to the uncertainty of a woman, Mother Mary Edward, who didn't quite anticipate her survival as a nun; the Bishop, at her clothing had simply been absentminded.

Mother Consilii delayed the celebration of her sixty years of service from March 1932 to August 22, 1933, when she was established at the Motherhouse.

She tried her best to seem grateful for the preparations, but her own great moment had already come. She had already seen the almost complete Motherhouse before her assignment to it, and that had been a joy, remembering the farmland as it had been, now seeing the whole hill covered with buildings, Riley's Brook with a strong bridge over it, the roads winding over it, dividing between Beaven Kelly and the Motherhouse, the chaste and modest cemetery crowning the hill, and then, to the north and almost indistinguishable from their own buildings, the novitiate of the Sisters of St. Joseph, and all the lovely arable, cultivated or cared for land between the facilities, with the great trees amongst them. Then, far below, she could see the winding Connecticut river, separating them from the distant city of Springfield, and the roadway that ran between, could lead you to the Berkshires, if you took one turn, to Mt. Tom or Northampton, to Holyoke center, even to Boston, if you went far enough. It looked beautiful and complete, these reams of blueprints that had sprung into bulk. Complete. She was happy in it.

At first, though, she had been licking her wounds, and residence in the Motherhouse felt penal. She could not help that, but she tried. How often she had told her subjects that it didn't matter where you were as long as you were doing God's work. That had been when she was working — and she had no work. Had she not, in her mind, criticized the St. Joseph Sisters for keeping Mother Valencia in office far too long? Wasn't she herself an octogenarian? But she felt young. That was the trouble. The human soul has no age.

290

God gave her joy, unexpectedly, not at the opening of the Motherhouse or at any of the fomal solemnities that blessed rooms and the stations of the cross and innumerable things—but on the day of the first Mass ever to be celebrated in their own chapel.

The main altar was consecrated on November 18, 1932. Her reaction, which she no doubt, as others did, thought was aesthetic, was perhaps not principally that, for the altar and chapel fixings proclaimed a period when ornateness and wealth of material substituted for dignity of line and construction. Though the chapel and altar were not in bad taste, they were impressive rather than significant, and unfortunately the impression was one of rather massive expenditure.

"If this is so beautiful," she said, "what must heaven be!"

After that glory, everything else must be anticlimax. And between was the long winter, the spring, and most of the summer.

Truly, at her festivity, they did everything they could for her and she responded warmly to the love that she knew was being poured out on her. Subtly it changed her. She remembered with nostalgia another fiesta, when the nuns had seated Sister Dolours beside her at dinner and how once she had touched her sister's hand but had been met only with a look of alarm. She had not pursued the intimacy. But from now on she would not be afraid to show affection. She was old enough not to fear.

Other than that, the celebration had little effect on her. She thought but never said, "I appreciated it. But I didn't like it." She tried her best to close her ears to the tributes, because they were dangerous—because they were all true. Suppose she were to believe them! What a terrible old lady she would turn out to be.

It was hard though to close her ears to the Bishop. He spoke with warmth, with feeling, yes, with love, doing his kindest and best to make amends. Telling the truth too.

It was many years since she had heard a bishop say nice things about her.

Fortunately Mother Mary had had ample time before her delayed celebration to improve her correspondence, and fortunately also, Helen, her adopted daughter, had preserved all her letters from the time of her leaving St. Luke's. Though they show little about the experiences, either outward or psychic, of Mother Mary herself, they are complete with revelations of her values and are interspersed with significant comments by Helen.

Helen writes:
Quite by accident I found that Mother was leaving St. Luke's. She was being transferred to the Mother-house. I did not know this. Mother intended to leave quietly, but I came upon a sad-faced Mr. Broderick and the same gray Cadillac that had brought me to Pittsfield. It was at the side door, and just then Mother came out and entered the car. Very briefly she bade me goodbye. It was a sad occasion. She told me that she had left something for me with Sister Marie Carmel. And then the car was gone! And Mother and her companion.

The something she had left for me was a little blue book entitled, "Heart Talks with Jesus", and the short note which follows:

St. Luke's Hospital
July 29, 1932

My dear Child:
It must be that our Heavenly Father wishes to strengthen you, by taking away one big prop. It is for you to develop strength of will and devotion to Duty. I can give you no better tonic, Write to me as often as you feel so inclined. I will answer according to your needs. I will pray daily that you may not disappoint
Your foster Mother.

The next letter came in August:

Convent of Our Lady of Victory:
My dear little Girl:
I have just come from the chapel, where I was making the afternoon visit and you came into my

292

distractions, so I said a Litany of the B. Virgin, a Memorare and Hail Holy Queen, strictly for you and decided to write you in case you may be lonely, it will give you assurance, that Mother is not forgetting her child. I am going to Providence in the morning; will return Thursday evening and I hope that a letter from you will greet me as I enter our little office and search the desk. There must be plenty that you can find to fill a few pages. I am so anxious to know what you are to do when school opens. Let me know the prospect; and what you have done to secure admission. I had a pleasant surprise in a visit yesterday (Sunday) from three of our girls and Teresa's mother, all of whom were on their way to Carmel. [the novitiate.] My little Eva was there, just as sweet as ever. After our return from Providence, I will make some plans to see you. Just wait and trust Mother. I am very well and contented tho' my truant thoughts often stray to St. Luke's. Pray earnestly my dear Child, for the execution of our plans, in some manner or other. Be faithful to duty, a stern mistress, but a faithful one too, who never fails to reward honest service. I think you should write to me often and confide in me, as you would if we were together. It is sometimes easier to write than give vocal expression to our thoughts, feelings and desires. Especially if you are discouraged, you should write. All letters to me are private.

Now I will close as it is nearly time for the supper bell.

May the Holy Trinity, our Blessed Mother and your Guardian Angel keep you safe! How is Alice? How is Albin? [*Helen's sister and brother*]. Tell him that I asked for him. I wish he would write to me and I will answer him, by a nice long letter.

With sincere and maternal love and solicitude,
Yours as you know,<br>Mother

Mother Mary had written, advising frequently, though not daily Mass and Communion, but in the meantime, had become convinced that Helen had a vocation to be a Sister of Providence, perhaps that she had applied for admission. Her letters now became somewhat sharper.

Providence Mother House
February 1, 1933

My dear Helen:

Perhaps the mail will bring me some word from you, but in the meantime I must find some relief in advising you on the basis of what I have been told. It is that you have not been going to Holy Communion daily for some time; *Sunday the only day.*

Also the party [Bishop O'Leary] whom you talked to on the day of annual meeting thinks you very delicate. I heard also that Helen just gets around in time to take a drink — no breakfast, and rush off to school.

I was so indulgent as to suggest that you go to Mt. Carmel Church to Mass two or three mornings a week, at least, but you grew self-indulgent. It has not been a good example to Nurses or Girls and to the Sisters very disedifying. We will not speak of the treatment to our Divine Lord, but He cannot be pleased with such tepidity.

My Helen has been starving soul and body. You know your family history in point of health. You need to really stuff yourself with nourishment and lay up a reserve supply. You have received a *check* that perhaps you will heed. Then, since that interview, you have not turned to me, but have left me to worry myself almost sick, Helen, you have been carried too kindly; a little severity would have done you no harm. You have been flattered and have rested in the good opinion of others. Wake up!! Nothing is ever gained in this world, except by strong effort. I know the Bishop and Reverend Mother; know that both are kind, but they must study character and surely yours will need strengthening.

I think you should write to Reverend Mother; tell her what the Bishop has said and ask her, if you may

294

not hope to be successful, if you take more care to nurture your strength and to improve in piety. You are now in their hands and I will not ask favor for you, because you must go on, on your own merits.

I believe that you have the qualifications that go to make a vocation but they must be fostered and developed. It does not matter *how soon* or how late you come to the novitiate; all that matters is that you be in *downright earnest* and that you show CHARAC-TER. No convent-bred girl shows that by lying in bed till eight o'clock. It looks very selfish. Perhaps too that you have not hurried to bed as soon as free. You know, my dear, that when you were going to school, you often talked before retiring, to a late hour.

The cross is good for you; humiliation is good for you. How many girls, going to work, would be grateful for the breakfast that you have not taken the trouble to eat. How can you be strong without it? Do you wish to fall through as Alice has: (Her sister was now a tuberculosis patient at Providence Hospital) If she had been watched as you have, she might not have been thrown down.

I do not mean to discourage you; rather do I desire to spur you on to action. I think you should be hard on yourself and change at once. How can I excuse you for not telling me how things stand with you? Have you been told that you will *not* be accepted at any time? Please, please tell me something and take kindly and act on what I say here.

Mother

The letter of the next day has a more benign tone, and the address changes from "My dear Helen." Also it gives some of the rare insights into Mother Mary's daily schedule, in her eighty-third year.

My dear little girl:
I received your letter yesterday and lest you might be disheartened by anything I have written, I write again today, more earnestly, because I know the

situation better than you can. I am much relieved to learn that you have really been accepted and since this good fortune is yours, we must begin in earnest.

You probably were made aware that the Bishop did not approve on long sleeping in the morning, to the loss of Holy Communion. Reverend Mother takes it very seriously and we must accept their view, as that of Our Lord, Himself.

Now that you are accepted, try to feel that you are already *one of us*, an adopted child of the Community. Lay up treasures of grace. Be a bit hard on yourself. It will be known among the Sisters anyway that you had an important interview and the purpose will be understood; therefore every Sister will expect. Probably you may meet Reverend Mother up there, and how glad you can be, if you know that no one can say: "Helen is neglecting Holy Communion, and daily Mass."

The nurses work just as hard as you do and in a more fatiguing way. If you will train yourself to early rising, for the next five months, it will not come hard here. *YOU SIMPLY MUST DO IT.* I wish you to engage some reliable nurse to awaken you every morning, when she rises. Ask her to stay until she is sure that you are really awake. Do not linger yourself. Every morning, except Saturday, for I understand that the nurses do not rise, that day, though I have often wondered why they cheat Our Lady, on her own day. By rising in that way, you will be ready for breakfast and that is another thing. No more running off on a cup of coffee. *A full breakfast.* It may nauseate you at first, for the stomach becomes weak, but by degrees, you will relish food. Your health comes next in importance, to your spirit of piety. Keep this letter and read it occasionally. If you fail, let me know why and how often. I will help you. My alarm is set for a quarter to five. Many times, I am tempted to rest until later, but I do not and now will offer this first sacrifice of the day, *for you.* Then we will both be hearing Mass and going to the Holy Table

296

at the same time. Can you do this for our Lord, to Whom I have given you *and for me* also?

Helen, it is prayer that has won for you this great gift and as the time approaches, you will need grace and strength all the more. In your letter to Reverend Mother, I hope you will tell her something positive.

You should tell her that you intend to go to Holy Communion and to nurture your health, for she is anxious about these 2 necessities. Now as to telling your Aunt, let it stand for the present. Do not bring any trouble about your head, until you are nearer the goal. I hope that you may be able to come to see me before very long and then we can settle other things. I wish to be proud of you Helen, in the edification you will give, by your attention to HOME DUTIES. By early rising, you will have time to do any little service assigned you, before school. Leave not yourself *in the power of any one*, to *find fault*. All for the love of God. Mother is not angry with you, but has been frightfully anxious. Write often to her.

I ought to have a letter from you every week.

Do not write next week as I expect to be absent for a few days.

Mother

The pleas for letters become increasingly plaintive through the months preceding Helen's entrance into the convent. Apparently the reform of daily Mass attendance was achieved and, in the interests of health, Mother Mary arranged for Helen to go to a Pittsfield orthodontist, to have her tendency to buck teeth treated. Also, she sent her brother Albin to a curative speech teacher, to conquer his stuttering. The bedridden sister Alice was, at Mother Mary's arrangement, fully cared for by Providence Hospital, varying from the euphoric improvements to the increasing setbacks, common to consumptives. Typically, when Helen's Aunt and Uncle came to see her, and she broke the news to them about her intention to enter the convent, they opposed her. They thought that Helen would be wasting her life, to devote it to such a great social cause.

Mother Mary's comments are brief and pointed:

Holyoke, Mass.
May 31, 1933
How is my little girl this morning? I remembered
her at Mass; in my Rosary too and in a visit to the B
Sacrament after breakfast. Dear Child, I hope the
good spirit that God has given you for Guardian, has
whispered to you, restoring peace to your soul. I am
quite certain that your Uncle came for the one
purpose of turning you aside from your purpose and
surely you are wise enough to realize that he would be
a very weak counsellor in such a case. He flattered
you. In the Gradual of the Mass of St. Angela, this
morning are the beautiful words: "Hearken O Daughter and see, for the King hath greatly desired thy
beauty." In these words, Bishop Beaven addressed the
first class of Postulants to whom he gave the Holy
Habit in Brightside Chapel, forty years ago. I repeat
them to you in Our Lord's name. Do not be deceived
by appearances. The world gives no lasting happiness
and human love is *freighted* with selfishness; no
stability, cares never cease, even on the death bed.
Then again it is so sweet to serve God for His Own
sake and to do some good in the world. You have had
a trial and came through quite bravely. Our Lord was
tempted by the Evil One and we expect the trial. Be
brave and joyful in the Lord.

Ever yours,
Mother

On July 22, 1933, a month before Mother Mary's jubilee,
Helen entered the postulancy, and after some trial names,
eventually emerged as Sister Mary Dosithea, taking Mother
Mary's confirmation name, which implies some conspiration-
al pressure on the part of Mother Mary.

After Helen's entrance, the letters from Mother Mary
became quite sparse, and her requests for Helen's replies,
practically cease. This is an important clue. Mother Mary had
been accused of over-influencing and attempting to form the

girls whom she sent to the novitiate, thus interfering with the true and main role of the Mistress of Novices. The lack of correspondence through this time is negative evidence to the fact that the accusation was unfounded. The good director, on sending a girl to the convent, withdraws counseling, withdraws even the self. So in this first period, did Mother Mary.

The months had gone on until the Great Day, which did not seem so very great, and the small and personal things that she could do, became the focal point of her interests, her values and her life.

## CHAPTER 22

Mother Mary had a regular employment now. It was to teach speech and drama to the younger nuns. She had not been in a classroom for half a century; she had never been to a theatre to see a play. It was a bit too late to learn by observation, as she always had. But she spoke well, herself, with her nice Kingston diction, and her low, clear voice, which now had attained a Berkshire overlay, for her perfect ear caught the nuances of every environment to which she was exposed, and unconsciously appropriated the inflection she encountered.

Also, through the years, the sloppiness of diction that she heard about her actually hurt her, and it was hard for her to understand why other people could find no difference between ugly noises and natural and beautiful tones. The new, so-called music, with its awful caterwaulling was physically distressing, yet she had frequently seen young nuns turn off Jessica Dragonette, singing purely and like an artist, for scooping and groaning vulgarians, some of whom could turn even an inoffensive commercial into a suggestive obscenity.

At least she could teach her nuns how to open their mouths, distinguish between d and t, and to some degree eliminate the South Boston brogue, which people were beginning to call a Boston accent, much to the distress of the Brahmins and the Beacon Hill Browning Societies. Mother Mary was also able to distinguish the various sounds of the letter a, and to train her little sisters in the correct shadings of "Half a gas mask."

As to the readings of her students, she demanded absolute and verbal memorization, and to the poor things who had had no memory training in the advanced grade schools, she was ruthless if they changed a word, saying, "The author writes better than you. Use his words — not your own."

Mother Mary Consilii was vaguely satisfied with Mother

Mary's occupation. It did no great harm, and though she suspected that Mother Mary was using her teacher relationship with the young for more training in rather old-fashioned spirituality than in speech teaching, there was not too much to worry about, as this new depression-trained youth would scarcely pick up the spendthrift, trust-in-God attitudes of the past generation. The new society was too thoroughly frightened to be prodigal, having lived through poverty and want. The lost generation, the new freedom, was as extinct as the dodo, and pray God, youth would not rebel again, at least during her lifetime. It had taken massive suffering to defeat them, but Mother Consilii knew that this was God's way. The Reverend Mother also did her best to make Mother Mary happy by consulting her when she could. Not that she need take her advice, but it did no harm and made the old lady happy. Besides, sometimes Mother Mary could straighten out things quite successfully, as in the case of one newly appointed superior who was too strict by far. She got Mother Mary to write her:

Providence Mother House, Holyoke, Massachusetts
August 18, 1933.

My dear Child;—

Your letter awakened in me sincere sympathy and I have been turning over in mind, its statements, while awaiting the opportunity to answer. In this letter, I may say something that will sting a little, but such is not my intention. The truth is generally bitter, *but is a tonic.* I have judged by the visitors here, that tranquility is disturbed, in your domestic circle, and your letter gives me assurance of the same. I understand conditions perfectly and am not surprised.

You are receiving your first lessons of experience in government. Among the Sisters of Charity, the Sister Superior bears the title: — *SISTER SERVANT* and it is well placed. I have also my personal views of what the Superior is expected to be. She must be, not so much a Mistress of Discipline, as a *Mother* of the religious family. It always surprised me to realize how much the Sisters, even the seniors look to every

Superior young or old, for support, understanding, forbearance, etc. etc.

They do not think so much of their duty to her, as to *her duty to them.* If she be younger in years of religious experience, it makes little difference. They are still exacting. I have been through the mill: have found occasions, even in those later years, when faith did not inspire them to take correction, conference on the spirit of religion, in the proper way and when I actually refrained from either personal counsel or general remarks. If I should meet with such opposition, how much more might you expect it. Here is where the little lesson or hint of *LENIENCY* might serve a good purpose. Many a time I have said to myself: "God bears with them; why should not I?" And again; — perhaps they are more pleasing in His sight than myself and many, many times, I allowed things to go by unnoticed, and frequently, *they corrected themselves.* Furthermore, perhaps the irregularities that disturb you, do not amount to even a venial sin. I am often surprised and much edified, by the forebearance that our Reverend Mother practises. I am not blaming you at all, dear Child, but if you find that your efforts to enforce discipline, do not ensure *PEACE,* then your efforts may be defined as *bitter,* rather than *holy zeal.* I would suggest that you change your attitude entirely. Be cheerful; be even gay. Try to be the centre of the family circle. Do not take life too seriously. Do not exaggerate your responsibility. They are all professed and are amenable to God and their own conscience and there can be nothing so serious in their conduct as to threaten disaster to community life. Many and many a thing I have allowed to pass unnoticed, (so far as verbal reference was concerned) for the sake of peace and above all, when I myself, was interiorly disturbed. I told Rev. Mother, when she would come for her visitation, or when writing,:— "Things are not as I would wish, but for 'peace' sake, I have let them pass." You will always find those who are ready to sympathize with one, who has had a correction from the head. My dear little girl, study to acquire tact; forbearance; long-suffering. Think of Our Divine Lord, with those clumsy Fishermen, His Disciples and how His sensitive nature must have suffered, by the merest contact with them: even to His St. Peter, he was obliged to check his curiosity about St. John. Those Sisters, young and senior are expecting as much, in your state, as you are expecting from them and it is and will be "Nip and tuck", unless you conquer by meekness and patient endurance of little things that have disturbed you. Am I harsh? I do not wish to be. By kindness and humility, you will gain a victory. Now cheer up. Be in good humor for the 22 NEVER show coldness towards anyone. Ignore insult.

I hope you will feel better. We know your people and adopt St. Teresa's Motto.

God bless you.<br>Mother

Beyond the insights into her own attitudes as Superior, there also appears here her very definite and candid evaluation of Mother Consilii. Several of the nuns, loyal to Mother Mary, analyzed her many defenses of their General Superior, as only the holy subterfuge of Christian charity and meekness; indeed some of the older nuns made very cutting criticisms of the General Superior saying that she was harsh with Mother Mary, that she could not wait until the old lady said something before she would contradict her, that Mother Mary suffered much from her. But the evidence seems reasonably contradictory. Mother Consilii was chosen by her peers in three free elections, the records now giving no hint of pressure from the Bishop. The majority of the voting members of her congregation must have approved of her. And the evidence furnished by Mother Mary is invariably laudatory.

Mother Mary thought that she understood her General Superior. She could only approve of Mother Consilii's reticence, and having had inside information on the state of finances for so many years, she guessed shrewdly at the conditions of the diocese, the negotiations with Bishop O'Leary and with Mrs. Creighton. True, Mother Consilii did have a habit of contradicting her, but if it were a fault, it went with her office. When she did not agree, she had a duty to reprimand, and Mother Mary knew that some of her own views — such as complete financial trust in Divine Providence — were antiquated by the very conditions of the times. Also, for she had experienced it before, the General Superior must be sure that it is she, inspired by the Holy Ghost, who must dictate the policies, outline the obediences of the community — and not an antique like herself. That some of her dear sisters who were loyal to her and to the old days, would uncharitably put this down to jealousy, she could understand. But they were wrong. The motivation was certainly one of righteous exercise of authority.

Two illuminations came to Mother Mary now. One was that though she tried to avoid being an old lady who lived in and praised only the past, remembering the earliest days of personal involvements with the people of God, greater ability and freedom to work with the poor, far more possibility of developing one's own personality as a woman, that, though she had had a hand in the structuring, even in the claustration of her own foundation — it had not been her fault, and she had fought with bishops every inch of the way. Now she could envision no return to such a manner of service to God. Rome had spoken; never again, she thought could there be nuns such as St. Vincent had envisioned, priests such as St. Ignatius had dreamed of, doing the work of God with personal dedication.

She had at first accepted, and now was accustomed through many years, to their almost cloistered life, the life of total dependence on the decisions of the Superior. The generations which had come since, and who had been trained to it, were not unhappy. Those many who survived, disciplining their wills and judgments in the methods she knew were being used effectively on her little Helen, were more than content usually; they had scratchy days, but their values of doing God's will, their life of prayer, dedicated to the grace of conformity, their mystique of obedience as the cardinal virtue, their abiding knowledge that what they were

304

doing was worthwhile, their deep communal devotion to
their own congregation, stressed by the identity of their garb,
their uniform, the total respect and the special privileges
given them by the laity, left precious few of them soured.
Mother Mary knew that the present system was working. She
accepted the great legal edifice of the Roman Catholic
Church; she took pride in the monolithic uniformity in
matters of dogma and morality. All Catholics held the same
faith, as all Catholics ate fish on Friday, spoke a single
language at Mass. Others who claimed to be Christian lived in
a welter of confusion and obscurity.

Mother Mary realized all these good things. If occasionally
she thought that some of the decisions made by Mother
Consilii were a bit too rigid, they were really trivial and she
could usually heal the wounds of the nuns who sought solace
from her, implanting in them the grace of Acceptance of the
divine will. And really, there were only little things which
brought her to a silent rejection. Now, without decree, the
nuns were assigned the names they would bear for the rest of
their lives, had no choice whatsoever and occasionally were
stuck with soubriquets that were ridiculously inappropriate
and sometimes downright outlandish. They all had saints to
back them up, but they were often martyred ladies from the
Roman martyrology who very probably never existed.

The other thing was the new regulations on visitors. Until
they were fully professed, the younger nuns, some of them
not that young, were allowed to see their own families for
only a couple of hours, in the overcrowded parlors, once a
month; and if the families could not visit on that assigned
day, they had to wait till next month or if they tried to
override the regulation and come out of season, be denied
entrance at the door of the convent. Mother Mary thought
that while one could make regulations for one's own subjects,
the General Superior's commands and rights did not extend
to the laity. The rule punished the families. Yet they
accepted it, as externs always did and the grumblings came
more from the sisters than from the families. About this,
Mother Mary kept her own counsel.

Her second recognition came gradually, but was devastating. Not for a moment had she ever thought, in either of her

terms of office, that she had been a member of a governing clique, much less, the head of one. Like any administrator, she had surrounded herself with people whom she trusted, who thought approximately as she did, and all that she had thought was that it was a blessing that the governing body got along so well together. Never once had it crossed her mind that she had surrounded herself with rubber stamps, though it was true that any dissident ladies had been, in a kindly fashion, eliminated from the Councils of the Great, or had had their opinions sidetracked with the greatest of firm sweetness.

Now that she was no longer of the inner circle, Mother Mary knew. She knew how some of her nuns, passed over, never consulted, guarded from the secrets of the Council, must have felt. She had compassion for her sister, Mary Dolours.

But before God, she had never realized it until now.

Yet she still had influence, though not within her community. Now that Mother Valencia was practically blind, it was the Superior General, Mother Josephine of the Sisters of St. Joseph of Hartford, an old lady herself, but still active and alert, a foundress, who sought and followed Mother Mary's advice on the new expansion of hospital services in Hartford, Waterbury and Stamford. And the Sisters of Providence of Holyoke claim that it was due to Mother Mary's advice that the Sisters of Mercy of Hartford bought and established their fashionable girls' school called Laurelton Hall in Hamden, which put them almost in the same bracket as the Madams of the Sacred Heart. Of course, the Sisters of Mercy had the Brady fortune in back of them, and that meant the Garvans and the O'Neills, so that the move was scarcely flying in the face of Providence. And of course at that time all congregations of nuns wanted their own select boarding schools, as many of them wanted and got their own tiny and independent colleges.

The depression had killed off the great estates. Nobody wanted them any more, and they fell for a song to the Catholic hierarchy and the religious congregations, often just for back taxes. As Father Stanton said, "It's like the reversal of the times of Henry VIII. Then they seized the monasteries and turned them into manor houses for the nobles. Now we are getting the mansions they built on the plans of the old monasteries and turning them back to the religious. How hath God wrought!" It was very nice of God.

Mother Consilii had started her second term of office at a time when, after constant expansion, retraction of effort and money was an absolute necessity. She had, after a lapse of two years, managed to push the Motherhouse to completion, but with that done, most of her plants were satisfactorily large, or at least adequate to the immediate needs.

Less significant matters also called for Reverend Mother's attention. After twenty years of shelving, Pope Pius X's Motu Proprio on Church music had at last been recognized, and the liturgists were coming into their own. The distractions of the immediate past, the operatic performances in the great churches, the terrifying hymnody that still retained its Victorian sentimentality, was, at last, doomed — and though the people still said that they did not feel married unless they had Lohengrin for a wedding march, there were now bishops' commissions to see to it that the music had something to do with the words of the sacrifice. "I Love You Truly" was more rarely heard by the more advanced congregations. To the delight of the Benedictines, Gregorian chant was being rediscovered, and many a person of good taste rejoiced that past vulgarities were finally being expunged. The curates might still scoop like Bing Crosby, and the Pastors appall the guilty and make mad the free, but at least, the choirs were better. There was hope for the future of music in the Catholic Church, since the nuns led all the rest in their devotion, and the children could sing the Mass of the Angels quite acceptably.

Mother Consilii had good taste and insisted that her nuns get the proper training. As the Professor said, anybody could chant Gregorian, given practice. The Reverend Mother had them imbued with the square notes, the punctum and the clivis — all of them with no exception. At least they could all chant the *Te Deum*.

She caught Sister Mercedes trying to skip rehearsal one night, but Reverend Mother was both watchful and spry. Sister Mercedes was personally and by the arm, conducted back to her pew.

"But I can't sing," she said.

Mother Consilii was aware both of that fact and that Sister Mercedes could mimic to perfection, any nun soloist they had had when there were solos.

"Then chant the words," she whispered. Sister Mercedes obliged with a counterbass, but the organ played quite loudly, and she amused only her neighbors.

Later, Mother Mary came upon Sister Mercedes imitating herself to the rollicking delight of the other nuns. It was one of the few times when Mother Mary's chuckle became a laugh. Not only was the situation droll, but she was in sympathy with the sisters who regretted the loss of the old hymns. She had always loved "To Jesus Heart All Burning," and she missed it.

Even at funerals, they had silenced the touching hymns at the grave. Now a long black procession wound up the hill to Calvary, chanting the *De Profundus* and the *Miserere*. "That's where this Gregorian belongs," Sister Mercedes mumbled, "at funerals."

But it touched Mother Mary on the day when they laid Helen's little tubercular sister Alice away, and she was almost glad that she could not attend the interment for this innocent girl. She wrote to Helen:

July 28, 1934

My dear child:

I know your heart is very sad and you have not had the comfort of Mother's sustaining presence in your grief, but I have been confined to our cell because of high blood pressure and even when I took the message of dear Alice's critical condition, though Reverend Mother was willing that I go with you, I did not feel equal to it.

Just as soon as I get out of the Doctor's grip, I will try to see you and learn details of the sad experience you've had.

There is another side to it dear little Sister. Alice is safe in God's care. She was too shy and frail to battle with life. She has gone to her Creator in her baptismal innocence, I doubt not.

If we know each other there in spirit-land, how

great your dear Mother's joy, to meet her darling, and Father too.

Of course I have prayed for her and offered this morning's Mass, and I can picture her only as a sweet virgin, welcomed by our Blessed Lady.

God has taken care of her, as He has of you; let us bless His Providence. Do not grieve unreasonably; rather rejoice in the Lord that she is safe.

Mother.

As Mother Mary sealed and sent the letter, she wondered if the Church would ever acknowledge the joys of attaining eternity, meeting the Beloved at last? Would it always be so pessimistic, stressing the dangers of eternal flame, praying for deliverance from past and heinous sins? Sins? Little Alice? Nonsense.

She guessed she was a heretic after all.

There was another moment in which Mother Mary had to console Helen, and it was also one in which the nun had mixed emotions, for her own happiness at the moment was so great that she found it hard to empathize.

Helen, looking very young and very tragic as a white-veiled novice, had told her that her best friend in the novitiate, Sister Rita had been dismissed from the convent.

"And only seventy-five days before profession — and she doesn't want to go — and she is being sent home."

"I know," Mother Mary said. "Sister, thank God it is seventy five days *before* profession." Helen understood, but not all.

For Mother Mary's happiness was very great. After all these years, her own child, her other child, had come home. Sister Ursula had returned to them. She had been a patient at Mercy Hospital, and signified that she would like to re-enter the convent. Mother Mary had not been at all sure, when she presented the case to the General Superior, of what the reaction would be. But Bishop Beaven had been dead these years, and there was no one now to remember the insurrection, the severity of the law. Like Sister Rita, she had not asked to go — she had been dismissed. Out of hand, the memory went. While trying to seek out the apostolic delegate. Out of loyalty to Mother Mary of Providence.

Mother Consilii and Bishop O'Leary said yes. Sister Ursula renewed her vows on the twentieth of June, returned to the Motherhouse on June the twenty-first, and remained there bedridden for eighteen years.

Mother Mary took her in her arms. "I am so glad you are home!"

"So am I." That was all, and quite enough.

It was now that Mother Consilii thought up a new thing to occupy Mother Mary's empty hours, to give her a sense of contribution.

"Mother," she said, "since you have an excellent memory, I should like to have you write the chronicle of our Foundation, from Montreal on — through Kingston — and here."

When this task was concluded, the General Superior assigned her duty of writing the necrologies of all the sisters who were laid away in Calvary. When this was summarily dispatched, Mother Consilii said, "Now you must write the story of your own life."

"My own life? Oh — I don't think I could do that!"

"It is an obedience, Sister."

There was nothing she could do about it. She started to write it.

The chronicle, the necrologies, the autobiography are clearly, and in the main, accurately transcribed. Yet Mother Mary was a woman who had never read a biography, except the lives of the saints and had carefully eschewed novels, for moral reasons. She writes facts, with impeccable grammar. She has the aggravating habit of glossing over important conflicts, stating them, and serenely going on to a development of factual details. Of what went on within herself or within her community, there are only the barest hints.

It is strange and disturbing, because her epistolary style was so much warmer, and often, so much more revealing. But in her account, which she knew would be read by many others, the habit of silence overcame her.

One of the very last of her letters to Helen deserves preservation. She writes:

310

God is Charity.

Rev. Sister Mary Dosithea:

My dear child:

So you packed your bag and labeled your trunk and took yourself off to other scenes and were you sorry and fearful, or were you glad to have a new experience, or were you just obedient and indifferent? Now there is the skeleton of a letter to Mother which indeed I should now be answering instead of suggesting to my little girl. How did I take your transfer? I was very much pleased, for though you were well off at the Mercy, it gives you a broader experience to see our little world of the Community.

Be careful of your health by wearing your rubbers, in crossing the yard, even though the ground be dry, it is still cold and damp and one easily takes cold in the feet. It is drafty in the ground floor where you work and it might be prudent to wear the jacket that Albin sent, under your arm; then do not forget your cape when you cross the yard. Thus you will avert trouble. Remember dear, that I am advising you for your own protection and please me by doing as I advise, for I know the climate of Worcester. It is cold . . .

I went up to Pittsfield on the sixth of January and remained there two full days . . .Dr. Young and Betty came to see me. We spoke of you and Betty seemed interested. She is expecting in the Maternity Department of St. Luke's any day now. I could not but compare your good fortune and hers, but as I looked at the young couple and realized that all her happiness under God, of course, is bound up in that frail young man I blessed Our Lord for his goodness to my little girl, and your good sense in following the call of vocation. Be ever and always in love with it.

I saw Albin. He will soon be eighteen and I have asked my M. Thrane to take an interest in getting him work in the G.E. Help us by recommending the matter to St. Joseph.

I hope you may find some time for good reading
and I warn you my dear Child against picking up any
of the secular papers or magazines that are so plentiful
in the hospital. It would be not only a loss of time but
also a dangerous pastime. Even in Catholic periodicals
today, there are things we cannot read: they are not
intended for us.

Mother.

It will make you think of old times to read this
epistle, but it will also tell you that I love you in the
same old way.

Yours, as you have known me,<br>Mother.

Whether it was due to the obvious self-consciousness
apparent in her public style or whether her speech truly
reflects her feelings, the choice of Mother Mary as eulogist
for Mother Consilii on her feast day was unfortunate. Mother
Mary spoke at some length, and said nothing, nothing which
could not be said of any good administrator, of any good
nun. But then again, her lack of warmth may just have been
that by that time she was tiring, for her niece was alarmed
when she saw her, and more alarmed when the admission
came that old age was making things difficult for her.

She who had never been very demonstrative with her
family, gave her Catherine one long look and then embraced
her tenderly. Catherine was shattered. There was no doubt in
her mind that it was intended as a last farewell.

It was in that year, in October of that year, 1936, the year
of the final restoration of Fort Henry in Kingston, the year
that Mother Mary quietly celebrated her sixty-four years as a
fully professed religious, that she received word that her old
friend, Mother Valencia, had gone to God.

It brought back so many things — the building of hospitals,
the conferences about the professionalization of their staffs,
the great meetings of the New England Conference of
Hospitals, the last tragic sight of Mother Valencia, blind and
old, old.

She herself was old now and so very tired. How much
discipline now went into her early waking, her refusal to take

the constant naps desired by the aged. How much it cost her to hold the pen in her — amazing, she noticed — still youthful, strong hands.

Well, she would rally herself and go to Hartford for Mother Valencia's funeral. Nothing must keep her from that. She prayed that the late October weather would hold out and be fine, as it had been. She would not give in as she had at Alice's funeral, but that was different, and the blood pressure, diastolic and systolic, was closer together a little more than it had been then.

Besides, this was different. This was Mother Valencia. Certainly she would go.

The morning of October twentieth was bright in Holyoke, but chilly. She would wrap herself up warmly, and the cars were all warm now, enclosed and comfortable. She would probably not dare to go to the burial, but the old brown cathedral in Hartford was always overheated.

Just before the car came, she penned a few lines more of her autobiography which really hadn't gotten very far. But the last lines were a scrawl, and she could not hold the pen right. It was odd.

Mother Mary did not go to the funeral. When they found her a few moments later, she was paralyzed and disfigured, crumpled there at her desk.

# CHAPTER 23

Eight years. Eight years.

And Mother Mary could not die.

At the first, though the cerebral hemorrhage had destroyed her speech and her locomotion, her daughters, could dress her every day and she could sit in a chair. With great effort she could write her initials. Those who understood her phrases translated them into "Duty" and "Good Will." It meant, they said, all charity and commitment to God and the Rule.

Tragically, her mind did not go. As Dr. Criscitiello said, when he came down to see her, "It's like operating without an anaesthetic. Usually, they're half senile. She knows everything."

She knew when they came to see her and when they did not. It was no one's fault because how could busy people take time off just to sit with a very old lady who could not communicate? When they could, they came; but for most of those years Mother Mary just waited. Mother Edward, the Bishop, Mother Consilii and now God kept her just waiting.

If only they knew how much the news of the house and of the Congregation meant to her. Sister Gonzaga, the artist, told her how she had crept down one dark night and restored the face of Sister Ursula to the group picture which had been defaced after the defection. No. Sister Genevieve's mutilated face had not been restored. Sister Genevieve was still in the world.

Sister Chantal embarrassed her by chanting the epic of her past glories, but she could not remonstrate. Sister Michael was relegated to a room right down the hall, but she was the one for anecdotes! The novice whom the Retreat Master told to make the election, but who didn't know who was up for voting; the time that she herself had heard that you could receive communion if you were in the infirmary, then, having done so, only if you were in bed, and how, when the priest

314

was coming, she had jumped in clothes and all.

It saddened Mother Mary though to see Sister James, although, or perhaps because she was always gay, she and her chickens; but she laughed when the dancing-master William V. McCarthy called, and once a month reminded her that she had slipped the glamorous V into his name, making him, consequently, a better dancing teacher. But when her orphan boy, now a priest, came to call, she was grateful indeed to God, grateful for her life.

And Helen.

Sometimes too she lived in the past. Bishop Beaven was with her, but more often, Father Harkins. Two great tears went down her cheeks when she heard. The last of his benefactions, The Father Harkins Home, his monument had been closed. His name too would be forgotten, even here in Holyoke. As would hers.

But the people who came to her were, except for Helen, all so old. She longed for youth about her. The young never came. No one told her that they were forbidden.

Many things were forbidden, so that the stories about Mother Consilii grew into a legend, a calumny of pride and jealousy and ambition. St. Therese Couderc had suffered so; Margaret Mary's Superiors had been harsh; Bernadette's persecution is of record. But it is scarcely necessary to make Mother Consilii into an ogress, to praise the eight last years left to Mother Mary.

One legend will do. Sister de Chantal witnessed it.

Mother Mary's hands, for so long young, were now gnarled and swollen. Mother Consilii was shocked when she saw the vow-ring almost embedded in the poor old fingers. Her hands were blue. The nurse in Mother Consilii cried out against the lack of circulation. She tried to remove the ring.

It was amazing how much strength the old lady had in her, how she fought for her ring — Mother Consilii had to use some force, until finally she gave up. Maybe good circulation was not as important as the ring. The bridal ring.

And this, and this alone, was what Sister de Chantal saw.

Mother Mary suffered quite enough as it was from her immobility, her inability to communicate. And the pain in her was clear when she heard of Pearl Harbor, and this third

315

great war, for wars had patterned her life, and she never had believed that war was sent to assist the Sisters of Providence, or as a scourge on the people who sinned. It hurt her not to be able to defend God when the nuns around her seemed to confuse Him with the Japanese warlords and with Herr Hitler, as if God had raised up these evil people to be His own personal scourge. She wanted to tell everybody that God did not approve of evil, that God did not seem to favor modern war. But she could not speak. She could and did offer her sufferings, the last three years of her life, that out of these horrors a generation might rise up that would defeat war, which would fight against and destroy war, that this might be what President Wilson promised her — the war to end wars.

To fill up the hours of her isolation, she began then, to invent a Utopia in which she could live when no one was about. It became very real to her, more real than the white room in which she lived or the news that was brought to her, full of confused alarms. On a deeper level of awareness, she knew, of course, that hers was an unforseeable dream that could never possibly be actuated; and yet, as her imagination shaped the future, she found her fantasies turning into prayer, that in some remote tomorrow some things might come true.

She put into this perfect world all the things that she had desired, canceling her defeats and actuating her values. In this world too she remedied her mistakes.

Naturally, her secret life centered around her own community and she saw the girl, still in the world, who would be given her name once she was dead — a new Sister Mary of Providence. Later she so identified with this girl, young and vibrant, that in her she could renew her youth. Those who came and found her thus, marveled at her serenity.

The new Mother Mary of Providence would be born into a time when the entire Church would be reawakened, when the spirit would breathe again as in a new Pentecost, and the face of the earth would be renewed. The Pope of that day sometimes looked to her like Bishop Beaven, but more often like the benign and aged Father Harkins. She could not see him very clearly, but once, at least, he looked like her father.

The young foundress would first of all return the sisters to

316

the original spirit of St. Vincent and of Mother Gamelin, and the people of God would accept the fact that nuns, to be nuns, need not all be cloistered. New nuns could go out into the world as the rule said and as they had done within her memory, as she and her sister and her beloved Mother Mary John had done, identifying with the very poor. Eventually the laity would accept them, and people and bishops alike, who could not remember a time before 1918 and the Code and thought that all nuns should be enclosed, would no longer say, "Why don't they act like nuns? Why don't they stay in their convents?" — mistaking a brief moment in history for tradition.

Thinking of the criticism she had received when she employed Protestants in her building programs, or the raised eyebrows when she made friends of the Mammon of Iniquity in the Berkshires, even with a smile at the recollection of Father Harkins' intransigence, he and his mixed marriages, her reincarnation would send her daughters out even to work in, even to combine with, those archenemies, secular hospitals. But right now, wouldn't everyone be shocked to know what she was thinking.

The hospitals and her trained nurses. Stopped during the depression. But maybe just as well. She had wanted for her sisters a professionalism in their own commitment; she had wanted them to be perfect bedside nurses like Miss Stoney — not just administrators as she herself had been forced to become, sitting in an office remote — but now, come to think of it, she had never really let herself get into that groove. But she had once or twice been depressed by the growth of her hospitals when their expansion had inevitably led to her sisters being less and less involved with patients and more and more with starched supervision. No. Souls were not saved by the efficient running of massive institutions; they were saved by moments of bending over a bedside.

It was like the schools. There were too many deans and vice presidents and executives. When she had been principal she had taught in the classroom with real live urchins whom she knew by name, right from the first day to the last. Her new nuns would be professional, but professional bedside nurses.

Then who would be the administrators? Oh dear. All her life she had fought off the encroachments of her staff of physicians, making it clear that the Sisters of Providence owned and ran their own hospitals. Had she been quite right? For her own time, perhaps, she consoled herself. But what would the future Mother Mary of Providence do? Could it not be that doctors, laymen and laywomen were as devoted to the Church and to society as nuns were? Perhaps. But she doubted it and did not pursue this idea to its ultimate. Yet it would free her nuns to be nuns again. Nursing nuns, nuns working with people.

People. Where had she found Christ, she wondered now. No. She had known this years ago. Not in the novitiate in Kingston — she had not found Him there; not in the cloisters of her immediate past. Had she not been secretly glad when Bishop Beaven had been forced to allow the nonprofessed to be engaged in the work — with people? She destructured her novitiate and worked out a new pattern of training and preparing novices for the active works of St. Vincent, not gearing them to be Carmelites and then turning them out into the world to be female Jesuits. What she evolved was alarming, but she pursued her train of thought with glee.

It would mean, of course, that in their future commitments, her sisters would be given more freedom, and one must rely on Divine Providence that had given them their vocation to this life, to carry their cloisters with them. God cannot give the call and refuse the grace. There would certainly be some who would be lost, but she became delightfully angry when she thought of how she had always fought for those who had — horrible word — *defected*. In her sleeping dreams one night, she went down and restored the picture of Sister Genevieve, and looking at the restoration, she was as sure as one can be without heresy, that Sister Genevieve would save her soul, even if she was an ex-nun. In her reformed community there would be more charity. If a live woman wanted to dedicate her life in the world rather than in the convent, if a woman even wanted marriage — God bless Mrs. Savage — well —

It was not her own way, God knows. She had never given up anything. She had chosen and preferred and united herself

318

totally to her beloved, and she knew that she would not be complete until she was one with Him in the eternal union that He was denying her so long. That would be her true mystical marriage, of which the time when she had become in symbol, the bride of Christ, would be only a foreshadowing. Such is love. Love is a choice, a preference over all things else, a total dedication of all, not part of one's self, and above all, love is a union, love is an identification. Sometime soon, she knew, she would put on Christ.

She clutched her wedding ring. She fought for her marriage band. The pain of love was exquisite.

She looked then at her habit, hanging lifeless by the wall. Strange, she thought, I have never thought of my garb as a marriage gown, as some of my sisters have. I never really liked it, its flatirons and all. I would rather have had the brocades of Mrs. Benjamin Harrison, and when, as a girl, I dressed plainly, it was a penance. As a uniform the habit has significance, but there is no real meaning in saying that you belong to the seventeenth century. So the new foundress spent several days in designing a new habit, sensible, comfortable, and twentieth century. All of a sudden, the individuality of her nuns emerged.

Oh yes. She must work at that too. That must be done in a deeper field and it would come in the Pentecost, when the crusted, rabbinical, Roman, medieval legalism would be swept behind the door and there would be a return to the Christ whose yoke would not be heavy, and whose burden would be light.

This coming had indeed been long, had been a frozen winter, a winter in which the old Mother Mary had lived, still lived.

So often she roused herself to know, and the dream shattered and lay about her like broken glass, all iridescence gone. Then she looked upon her life and though she had never heard the doggerel William Shakespeare had cut upon his headstone or had read the inscription John Keats had dictated for his own, she thought in paraphrase, "Here lies one whose name is writ in water." For she was certain, with the cloisterization, with the new legalistic penalties, with the strictures of the Index of Forbidden books, with more stringent oaths imposed on the nonCatholic partners of marriage, with the Legion of Decency, with tighter and more condemnatory censorship on writers, with increasing insistence on the armed forces not to worship together with heretics even when going into battle, with the defense of the marriage bond and the long years of agony before a possible declaration of nullity would — or would not — come from Rome, with Armageddon, with a million Jews in gas chambers, with our ally, Godless Russia — that it was indeed winter.

From this she would rouse herself. The resurrection had always followed the crucifixion. There had never been a night without dawn, and if winters came, spring was not far behind.

Long? She had been accustomed to wait. She waited now. But the coming of the world's spring, she was certain, would be very long. Centuries, she thought. Every sign of the times pointed against its coming soon. But spring would come. There was Divine Providence.

Must it be so long, everything so long? Many times, for patience was the hardest virtue. Many times, for herself, she had desired death and had dared to rebuke God when she heard of others attaining at last to the unity of love. Her beloved left her here, not in any great physical pain but not with Him or with His Mother or with hers. Had not every good thing in her life been delayed? So long — so long — but not eight whole years.

At the end she was not denied pain. Like the Pope whom she would not live to see and could not envision, but who would indeed look a little like her father, pain came to her in terrible, final agony.

An inner obstruction, or perhaps more accurately, an atrophying of worn-out muscles brought to her three days of identification with the three hours of her Lord's agony.

Only once, voiceless, she wanted to cry out against the well-meaning prayers that were said about her, for the prayers seemed to imply that God was sending her this pain as a penance for her sins. For so many years she had taught her daughters and still they did not understand.

Where else would the lover be when the loved one is in

pain? She could not feel the crucifix they pressed into her
hands. She did not need to. Now she was one with her
beloved.

For strange, for such is love, that her lover did not deny
her the sharing of His pain.

Of these last hours let those who loved her speak:

The Annals of the Sisters of Providence, Holyoke,
Massachusetts:

Jan. 4, 1943: Mother's condition poor today.

Jan 7: Mother was annointed this afternoon; she
requested that the Sacrament be administered
privately.

19. Mother's condition is much weaker.

20. Mother suffered a very bad attack; Doctor called
to see her late this afternoon, and gave her about
two hours to live.

22. Mother was able to receive Holy Viaticum this
morning.

23. Mother requires constant watching; Sister Mary
Seraphina remained with Mother; Mother Assistant, Sister Mary Incarnatus, and Sister Mary
Consuela took turns in remaining with Mother
through the night. Mother was not able to receive
Holy Communion this morning. Mother is in a
semi-conscious condition; has paroxysms of pain;
she appears to be suffering great pain when these
attacks come on. Mother has great difficulty in
breathing. Sisters permitted to pay Mother a visit
as they pass her room to and from the Chapel.

25. Mother decidedly worse; A group of Sisters
gathered about her bed to recite the Rosary.
Reverend Mother was obliged to go to St.
Vincent's to attend the Annual Corporation
Meeting of the Hospital.

NOON. Mother's life seems to be slowly ebbing
away; heart attacks are more frequent.

1:30 P.M. Our beloved Mother Mary of Providence dies. The Reverend Chaplain was called but
Mother's dear soul had winged its flight before he
arrived. The Community had gathered for the

noon recreation; they learned of dear Mother's
death as they left the Community Room for the
Chapel. There was evinced general signs of regret
that they were not at Mother's bedside when she
died. Reverend Mother was notified, as also
Mother's relatives in Washington and California.
At supper an article which appeared in the
Holyoke Transcript was read. Mother's body was
placed in the Relic Room where so many of her
dear children had lain awaiting interment. At
seven o'clock the Sisters gathered together with
Father and recited the Rosary for the repose of
her soul. Later in the evening a group of boys
from Brightside came over to pay their respects
and they also recited the rosary. Mother must
have viewed the sight of these little ones as they
grouped about her casket with pleasure and
complacency.

26. Before the Community Mass this morning, Father
addressed the Sisters. "It was my happy privilege
to say Mass for Mother yesterday morning to
petition Almighty God for the grace of a happy
death; and today it is also my privilege again to
say Mass for the repose of her soul that God may
grant her the peace and rest that she merited
during life.
It was learned today that Mr. Dillon, the undertaker, is donating Mother's casket and also
assuming the expenses incidental to the funeral.
Alfred Logan and another group of boys came
over this evening to recite the Rosary. At the
conclusion of the prayers, Alfred told the children, encircled about Mother's casket, that
Mother Mary of Providence was the only Mother
he ever knew. This touching remark saddened
those who were listening but it is true that many
a Brightside Alumnus never knew any other
Mother than Mother Mary of Providence.
Four Sisters remained each Night that continuous
prayers might be offered for our beloved Mother.

L. L. Driscoll of the Police Department and Mr. Sheehan of the Board of Public Works called to extend their condolences, also to offer the services of their respective departments if they were needed. It was a timely offer as the road to the cemetery was in bad condition, and there is not one at Brightside to attend to it.

28. A High Mass of Requiem was offered in our Chapel this morning for Mother. It was the loving tribute of the Brightside Alumni to Mother. The Sister's choir sang the Mass. None of the Alumni members were present with the exception of the altar boys. Miss Catherine Horan, Mother's niece arrived here from Washington. Mother Clara of the Sisters of Mercy from Manchester, N.H. also came.

29. Day of Mother's Funeral
Reverend Father McEleny S.J. said the Community Mass. Father remained at the Mother House last night. Reverend Father John McCarthy received hospitality at the Beaven Kelly Home.
Despite the kindly offer of the Board of Public Works to clear the driveway and have it at least passable for the funeral, our repeated calls for the service of the Snow Tractor failed to get any response. It was indeed disheartening to look out the door and see the great drifts of snow piled up at the entrance and no men to remove it. Several appeals had been made to the Board of Public Works, even the Mayor had been called upon, but up until nine o'clock nothing had been done (the previous storm had taken on the aspects of a severe blizzard) Sisters from the Mercy got into Holyoke all right, but had to abandon their car at the line and walk up the hill. About 9.30 the plow put in an appearance and opened up the road for the automobiles. A long line of cars followed in its track, even the undertaker and several cars, for a long time stalled at the foot of

the hill, many of them our Sisters from the various missions.

Up to this time the tension was severe. His Lordship had not arrived, neither had the Officers of the Mass. However the Bishop arrived shortly before ten o'clock and some of our fears were allayed.

As soon as his Excellency was vested the procession formed in line in the corridor near the Rotunda and entered the Chapel from the Front Rotunda. Following in the line after the Priests were the little girls from Mount Saint Vincent, the boys from Brightside; a delegation of Nurses in uniform from the Mercy and Providence Hospitals, then the casket and lastly the Sisters. Mass began about ten-fifteen; the Pontifical ceremony was carried out very impressively and orderly, and the choir, though few in number, contributed to the solemnity of the Holy Sacrifice with their liturgical music. The last blessing was conferred by His Excellency, our Bishop. After the singing of the "In Paradisum." silence prevailed for a few moments, then Father P.H. Sullivan came from the sacristy and announced that because of the conditions at the cemetery it would not be possible to take the body over until 2.30 P.M. It just seemed, as some one remarked — that Mother was loathe to leave us. The people filed out of the Chapel and made their way to their cars. The Officers of the Mass were invited to dinner, fourteen in number. A guard of honor (Sisters) remained near the bier whilst the Community took dinner. At two o'clock the Sisters assembled in the Chapel and recited the fifteen decades of the Rosary. Just as the prayers were finished, the undertaker arrived and slowly removed the sacred remains of our beloved Mother Mary of Providence to Calvary. As the Sisters wended their way down the aisle of the Chapel, the Sister Organist played "Let a Pious Prayer be

Said" and the Sisters in the body of the Chapel sang the hymn. Only four Sisters from the Mother House accompanied the remains to the cemetery, although a larger number had been planned for, if weather conditions had been normal. Reverend Father Keating, Mother's confessor recited the prayers at the grave; Father Mahoney and Father Van Valkenburg of New York were also present. From the Mother House windows we could see the forms of the Sisters moving about in Calvary. Sorrow filled our hearts as we gazed from afar at the snow clad hills and thought of our dear little Mother, beloved by all, being consigned to the grave. It was Reverend Mother's plan and intention to have the "Benedictus" sung at the grave, but God ruled otherwise. However Father Keating said the commital prayers with such devotion that it made up in part for the privation of the Chant. It was with sad hearts that the Sisters returned home.

Sadness penetrates the very depths of our soul as we chronicle these facts. Fain would we eulogize her who received us into the bosom of the Community and by her wise counsel and edifying example, helped us to rear the spiritual edifice . . . small, it is true, in proportion to what it might have been, had we been more faithful in following the path of sacrifice, but undoubtedly bigger than it would have been, had we never come under the influence of her stimulating precepts. Some day, please God, abler hands will pen the story of her heroic and saintly life . . . a life full of inspiration and worthy of imitation. Then will her courageous spirit be lauded . . . then will her humble followers rejoice in having her for a leader, the humble and loving Mother Mary of Providence.

Mother Mary had waited for her funeral.
Soon after Mother Mary's demise, Mother Mary Consilii

and her companion, Mother Mary de Chantal, went once more to join with the Sisters of Providence both of Montreal and of Kingston, in the mutual charity of their common foundation a hundred years before, by the widow, Mother Gamelin.

As a gift, the Montreal Sisters gave the Sisters of Providence a beautiful volume of the original Rule of St. Vincent de Paul. The Sisters of Holyoke and their General Superior read it.

Many of them believed then that the unforseeable day would come when once again their sisters might lead such a life as Mother Mary had begun and had fought to preserve, a life-style which, though eradicated during her own near century of living, could be as holy to a later generation as it had been to her and to her religious ancestors, in what was truly not a modern aberrance, but in reality, the Great Tradition.

Now, after Good Pope John, after the *aggiornamento*, putting away the whispers of those who say, "It came too fast. . ." for, after all, it was not far behind — we go down Dwight Street.

Past the treeless streets, Maple, Locust and the rest, Elm Street cuts through between a parking lot and a tiny green, which used to be The Patch.

It is winter and too cold today for the old people to catch the sun. Save for one man, the benches are empty. Beyond the parking lot is the ancient and decaying Catholic High School. Debris from the construction of the parking lot has covered the foundations of the Father Harkins Home for the Aged.

Here the first mass in Holyoke was said under the tree. There is still one tree on the side facing the main entrance of the post-office, but it is not the same tree. It seems to be a sycamore, but it is hard to tell because it looks as if it were dead.

But the one man left in the park says it is not so. He says it is only winter. There will be leaves come the spring.

## EPILOGUE

### by the Sisters of Providence of Holyoke

A plain wooden cross marked Mother Mary's place in God's Acre, but the life of her family and her spirit went on.

That she and her sisters had a special place in the history of Holyoke became evident when, in 1948, the city celebrated the seventy-fifth anniversary of its founding. The sisters prepared exhibits and a pageant depicting the coming of the Sisters of Providence from Kingston in 1873 in a program directed by Reverend Edmund Walsh and presented at the War Memorial.

Thirty-eight years had elapsed since 1911 when Mother Mary of Providence had revised the Rule brought from Kingston for her Sisters in Holyoke. Since that time the laws of the Church had been codified and Rome had prepared the *Normae* on which all the Constitutions governing religious women were to be based. Hence the Sisters of Providence, assisted by the Reverend Constantine Phillips, C.P., a Canonist, prepared a revision of their Constitutions, which Bishop O'Leary approved.

In October of 1949 Bishop O'Leary died. His passing marked the close of a chapter in the history of the Diocese of Springfield. For four months the See was vacant. When finally a successor came on February 1, 1950, everyone knew that things would never be the same. The diocese was divided: the eastern section of Worcester County became the new diocese of Worcester; the western section, Hampden, Hampshire, Franklin and Berkshire Counties remained in the Springfield diocese.

Auxiliary Bishop John J. Wright of Boston was named the first Bishop of the new See of Worcester, a Bishop without Chancery office or home. The Sisters of Providence welcomed him at St. Vincent Hospital, and there he dwelt for several months.

Monsignor Christopher J. Weldon, Director of Catholic

Charities in New York, was appointed the fourth Bishop of the See of Springfield. Some of the Sisters of Providence attended his consecration by Cardinal Spellman in St. Patrick's Cathedral on March 24 and his installation in St. Michael's Cathedral by Archbishop Richard J. Cushing four days later.

The Sisters of Providence were concerned. They were now working in two dioceses. Would they, like the priests be frozen wherever they were? Things were changing. No one could be sure what would happen.

One of the first changes affecting the Community occurred that summer when the new Bishop gave permission for sisters born in Europe to return for a visit with parents and relatives still living there. No one had ever dreamed of it, least of all the Sisters who had bade what they thought was a final goodbye to their loved ones in Ireland years before.

For a Belgian, Sister Mary Paula Schillewaert, who was unable to travel, there was the joy of hearing her brother's voice and conversing with him over trans-Atlantic telephone. It was the first contact, except by letter, she had with her family since she left her native Belgium for the Foreign Missions (the United States) some fifty-five years previously.

Bishop Weldon led a pilgrimage to Rome for the Holy Year of 1950, and among the pilgrims, nineteen Sisters of Providence brought the prayerful tribute of the Community to the Holy Father. Of that group, however, Sister Mary Assumpta did not return. Four years previously major surgery had interfered with her role as a Sister-nurse. On their way back, she had stopped at Lourdes and prayed that either she be cured or be taken home to heaven. Forty-eight hours later she had gone home indeed, and they brought her body from Paris to Holyoke, placing her among her own on the very day of the Proclamation of the dogma of the Assumption.

Though the General Elections had been due in September 1950, it had been postponed to the following year. The choice of the delegates for Reverend Mother was Sister Mary de la Salle, a native of Springfield who had entered the Community when Mother Mary Immaculata was Mistress of Novices. Though she had often been corrected and formed by

328

her mistress, she loved and admired her and seemed to have caught her spirit of gentlewomanliness and prayerfulness. Later she became Mother Immaculata's secretary during her term of office as Mother Superior and spent many years at the Mother House at Brightside where she met Mother Mary of Providence, Bishop Beaven and the older members of the Community. She brought with her to the position of leadership in the Community a knowledge and appreciation of the past and its traditions and an awareness of the needs of the present.

When the First National Congress of Religious of the United States was held at the University of Notre Dame in 1952 as an outgrowth of the International Congress held in Rome by Pope Pius XII two years before, three Sisters of Providence attended. The purpose of the Congress was: To deepen and strengthen religious life. As a result institutes and schools for the study of religious life and the preparation of those responsible for the religious formation of others were established. A group of Sisters attended the Institutes of Spirituality at Notre Dame each summer and others attended similar institutes and workshops in various places. These workshops provided a unique experience: the sisters themselves discussed the needs of their communities in the light of the ideals proposed by the experts in the lectures and panels. Other sisters attended courses in Canon Law and schools of theology. The sisters' world was growing larger.

The horizon was broadening at home too. The Mission Exhibit in Springfield in 1952 and the Congress of the Confraternity of Christian Doctrine in 1953 brought approximately a hundred sisters of various communities to Providence Mother House on each occasion giving an opportunity of mutual exchange — a sharing of ideals and goals, long remembered by all who participated.

Attendance at the Notre Dame Institutes made Mother Mary de la Salle more keenly aware of the need for and importance of the advanced education of her Sisters. A few who were teaching in the Schools of Nursing had been sent to college at the suggestion of the members of the Board of Registration and at the further insistence of the League of Nurses. Extension courses had been offered at the hospitals, it was true, but only a few credits could be earned each year by Sisters engaged in full time hospital work. A more adequate program was indicated. A House of Studies was opened in Chestnut Hill close to Boston College, which had recently established a School of Nursing. Sisters already in nursing service who had taken extension courses were given the opportunity of completing their work for a degree; young sisters came there to prepare for their professional work. Later the young sisters were sent, after first profession of vows, to Marillac College in Saint Louis, Missouri, which had been designed for Sister Formation and was conducted by the Daughters of Charity of Saint Vincent de Paul. There, together with young sisters from several other communities, they studied for their baccalaureate degrees.

Now the Sisters of Providence were living in three different dioceses. Soon there would be a fourth. A small hospital was offered for sale in Murphy, North Carolina, a town that had only seven Catholic families. This was brought to the attention of the Community by a zealous Glenmary Father, Rev. Joseph Dean, who was pastor of the only Catholic Church in Murphy and who saw the possibilities for the work of the Sisters in the China of America. This priestless land offered considerable missionary appeal when the almost foreign mission was communicated to the Community at Christmastide, and the sisters were enthusiastic in their attitude towards sponsoring this new Bethlehem.

From the many volunteers, the following Sisters were selected: Sister Mary Anthony Reimann, as Sister Superior, Sister Mary Francis Xavier Rupprecht, Sister Marie William Pearson and Sister Mary Francina McGrath. Six months later, two other Sisters joined them: Sister Mary Fidelis Kennedy, who had just been graduated from Regis College, and Sister Mary Dosithea, the Helen of the story, and Mother's protege.

It seemed peculiarly appropriate that their arrival in the South should concide with the anniversary of Mother Mary of Providence's death. Her spirit was indeed alive in the actions of her followers, who, like their foundress, were willing to risk all to reach out to those in need. This day marked the feast of Saint Paul, patron of all missionaries.

The first little missionary band, like their Kingston pioneer

Sisters of 95 years previously, entrained in the afternoon of January 23, 1956, on the first lap of their journey, which was to take them one thousand miles from home. The following morning at nine o'clock they arrived in Asheville, North Carolina, where they were met by Rev. William Pearson, brother of Sister Marie William, who conducted them to St. Joseph's Hospital of which he was chaplain. The Sisters of Mercy who operate the hospital took them in and after dinner Father Pearson drove them to Murphy some 100 miles away. It was a breath-taking trip, along tortuous mountain roads, narrow and precipitous and protected by a single guard railing. When twilight approached, the countryside was very sparsely illuminated. The brave, but as yet untried missionaries, experienced some trepidation as they passed the Cherokee Indian Reservation and a Bear Reservation.

Their coming aroused local interest when it became known that they were taking over the management of the hospital, and the sentiments of two opposing factions were evidenced. The Baptists, coached by their ministers, vigorously resented what they termed the encroachment of the Roman Catholics on their territory. A stirring article appeared in "The Biblical Recorder" under date of January 21, 1956, just before the sisters' arrival. It purported to have been written by a Missioner, G. E. Scruggs, and was entitled "Baptists Are Fast Losing the Mountains to Roman Catholics." In it he deplored the fact that the Roman Catholics were opening a hospital there. The majority of the people, however, who had apparently no acquaintance with the Catholic sisters before, were plainly mystified, puzzled, but on the whole, friendly and responsive to the Sisters' advances of friendship. It was only after considerable association with them, that they adopted the appellation of Sister, addressing them instead with the familiar Ma'am, which to nuns' ears was *not* familiar.

The sisters' first six months in Murphy were a series of setbacks, delays, obstacles and frustrations. They received the first intimation of impending conflict when their application to the North Carolina Medical Care Commission for a license to operate Murphy General Hospital was denied on the grounds that the building created a fire hazard. Only then did

331

they learn that the owner, Doctor Taylor, had been operating on a provisional license with the understanding that the deficiencies would be corrected, which he had made no attempt to do.

Later when Petrie Hospital across the street, owned by Dr. Hoover, was offered for sale and it became known that the sisters were interested in buying it, the Baptist community exerted great pressure to prevent it falling into the hands of Catholics. Then came a period of weary waiting while the Sisters strove to abandon themselves into the hands of Divine Providence. They remembered that their founder, Saint Vincent, had told them that "the works of God have their proper time and His Providence accomplishes them only then and neither sooner or later." Confident that "Divine Providence is never wanting in things undertaken at Its command," they surrendered the outcome of the affair to His guidance. And Providence did not fail them. They took possession of Providence Hospital on July 1st and one week later the first Catholic patient was admitted, a Navy boy on leave. On July 25 the first baby was born to Catholic parents. The sisters had their first Baptism.

The interest and support of the Community in Holyoke in this mission is evidenced by the success of the annual bazaar held at the Motherhouse for its benefit each year since its foundation.

In 1966 the Most Rev. Vincent S. Waters, Bishop of Raleigh, invited them to take over the administration of another hospital in his diocese, St. Joseph of the Pines in Southern Pines, about three hundred miles from the Providence Hospital in Murphy. Although located in a wealthy area, on its outskirts live the poorest of the poor, both white and black.

Meanwhile back in Springfield, Bishop Weldon in his newly acquired diocese was deeply concerned with the need to replace some of the outmoded facilities in which the works of charity were conducted and which had not only outgrown their usefulness, but in some instances at least, were a fire hazard. The Home for Children at Brightside first claimed his attention. It was the current trend of thought then that children should be cared for in a homelike atmosphere rather than in an institutional setting. Accordingly the design for the new Child Care Center consisted of a cottage type group of dwellings surrounding an administration building. On its completion, December 8, 1954, it was designated as Our Lady of Providence Home for Children.

Other building projects were in progress. A new St. Vincent Hospital was completed in 1954 making it the second largest hospital in Massachusetts. The Farren Memorial Hospital added a new wing and the Guild of the Holy Child (Home for Unwed Mothers), in operation in Westfield since 1932, acquired a completely new facility.

On the opening of a fund-raising campaign towards the close of 1955 to replace the long outmoded Providence Hospital buildings, Mrs. Minnie Dwight, the publisher-editor of the Transcript-Telegram wrote in the local newspaper an editorial entitled "A Challenge to the Heart of Holyoke," and paid tribute to Mother Mary.

A Challenge Well Met

Holyoke being only three generations distant from its beginnings with the great dam across the Connecticut river for its mainspring can clock back to the 'firsts' more easily than other New England communities. And whoever turns the hands of the clock back to check the beginnings of Holyoke mothering of orphan children or binding up the wounds and easing the fevers of the sick always comes to that gallant lover of God and man who came down here from Canada with her little band of sister nuns and plowed the ground and sowed the seed for the magnificence of today's houseful of children at Brightside and for the great hospital that is to tower under the very hillside that Mother Mary of Providence selected for the Brightside and Ingleside homes for homeless childhood.

So Bishop Weldon has measured the ground in the more than 100 sessions he has devoted to solving the problems of the outgrown, out-moded Providence hospital. In his initial call to the heart of Holyoke, the Bishop came back to those "firsts" built in the life of early Holyoke by the courage of the great hearted nun who rose up from her most personal care of individual children and sick people to bring the Providence Order to Holyoke and house it where it can look over the new Brightside with its beautiful home for children and its forthcoming palace of healing.

What seed that great and even glamorous woman sowed during her long life! We can properly use the term "glamorous" for this active saint of our city streets, because she had the rare gift of charm.

If there are as many changes in the field of medicine during the next 50 years as there have been since the start of this century it can be foreseen that there will be hospitals of different purpose and structure. There are great things yet to be done in the field of preventive medicine. For the childhood of the race and the golden years at the other end, modern medicine has wrought what would seem miracles a century ago.

When a community like this Holyoke area projects a multi-million dollar hospital as part of its Christian responsibility, it is doing something with its hands and feet, but, as Bishop Weldon said over and over last night, in its major ideal the new Providence hospital is a challenge to the heart of Holyoke.

It was good, too, that Bishop Weldon should stress this brave undertaking in community health as an expression of free men and women, in a free land. The many hundreds who listening with tense interest to every word spoken at the call of Chairman Begley by representatives of our interfaiths of Holyoke were eager to go along with Bishop Weldon in his challenge for the freedom of medicine as against its socialization.

And let this be the answer to the one criticism one hears about choosing a site for the new hospital so far distant from our City Hall. When the young Sister Mary of Providence back in 1873 was seeking a center for the great work she was pioneering, she went down the river to that handsome knoll, with its meadow spread apronlike to the river, and there built for Holyoke's future.

The choice of that site for the new Providence hospital is just catching up with the nun who became Reverend Mother of the Providence Order in this country. His audience last night liked Bishop Weldon's reiteration of the campaign to finance the new hospital as a "challenge to the heart." So be it.

The people of Holyoke met the challenge and responded wholeheartedly. On the opening of the new Providence Hospital in Holyoke in 1958 the dedication ceremonies marked the 85th anniversary of the coming of the Sisters of Providence to Holyoke, the 65th anniversary of the building of the old hospital and the 55th anniversary of the first nurses' graduation there. Ten years after its opening it was the scene of the last months in the life of Mother Mary de la Salle, who had labored tirelessly for its building.

At the next General Chapter, 1963, Sister Mary Loreto was chosen by the delegates. She was a woman accustomed to authority. As soon as she had pronounced her perpetual vows Mother Consilii appointed her as Superior-Administrator of the Farren Hospital. From there she went to Providence Hospital and then on to St. Vincent Hospital in the same capacity. She was a gifted administrator, whose genius for organization was recognized by the civic community as well as by her own religious community. A citation from the City Council of Worcester, an appointment by Governor Furcolo to the Scholarship Board for Nurses, the distinction of being chosen the outstanding Catholic woman of the Worcester Diocese were among the tributes paid her. She was, for all this, a quiet person and only those who knew her were aware of her warmth, the kindliness and sensitivity that lay hidden beneath a somewhat severe professional exterior.

Mother Consilii had lived to see the office she had held for so many years taken up by her protege. She died after a long illness on October 2, 1963.

At this time everyone was talking about the extraordinary man, the well loved, Pope John XXIII. The Council he had

called would bring the winds of change to Holyoke very
soon.

The Apostolic Letter *Ecclesiae Sanctae*, issued Motu
Proprio by Pope Paul VI, August 6, 1966, contains Norms for
the Implementation of the Decree of the Second Vatican
Council, *Perfectae Caritatis*. Part 1, Article 3 reads: "A
special general chapter, ordinary or extraordinary, should be
convened within two or at most three years to promote the
adaptation and renewal in each institute."

In obedience and delight, Mother Loreto wrote:

February 16, 1967

Dear Sister Superior and Sisters:

*The Decree on Adaptation and Renewal of Re-
ligious Life* has stressed, as you know, a return to the
spirit of the Founder. Those of us who lived in the
Community during Mother Mary of Providence's
active years came to know and love her, and to hold
in veneration the nuggets of spiritual wisdom which
were the product of her deeply interior life.

For the benefit of the younger members of the
Community, and also to refresh the memories of the
seniors in religion, it was proposed that the missions
be sent a copy of excerpts taken from Mother Mary of
Providence's writings. These should first be read in the
refectory and then kept permanently in some kind of
notebook, so that they may be available to the Sisters
for re-reading at their leisure. From time to time other
writings of Mother's will be sent to you, and the same
procedure should be followed.

May these timeless messages from the heart of her
who suffered and labored so joyfully for the development of our Congregation awaken in all hearts a desire
to serve God with the same full measure of devotion
which characterized our Late Mother Mary of Providence!

Devotedly yours in Christ,
Mother M. Loreto, S.P.
Superior General

Preparations and preliminary committee meetings for the Chapter continued throughout Sister Mary Loreto's six year term. Professionalism, long advocated by Mother Mary of Providence, was now accepted as an essential ingredient for mixing well with contemporary society. Such professionalism was not only related to the educational preparation of the Sisters but also to the internal workings of the Congregation.

To assure realistic planning the Sisters of Providence called upon a consultant agency to work jointly with their own committee during an intense year-long self-study of the Community. This comprehensive survey provided a panoramic view of the health and social needs of the dioceses where the Sisters of Providence were involved as well as a closeup view of the financial status of the community, its present and potential manpower forecast, a critique of its existing apostolic endeavors together with a five-year action plan. The consultants and the committee scrutinized and discussed every aspect of community life and apostolic involvement.

This data provided the background for the Special Chapter of Affairs of 1967, which produced the revised Interim Constitutions of 1968. In this document a multitude of minute legal restrictions were swept away leaving a clear path with freedom for the Sisters to participate in social action, to discover more meaningful ways of providing direct service to the poor, to join with family and friends in celebrating the Sacraments and for home visits, to move into new areas of service. The contemporary daughters of Mother Mary of Providence were grasping again the Vincentian concept she treasured: that the works of the Sisters of Providence would allow them to be cloistered only in spirit.

A deep and far-reaching transition was taking place. Winds of change were whirling through the halls of the Mother House as the Chapter of Elections of 1969 appeared on the horizon. Not only the Chapter delegates, but all the sisters were encouraged to read, to study, to evaluate the many documents and books published after the Second Vatican Council. The Chapter Committees actively sought the advice and ideas of the sisters. Never before had the government of the Community openly urged each sister to assume personal responsibility for decision-making regarding her own life and the future directions of the Congregation. Unquestioning blind obedience was supplanted by the principles of collegiality and subsidiarity, challenging exchanges of healthy dialogue leading toward consensus. Mother Mary of Providence's dream of a person-oriented approach to community living was coming into its own.

Prior to the Chapter, the delegates visited each of the local houses to share with the Sisters the results of their months of research and to discern how the Spirit was working among the Sisters. At this same time, experts were consulted and special educational sessions were held for the entire community on topics relating to new theological trends, spirituality, changes in the apostolate, communication and finance. For the first time, the Chapter of 1969 was to be an open Chapter where any Sister could attend and express her convictions.

Into this climate of renewal and change came the woman chosen by the Sisters of Providence on September 20, 1969 to serve as their seventh Major Superior, Sister Mary Caritas. Known in secular life as Jean Geary, she was a native of Springfield and a graduate of its High School of Commerce and of Mercy Hospital School of Nursing before her entrance into religious life. She earned a Bachelor's Degree from Regis College and a Master's Degree in preventive medicine from Tufts Medical School. Following an internship in nutrition at New England Medical Center in Boston, she was appointed administrative dietitian of the Providence Hospital, and the diocesan consultant for food facility planning.

In 1967, prior to her election as Major Superior, Sister Caritas was the administrator of St. Luke's Hospital. She rode the helm through the turbulent and unchartered waters of the merger between Pittsfield General Hospital, a secular hospital with strong Protestant leanings and St. Luke's Hospital, operated by the Sisters of Providence. In testimony to her leadership and administrative ability, the Boards of Directors of the two hospitals named her the associate director of the newly formed Berkshire Medical Center where she served until her election as Major Superior.

With Sister Mary Caritas' support and encouragement, the

Chapter delegates worked steadily for one year re-evaluating and revamping, to some extent, every phase of the life-style of the Sisters of Providence. The delegates enacted changes that had far-reaching repercussions and touched the lives of each of the Sisters causing some to respond positively to the new forms and others to be threatened by the effects of the changes.

Sister Caritas, in an interview with a reporter from the Catholic Observer of Springfield, September 26, 1969, painted a picture of the community caught in the turmoil of renewal with its fears and tensions, challenges and conflicts, issues and dilemmas, yet urged on by a vision of hope and of rebirth.

*"What does the future hold for the Sisters of Providence?"*

"We must evaluate what the needs are and what we are capable of doing, how equipped we are to meet these needs. Our future lies within these two perimeters. Of course we cannot attempt to meet all the needs or we will spread ourselves too thin."

*"Do you foresee any difficulty in getting the Sisters to participate?"*

One of the great problems — because of the once prevalent idea that Religious should be humble and passive — is that Sisters find it difficult to be active, to participate as much as they might. I had occasion as an administrator to assign Sisters to positions for which they did not feel capable. Once started, they did a magnificent job.

*"Do you anticipate changes in your apostolate?"*

"We are at the peak of our membership right now. We have not had many vocations recently. We trust that God will favor us with more candidates. But if he does not send them to us, we will have to retrench."

"Then, of course, our work in hospitals will change; in fact, it has begun to change already. In Pittsfield, I was in the middle of it. I felt when we merged the two hospitals [St. Luke's Hospital and Pittsfield General merged in 1967 to form the Berkshire Medical Center — ed.] we were not losing anything, but rather opening up a whole new apostolate.

"If we are going to be relevant, we are going to be so as Christian women who are Religious.

339

"Another thing — some 10 Sisters are working outside our own institutions now. I feel they are witnessing in a very special way. It's a trend for us. We have been tied to our institutions in the past. While we did not own the hospitals, we looked upon them as "our own". We were tied to them.

"This is changing, even now, if a person is assigned to a hospital, she is working more with lay people than ever before. Her relationship to the hospital is not quite the same."

*"You mention a decrease in vocations. How can the Sisters of Providence attract more candidates?"*

"We have to be in works that are meaningful and relevant in giving service. Young people of our age are service-minded and anxious to help people. That is why our community is a natural — we are where the action is.

"I think young people are just as interested in making sacrifices as they were in an earlier age. But they are extremely honest and they cannot stand duplicity in any form.

"For instance, our young Sisters are marvelous. At the Chapter, five from among the junior professed — most under 25 years of age — have been invited to take part, in a non-voting way. They have been a stimulus to our thinking. These young people are very articulate and interested. Even more than that, they are committed. And I think this is what we admire most about them — their sense of commitment."

*"You have just been elected the major superior of the Sisters of Providence. What is your philosophy of leadership?"*

"I feel the role of a leader is to set the tone and try to create an atmosphere in which each Sister can participate and contribute. I have no doubt about the abilities and talents of the members of this community. I see my role as trying to bring out what the Sisters have."

"Together we will make it, because I certainly cannot take the community and alone bring it anywhere.

*"A Canadian layman was recently quoted as saying, "We don't need Sisters today. They can teach and do social work outside the convent. Religious life is a thing of the past in our 20th century when the focus is on the laity." What would be your comment on his opinion?"*

340

"I don't agree with him. I think there is a certain witness value that the Sisters bring. And I believe a Religious is living a baptismal commitment to Christianity in a more intense form.

"There is no basic difference between Sisters and the laity. Religious profession is not a sacrament. But it is a matter of living the basic Christian commitment we all share in a more intense way.

"I am one of those people who do not believe Sisters should be living behind convent doors. I think we are only as relevant as a community as we are as individuals.

*"What do you think of the experimentation being done in religious communities?"*

"Very often, what has been called experimentation has really been change, not experimentation. True experimentation means trying something out to see how well it works. In order to experiment properly we must have definite purposes and goals and constantly measure progress.

"Evaluation is the key to successful experimentation. We are planning to set up a board of experimentation to initiate and evaluate experiments.

*"Is it possible that the Sisters of Providence might be doing entirely different work in the future from what they are now doing?"*

"We are not limiting ourselves in any way. We are not planning at the moment to change or leave any of our apostolates. But we are not approaching the future with a closed mind either. We want to be where we are needed."

*"How much has Religious life changed since you entered 22 years ago?"*

"The environment is much different now. When I entered there were strict rules of conduct to be adhered to. Conforming behavior identified the good religious.

"Things have changed. There is a new freedom. Each person is encouraged to grow from within and develop her own uniqueness. Formation is based on creative discipleship where each Sister deepens her relationship with Christ and with the members of the community.

"There are those who believe that the present increase of defections from Religious life are the result of this new

341

freedom. This is not the case at all. It is the misuse of freedom.

"In the past Sisters were expected to be very passive and conforming to rules and regulations. Now all of a sudden, we are asking these same people to take a more active part in the direction of their lives and in the exercise of personal responsibility. This is difficult for many of our Sisters. I think we have to support them in making this transition. If there is a generation gap in Religious life, it is one based on training.

*"What is your attitude about the Sister's habit?"*

"In this time of renewal, I think the Religious habit has certainly been overplayed. As far as we are concerned, we have to establish a basic philosophy about the sign value and witness value of the habit. Then it is a matter of dressing appropriate to the occasion."

*"When a bishop is appointed, he chooses some motto for his coat of arms. If the same held for major superiors, what motto would you choose?*

"Hope."

Of vital importance in this renewal was the redefinition of the community objectives and goals. All the Sisters of the Community cooperated in this joint effort.

The need for total development of the person, the necessity of prayer as the core of religious life, and the acceptance of trust and friendship as the key to community relationships were concepts affirmed by the objectives. These convictions became the framework for the development of a new formation program that closely resembled the type of assimilation into religious life which Mother Mary of Providence had envisioned.

In the revised program, the candidates were to be gradually incorporated into the community, to learn its ideals, traditions, and objectives while absorbing the spirit of the Congregation by actively living and working with the Sisters in the various missions. Formation was to be personalized to meet the specific needs and level of growth of each candidate.

In the area of the apostolate, the Sisters of Providence

342

prepared the following objectives:

1. To work for the unity of mankind by building the world into a community of justice, freedom and love.

2. To be active participants and leaders in the human quest for meaning.

3. To be committed to the Church's mission, involved with all others who are actively present at the centers of need in the world.

4. To manifest radical commitment to the poor, dispossessed and outcasts of society.

De facto they recommitted themselves to the type of social involvement, and responsiveness to the poor that Mother Mary of Providence strove to incorporate into the first rule of the community. In concrete goals, the Sisters assumed responsibility to become actively involved in diocesan, and civic affairs, and in professional and national organizations, to support and participate in ecumenical, political, social and racial justice endeavors, and to work toward the elimination of unfair employment practices and any other injustices they encounter in their care of those in need.

Moreover, the Sisters spelled out their special interest in those who have opted out of the search for meaning through use of drugs and alcohol as well as their understanding of the need to work cooperatively with existing diocesan, civic and federal programs. Inspired by Mother Mary of Providence's vision, the Sisters of Providence reiterated their predilection for the poor, the dispossessed and outcasts of society in their choice of future works.

By 1970, the experimentation in life-styles, clothing and apostolates was a reality. Dressed in white uniforms or in modest contemporary attire and wearing a modified veil, a silver cross and ring, the Sisters of Providence were witnessing to Christ in ever-increasing numbers in apostolates outside their own institutions and in such diverse activities as drug programs, Spanish Apostolate, working with retarded and emotionally disturbed children, visiting the aged in their homes and in nursing homes, visiting prisoners in rehabilitation centers, assisting the visually handicapped, participating in youth programs in detention centers and summer programs, teaching in Community Colleges, contributing to State and civic commissions, doing catechetical work, and becoming involved in the Newman Center apostolate.

The fruit of the efforts of the Chapter 1969 — 1970 was crystallized in two documents: a *Book of Chapter Proceedings* and in *Signs of Hope*, a 72-page booklet that expressed in modern terminology the meaning of the life-style of the Sisters of Providence. As the Introduction to *Signs of Hope* stated: "It reflects the collegial thinking of the whole community; its shared experience and understanding of the religious life and of our rich traditions; its fresh approach to present challenges; its hope for future development."

The following excerpt on the "Charism of the Sisters of Providence" offers a glimpse of the content of *Signs of Hope* and of the rich heritage and spirit bequeathed by Mother Mary of Providence:

The Congregation of Sisters of Providence is a community evolving in hope.

Open to the future, the Congregation seeks to live the Gospel message fully by responding to the ever-changing physical, emotional, social and spiritual needs of modern man through dedicated service in the fields of health, education, and social welfare.

Alive with the pioneering spirit of their foundress, Mother Mary of Providence, the community is constantly "pressing forward to higher and better things" while "resting their hopes on the Providence of God."

A gifted woman of vision, Mother Mary of Providence, prophetically, courageously risked hardships, trials, failures to live out the social implications of the Gospel.

Her love knew no barriers; for her undaunted faith and hope in Providence urged her to undertake the seemingly impossible.

344

Captivated by her prophetic spirit, Sisters of Providence today willingly risk all for the sake of the kingdom.

By their witness of hope, they strive to bring life to the dying, courage to the sick and needy, comfort to the aged, meaning to the doubtful, hope to the hopeless.

By their womanly love, understanding and capacity to share human joys and sorrows, they reflect the Providence of God in their sympathetic concern and care for those in need.

At the official closing of the Chapter, Sister Mary Caritas said, "At a time when the greatest threat to religious life is a failure of hope, we have stressed this virtue. Our present-day response is rooted in hope and is based on the principles of unity in diversity and personal responsibility."

She continued in her dynamic enthusiasm, "We are not closing anything. . . . We have just begun to move!"

When we see these signs — the stirring of new life, renewal and hope — we ask: CAN SPRING BE FAR BEHIND?